Lectures on
ANALYTIC AND PROJECTIVE
GEOMETRY

ADDISON–WESLEY MATHEMATICS SERIES

Eric Reissner, *Consulting Editor*

Lectures on

ANALYTIC AND PROJECTIVE GEOMETRY

by

DIRK J. STRUIK

Professor of Mathematics
Massachusetts Institute of Technology

1953

ADDISON–WESLEY PUBLISHING COMPANY, Inc.

CAMBRIDGE 42, MASSACHUSETTS

PREFACE

The extension of the mathematical curriculum in our colleges has not infrequently been at the expense of some of the most valuable fields of more "old-fashioned" mathematics. Among the victims we find elementary, projective, and algebraic geometry, fields which used to stir the enthusiasm of an older generation. This decline into relative neglect not only means that mathematicians grow up poorly acquainted with one of the most attractive parts of their science, elegant in form and in results, but also means a loss of more fundamental values. This "modern" geometry of the nineteenth century was to a considerable extent responsible for the whole revolution in mathematical thinking typical of that period; out of it came the concepts of non-Euclidean geometry and geometry of more than three dimensions, and it contributed substantially to the formation of such concepts as transformation, group, invariant, and oriented quantity. Moreover, it has profoundly influenced axiomatics. Neglect of this part of mathematics therefore tends to stifle the understanding of some of the most important notions of modern mathematics, physics, and engineering. The task is set to find the legitimate place for this field inside our present mathematical curriculum, and to stress those fundamentals which are most vital for the understanding of our science as a whole.

The present book represents an approach to this task by means of a one-term course, mainly for juniors and seniors, given at the Massachusetts Institute of Technology. Those students have passed through a three-term course of the now traditional "analytical geometry and calculus" type, so that they have some understanding of Cartesian coordinate work in the plane and in space applied to straight lines, conics, and some other curves, have had some vector algebra, and enough of space geometry to recognize a quadric surface. This knowledge is presupposed in our text, so that we can start with affine and projective concepts concerning points on a line and lines through a point. Then the geometry of plane and space, leading up to conics and quadrics, is developed inside the triple frame of metrical, affine, and projective transformations. The algebraic treatment is occasionally exchanged for the synthetic one. At many

v

places the connection of the geometrical material of the text with other fields is indicated, notably with axiomatics, algebra, descriptive geometry, vector analysis topology, and statics. Further developments serve the purpose of allowing the student to find his way in the literature. Care is bestowed on the figures as well as on the problems for further exercise. The Special Exercises at the end are not necessarily meant as a further elaboration of the material of the text; they are rather aimed at allowing the student to take notice of interesting problems on the periphery.

The transliteration of Greek and Russian names should follow some consistent rule; for instance, that adopted in Sarton's "Introduction to the History of Science" and in the "Mathematical Reviews." The names usually spelled *Apollonius*, *Pappus* would then be transliterated as *Apollonios*, *Pappos*, and the name of the co-discoverer of non-Euclidean geometry as Lobačevskiĭ. Since the spelling *Apollonius* and *Pappus* is customary in mathematics, we have compromised on these names, just as Sarton has compromised on *Euclid* instead of *Eucleides*, since the word Euclid has become part of common language.

In preparing the manuscript I have had the advice of Mr. L. Cross, Dr. Ruth Struik, and especially of Professor H. S. M. Coxeter, to whom my thanks. I also take this opportunity to pay respect to the memory of Professor P. Zeeman of Leiden University, who introduced me to the charms of analytical and projective geometry, and whose lecture notes, after all these years, have still been of use to me in preparing my own text.

May 1953   D. J. S.

CONTENTS

CHAPTER 1

POINT SETS ON A LINE

1–1 The oriented line. A point can move on a line l in two different ways, from a point A to a point B, and from B to A (Fig. 1–1). We can thus distinguish between a *positive sense* on l (say $A \rightarrow B$) and a *negative sense* $(B \rightarrow A)$. Such a line is said to be *oriented* and is called a *ray*. We shall always use the term "line" in the sense of "straight line." On a ray we can differentiate between the positive segment AB and the negative segment BA, and express this as follows:

$$AB + BA = 0. \tag{1–1}$$

If P is a third point on l, then we always have (Fig. 1–1)

$$AB + BP + PA = 0, \tag{1–2}$$

regardless of whether P lies between A and B or outside of A and B.

A. F. Möbius, who introduced this concept of the oriented line in 1827, stressed an idea which was implicit in the work of those geometers who, beginning at the time of Newton, assigned both positive and negative values to the Cartesian coordinate x of a point P on a line l with respect to a fixed origin O on l (Fig. 1–2). When x runs from $-\infty$ to $+\infty$ we obtain all points on the line and every point only once. *We consider here only real points*, that is, points of which the coordinates are real (see Sec. 1–8).

This one-to-one correspondence of points on a line and real numbers is not obvious. To obtain it, take a point O on line l and another point U (the unit point) on l, and let O correspond to the number 0; U to the number 1. By well-known methods we can then associate one and only one point on l with every positive and negative rational number (for instance, the number $\frac{1}{2}$ is associated with the mid-point of OU). Every

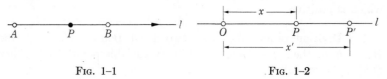

Fig. 1–1   Fig. 1–2

interval ϵ of the line contains such labeled points, where ϵ may be taken as small as we like: the "rational" points are *everywhere dense*. There remain points on l to which no rational number can be attached, for instance the point P for which OP is equal to the diagonal of the square described on OU as side. We can represent OP by an endless decimal fraction, in this particular case 1.4142136. . . . If we now postulate that to every such fraction a so-called irrational number belongs (in the previous case we write $\sqrt{2}$), then we can combine the rational and irrational numbers in ascending order to the *arithmetic continuum*. Then we postulate that there is a one-to-one correspondence between the points on l and the numbers of the arithmetic continuum. The points corresponding to the rational and irrational numbers then form the *geometric continuum*. We here deal with these continua.

The sense of increasing x can now be taken as the positive sense on the line. If we indicate by $P(x)$ the point P with coordinate x, then we have for two points $P_1(x_1)$ and $P_2(x_2)$ on l:

$$P_1P_2 = x_2 - x_1, \quad P_2P_1 = x_1 - x_2. \tag{1-3}$$

Four points P_1P_2, Q_1Q_2 on l satisfy the relation

$$P_1P_2 \cdot Q_1Q_2 + P_1Q_1 \cdot Q_2P_2 + P_1Q_2 \cdot P_2Q_1 = 0, \tag{1-4}$$

which follows from the algebraic identity

$$(x_2 - x_1)(y_2 - y_1) + (y_1 - x_1)(x_2 - y_2) + (y_2 - x_1)(y_1 - x_2) = 0. \tag{1-5}$$

Möbius also extended his idea to other figures. For instance, he remarked that we can orient a triangle ABC by assigning to it a sense ABC (counterclockwise) and a sense ACB (clockwise). If one of the oriented triangles has the area α, then we can assign to the other the area $-\alpha$.

Möbius was preceded by G. Monge [Journal Ecole Polytechnique, cah. 15 (1809), pp. 68–117], who had already oriented triangles and tetrahedra and thus distinguished between positive and negative areas and volumes.

The length of a segment AB shall, as usual, be indicated by $|AB|$, which is positive.

1–2 Division ratio. We take two fixed points $A(x = a)$ and $B(x = b)$ on the ray and also an arbitrary variable point $P(x)$. Then (Fig. 1–1), we call

$$\lambda = PA:PB = (a - x):(b - x) \qquad (2\text{-}1)$$

the *division ratio* of P with respect to A and B. This division ratio is positive for P outside of the segment AB and negative inside of it. It is independent of the orientation of the line. From Eq. (2-1), we find for x:

$$x = \frac{a - \lambda b}{1 - \lambda}. \qquad (2\text{-}2)$$

Each point of the line, except B, determines one value of λ. We can include B if we admit for λ an infinite value, but in this case we are obliged to assign to this point the values $\lambda = \pm \infty$. It is geometrically evident that no two points have the same value of λ (see Ex. 3-1). We also see that every value of λ gives a point $P(x)$, with the exception of $\lambda = +1$, when x in Eq. (2-2) loses its meaning. We see that when P moves away from A to the left (Fig. 1-3), λ grows from 0 to $+1$, approaching $+1$ as closely as we like from the lower side; and when P moves away from B to the right, λ decreases from $+\infty$ to $+1$, again approaching $+1$ as closely as we like, this time from the upper side. We now introduce a new concept by saying that to $\lambda = +1$ also belongs a point, the *ideal point* or *point at infinity* P_∞ of line l. All other points of l are now called *ordinary points*. The x-coordinate of P_∞ is $\pm \infty$. In Fig. 1-3 we can see how a continuous change of λ from $+1$ via 0 to $-\infty$, and from $+\infty$ to $+1$ corresponds to a continuous motion of P on the line.

There is, in English, no generally accepted name for elements "at infinity" — except the term "at infinity" itself, which is, as we shall see, not always adequate. The terms "improper," "ideal," "extraordinary," "inaccessible" have been used as equivalents of the German "uneigentlich." We use the terms "ideal" versus "ordinary."

We can think, in a rather loose way, that the line is closed by the introduction of P_∞ (somewhat as in Fig. 1-4), even if the corresponding λ has to jump from $-\infty$ to $+\infty$ at B. This idea will later be clarified.

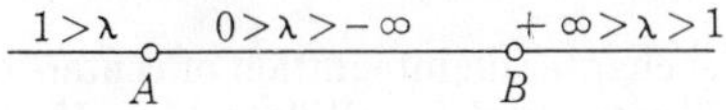

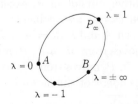

$$\underset{A}{\overset{1 > \lambda}{\vrule}} \qquad \underset{}{0 > \lambda > -\infty} \qquad \underset{B}{\overset{+\infty > \lambda > 1}{\vrule}}$$

Fig. 1-3

Fig. 1-4

The points A and B are called the *basic points* of l in the representation of points P by means of division ratios. We can consider λ as a *new kind of coordinate* of a point on l.

The division ratio was also introduced by Möbius, in his book *Der barycentrische Calcul* (1827) [parts of it translated in D. E. Smith, *A Source Book in Mathematics* (New York, 1929)]. In this book Möbius, who was a professor of astronomy at Leipzig, based his "calculus" on the concept of center of gravity. If we take two points A and B on line l, and place a mass m at A and a mass n at B, then one and only one point P on l is the center of gravity of these masses. If m and n are given all possible values (and we admit positive as well as negative masses, like electric charges), every point on l can be made the center of gravity, except in the case of $m = -n$. If A, B, P have the coordinates a, b, x, then, according to elementary statics*

$$x = \frac{ma + nb}{m + n}, \tag{2-3}$$

which passes into Eq. (2-2) by the substitution $\lambda = -n/m$. If we consider m and n as parallel forces applying at A and B in some direction different from that of l, then the point $P(x)$, determined by Eq. (2-3), is the point where the resultant force $m + n$ applies. The case $m = -n$ is that of the torque (see Sec. 1-7).

1-3 Harmonic sets. Two points P_1, P_2 on a line, for which the division ratio with respect to A, B is equal in absolute value but different in sign, are called *harmonic with respect to A and B*. P_1 is the *harmonic conjugate* of P_2, and conversely. We also say simply that the four points are *harmonic*. The definition requires that for such points the relation

$$P_1 A : P_1 B = -P_2 A : P_2 B \tag{3-1}$$

holds. One of the two points P_1, P_2 must lie inside the segment AB, the other outside of it, except when P_1 coincides with A (or B), in which case it also coincides with P_2. When P_1 lies at M, halfway between A and B ($\lambda = -1$), P_2 is identical with P_∞ ($\lambda = +1$). When P_1 moves from M to A, P_2 moves from P_∞ to A; when P_1 moves from M to B, P_2 moves from P_∞ to B. The harmonic property is obviously independent of the orientation of the line.

---

* See, in any book on the calculus, the chapter on integration of centers of gravity. Also L. Brand, *Vector and Tensor Analysis* (Wiley, New York, 1947), p. 9.

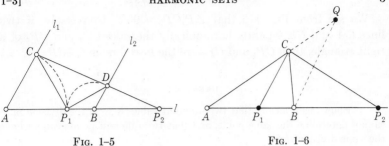

FIG. 1-5   FIG. 1-6

Since Eq. (3–1) can be cast into the form

$$AP_1:AP_2 = -BP_1:BP_2, \tag{3-2}$$

the points A and B are harmonic with respect to P_1 and P_2, when P_1 and P_2 are harmonic with respect to A and B.

In order to construct the harmonic conjugate P_2 of a point P_1 with respect to the points A and B, we draw (Fig. 1–5) through A and B two parallel lines l_1 and l_2 in an arbitrary direction, different from l. Then, by taking $|P_1A| = |CA|$ and $|P_1B| = |BD|$, we obtain P_2 by intersecting the line l with CD.

A construction with the straightedge alone will be given in Chapter 3.

THEOREM. *The inner and outer bisectors of the angle C of a triangle CAB intersect the opposite side AB in two points P_1, P_2 which are harmonic with respect to A and B (Fig. 1–6).*

This follows immediately from the two relations (the lengths of the segments AP_1, BP_1, etc., are all to be counted positive):

$$\frac{AP_1}{BP_1} = \frac{CA}{CB}; \quad \frac{AP_2}{BP_2} = \frac{CA}{CB}.$$

The proof of the first of these two relations is obtained by making CQ (Fig. 1–6) on side AC equal to side CB. Then $\angle Q = \frac{1}{2} \angle ACB$ (since $\triangle CQB$ is isosceles), hence QB is parallel to CP_1. This leads immediately to the required relation, because $CA:CB = P_1A:P_1B$, which is the well-known theorem of Euclid (*Elements* VI, Prop. 3); in words:

The bisector of an angle of a triangle intersects the opposite side in two segments which have the same ratio as the adjacent sides.

A similar relation holds for the bisector of the outer triangle.

We see from Fig. 1–6 that $\angle P_1 C P_2 = 90°$. Conversely, if two lines CA and CB separate harmonically the sides CP_1 and CP_2 of a right triangle, then CP_1 and CP_2 are the bisectors of $\triangle AC\mathring{B}$.

EXERCISES

1. Show algebraically that two different values λ_1,λ_2 of the division ratio cannot determine the same point, and that two different points cannot have the same division ratio.

2. The points A,B,P_1 have the coordinates 3,4,7 respectively. Find the harmonic conjugate P_2 of P_1 with respect to A and B.

3. Show numerically that in Ex. 2, B is the harmonic conjugate of A with respect to P_1 and P_2.

4. The locus of all points C in the plane for which the distance CA and CB to two fixed points A and B is a constant $\neq 1$ is a circle. This circle is called the *circle of Apollonius* of $\triangle ACB$ (with respect to C).

5. To every vertex of $\triangle ABC$ belongs a circle of Apollonius. Show that these three circles pass through two points. These points are called the *isodynamic points*.

6. A necessary and sufficient condition that P_1 and P_2 are harmonic with respect to A and B, is that $MP_1 \cdot MP_2 = a^2$, where M is the middle of AB and $AB = 2a$.

7. Show that the points with division ratio λ_1,λ_2 are harmonic with respect to the points with division ratio λ_3,λ_4 if $(\lambda_1 - \lambda_3):(\lambda_1 - \lambda_4) = -(\lambda_2 - \lambda_3):(\lambda_2 - \lambda_4)$. Another form of the condition is:

$$(\lambda_1 + \lambda_2)(\lambda_3 + \lambda_4) = 2(\lambda_1\lambda_2 + \lambda_3\lambda_4).$$

8. *Harmonic mean.* When the points O,P on a line are harmonic with respect to the points A,B, then

$$\frac{2}{OP} = \frac{1}{OA} + \frac{1}{OB}.$$

We call OP the *harmonic mean* of OA and OB, a term going back to the ancient Pythagoreans (Archytas, *On Music*, c. 350 B.C.).

9. Write identity (1–5) in the form of a determinant.

10. Prove that for four points on a straight line not only (1–4), but also the following identity holds

$$P_1P_2^2 \cdot Q_1Q_2 + P_2Q_1^2 \cdot Q_2P_1 + P_2Q_2^2 \cdot P_1Q_1 + Q_1Q_2 \cdot Q_2P_1 \cdot P_1Q_1 = 0 \text{ (Pappus)}.$$

11. Show that the points for which $\lambda = -a,+a$ and those for which $\lambda = 1,a^2$ are harmonic conjugates.

1–4 Cross ratio.   We now consider two points $P_1(x_1)$ and $P_2(x_2)$ on a line, with division ratios λ_1 and λ_2 with respect to the two points $A(a)$ and $B(b)$.   Then the quotient of these ratios,

$$\mu = \frac{\lambda_1}{\lambda_2} = \frac{P_1A}{P_1B} : \frac{P_2A}{P_2B} \qquad (4\text{–}1)$$

$(P_1A = -AP_1,$ etc., as usual), is called the *cross ratio* (or *anharmonic ratio*) of P_1, P_2 with respect to A and B.   For μ we introduce the notation

$$\mu = {}^{\cdot}(P_1P_2, AB), \qquad (4\text{–}2)$$

hence

$$\mu = \frac{P_1A}{P_1B} : \frac{P_2A}{P_2B} = \frac{P_1A \cdot P_2B}{P_1B \cdot P_2A} = \frac{a - x_1}{b - x_1} : \frac{a - x_2}{b - x_2}. \qquad (4\text{–}3)$$

The cross ratio of four points is independent of the orientation of the line.   When the cross ratio is equal to -1 the points P_1 and P_2 are harmonic with respect to A and B.   When $\mu < 0$, λ_1 and λ_2 differ in sign, so that P_1 and P_2 *separate* A and B.   When $\mu > 0$ the points P_1 and P_2 lie either inside the segment AB or A and B lie inside the segment P_1P_2.

Both cases are identical if we think of the line as closed by the introduction of P_∞ (Fig. 1–7). (See Sec. 1–2, Fig. 1–4.)

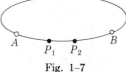

Fig. 1–7

When A, B, P_2 are fixed, that is, if λ_2 is kept constant, then μ is proportional to λ_1.   Therefore, when P_1 passes through all the points of the line (including P_∞), μ passes through all values from $-\infty$ to $+\infty$, and only once:

If three points are fixed, then the cross ratio determines uniquely the fourth point.   In other words, from

$$(AB, P_1P_2) = (AB, P_1P_3) \qquad (4\text{–}4)$$

it follows that $P_2 = P_3$.

The four letters A, B, P_1, P_2 can be permuted in 24 different ways. Four points, therefore, determine 24 cross ratios.   They can be divided in six groups, each of which contains four equal cross ratios.

These equal cross ratios are given by the identity

$$(P_1P_2,AB) = (AB,P_1P_2) = (P_2P_1,BA) = (BA,P_2P_1), \quad (4\text{--}5)$$

which can be verified by means of Eq. (4–3).   From this equation also follows

$$(P_2P_1,AB) = \frac{\lambda_2}{\lambda_1} = \frac{1}{\mu}. \qquad (4\text{--}6)$$

A third relation follows from the identity (1–4), which we can write as

$$P_1P_2 \cdot AB + P_1A \cdot BP_2 + P_1B \cdot P_2A = 0.$$

When we divide this by $P_1B \cdot P_2A$, we obtain [cf. Eq. (4–2)]

$$-(P_1A,P_2B) - \mu + 1 = 0,$$

or

$$(P_1A,P_2B) = 1 - \mu. \qquad (4\text{--}7)$$

From the three relations (4–5), (4–6), (4–7), we obtain all other relations.   The final result is expressed by the table below.

$$(P_1P_2,AB) = \mu, \qquad (P_1A,BP_2) = \frac{1}{1-\mu},$$

$$(P_2P_1,AB) = \frac{1}{\mu}, \qquad (P_1B,P_2A) = 1 - \frac{1}{\mu} = \frac{\mu-1}{\mu},$$

$$(P_1A,P_2B) = 1 - \mu, \quad (P_1B_2AP_2) = \frac{\mu}{\mu-1}.$$

These six cross ratios are, as a rule, all different from each other. If $\mu = \mu^{-1}$, then $\mu^2 = 1$, and $\mu = \pm 1$.   The case $\mu = +1$, according to Eq. (4–1), means that either P_1 coincides with P_2, A and B being different, or A coincides with B, P_1 and P_2 being different.   Then the cross ratios are $1, 0, \pm\infty$.   The case $\mu = -1$ is that of harmonic sets; here the cross ratios are $-1, 2, \frac{1}{2}$.   (For other special cases see Ex. 5 below.)   We combine our results in the following theorem.

The 24 cross ratios determined by four points on a line fall into six sets of four cross ratios each.   The four cross ratios of each set have the same value, and the cross ratios of the different sets can be written

$$\mu, \ \frac{1}{\mu}, \ 1 - \mu, \ \frac{1}{1-\mu}, \ \frac{\mu}{\mu-1}, \ \frac{\mu-1}{\mu}.$$

The term *cross ratio* seems to have been introduced by W. K. Clifford in place of the term *anharmonic ratio,* which is a translation of Chasles' *rapport anharmonique* (Aperçu Historique sur l'Origine et le Développement des Méthodes en Géométrie, 1837). The German term is *Doppelverhältniss,* first used by Möbius in his book on the barycentric calculus in the longer version *Doppelschnitt-verhältniss* (1827). Von Staudt, in his axiomatics of projective geometry rejecting the metrical implication of the term *ratio* (Verhältniss), used the term *Wurf* ("throw").

EXERCISES

1. Show that for four points A,B,C,D on a line:

$$(AB,CD)(AB,DC) = 1,$$
$$(AB,CD) + (AC,BD) = 1.$$

2. Show that for five points A,B,C,D,E on a line:

$$(AB,DE)(AB,EC)(AB,CD) = 1.$$

3. Show that for three points A,B,C on a line the division ratio λ also takes the 6 values λ, $1/\lambda$, $1 - \lambda$, $1/(1 - \lambda)$, $\lambda/(\lambda - 1)$, $(\lambda - 1)/\lambda$ (e.g., $AC/BC = \lambda$, $BC/AC = 1/\lambda$, etc.).

4. Investigate the case that two of the six values of the division ratio of three points are equal (see Ex. 3).

5. Show that the cases $\mu = 1 - \mu$ and $\mu = \mu/(\mu - 1)$ do not lead to new cases, but that $\mu = 1/(1 - \mu)$ does lead to a new case. In this new case, however, μ is imaginary. We speak of the *equianharmonic case.*

6. Show that $(AB,PP_\infty) = AP:BP$. Also find a simpler expression for $(AB,P_\infty P)$, $(P_\infty A,BP)$.

7. Find the cross ratios of the four points with coordinates $5,7,-1,0$. Similarly, try to attach a meaning to $(0,\infty,a,b)$, $(\infty,0,a,b)$, $(a,b,\infty,0)$.

8. If $A(x = 2)$, $B(x = 3)$, $P(x = 1)$ and $\mu = (AB,PQ) = -3$, find Q.

9. Show that the cross ratio (P_1P_2,P_3P_4) of four points P_1,P_2,P_3,P_4 on a line with division ratios $\lambda_1,\lambda_2,\lambda_3,\lambda_4$ is given by

$$(\lambda_1,\lambda_2; \lambda_3,\lambda_4) = \frac{\lambda_1 - \lambda_3}{\lambda_1 - \lambda_4} : \frac{\lambda_2 - \lambda_3}{\lambda_2 - \lambda_4}$$

(cf. Ex. 7, Sec. 1–3).*

10. Find by geometrical construction the point having a cross ratio 3 with three given points on a line.

---

* Sometimes we shall write for the cross ratio $(a,b; c,d)$ instead of (ab,cd).

1–5 Projectivity. We consider two lines l and l'. The points P on l are determined by their division ratios λ with respect to two basic points A,B on l, the points P' similarly by their division ratios λ' with respect to A',B' on l' (Fig. 1–8). A bilinear relation between λ and λ',

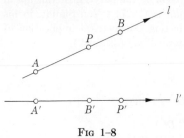

Fig 1–8

$$\alpha\lambda\lambda' + \beta\lambda + \gamma\lambda' + \delta = 0 \quad (5\text{–}1)$$

($\alpha,\beta,\gamma,\delta$ constants, not all zero), determines one and only one λ when λ' is given, and one and only one λ' when λ is given, provided the coefficients do not satisfy some special condition discussed below.

The equation (5–1) is called *bilinear*, because it is linear in λ and linear in λ'. It is the most general equation of this kind.

This means that in this case we can associate with every point P on l one and only one point P' on l' and conversely. Such a one-to-one correspondence, expressed by Eq. (5–1), is called a *projectivity* on the lines, and the points form *projective point sets*.

When the points $ABCD\ldots$ correspond to $A'B'C'D'\ldots$ in a projectivity, then we write with Von Staudt

$$ABCD\cdots \overline{\wedge}\ A'B'C'D'\ldots.$$

An exception occurs when Eq. (5–1) can be split into two factors. This is the case only if

$$\Delta \equiv \alpha\delta - \beta\gamma = 0 \qquad (5\text{–}2)$$

(see Ex. 1, Sec. 1–6). In this special case, supposing $\alpha \neq 0$, Eq. (5–1) can be written in the form

$$(\alpha\lambda + \gamma)(\alpha\lambda' + \beta) = 0, \qquad (5\text{–}3)$$

or

$$\alpha\lambda + \gamma = 0, \quad \alpha\lambda' + \beta = 0.$$

To every point P corresponds the same point P' with $\lambda' = -\beta/\alpha$, to every point P' the same point P with $\lambda = -\gamma/\alpha$. The projectivity is *singular*. If $\alpha = 0$ and $\delta \neq 0$, we can proceed similarly; if $\alpha = 0$ and $\delta = 0$ the projectivity is also singular, since β or γ must be zero.

We take $\Delta \equiv \alpha\delta - \beta\gamma \neq 0$ and select the basic points in such a way that A corresponds to A' and B to B', which can be done without affecting the generality of the projectivity (see Ex. 3, Sec. 1–6). Then Eq. (5–1) must be satisfied by $\lambda = 0$, $\lambda' = 0$, hence $\delta = 0$; and also by $\lambda = \infty$, $\lambda' = \infty$, hence $\alpha = 0$ [this we can show by dividing the left-hand member of Eq. (5–1) by $\lambda\lambda'$]. The projectivity then takes the form

$$\beta\lambda + \gamma\lambda' = 0 \quad (\beta,\gamma \text{ both } \neq 0). \tag{5–4}$$

This relation is uniquely determined if one more set of corresponding points is given, since this will determine the ratio $\beta:\gamma$. Hence we have the following theorem.

A nonsingular projectivity between the points of two lines is uniquely determined by three pairs of corresponding points.

This theorem can also be deduced from the fact that the left-hand side of Eq. (5–1) contains four constants, of which only the ratio counts.

We now prove the *fundamental theorem* of projectivities:

When four points on a line correspond to four points on another line by means of a projectivity, then the cross ratio of the four points on the first line is equal to that of the four points on the other line.

Indeed, let A,B,P_1,P_2 on l correspond to A',B',P_1',P_2' on l', and let the division ratios of P_1,P_2 be respectively λ_1,λ_2 (with respect to A,B), and those of P_1',P_2' be λ_1',λ_2' (with respect to A',B'). Then, according to Eq. (5–4), the relations hold:

$$\beta\lambda_1 + \gamma\lambda_1' = 0, \quad \beta\lambda_2 + \gamma\lambda_2' = 0,$$

hence

$$\lambda_1/\lambda_2 = \lambda_1'/\lambda_2',$$

or [see Eq. (4–1)]

$$(AB,P_1P_2) = (A'B',P_1'P_2'), \tag{5–5}$$

which proves the theorem. We can also express it by saying that *the cross ratio of four points on a line is invariant under a (nonsingular) projectivity.* We return to this theorem in Chapter 2.

Since λ, according to Eq. (2–1) or (2–2), is a linear function of x, a projectivity can also be given by means of a bilinear relation in the Cartesian coordinates x and x' of P and P' respectively, and also conversely, according to Eq. (2–2). If such a relation is given by

$$\alpha_1 x x' + \beta_1 x + \gamma_1 x' + \delta_1 = 0 \quad (\alpha_1, \beta_1, \gamma_1, \delta_1 \text{ constants}, \quad (5–6)$$
$$\text{not all zero}),$$

then $\alpha_1 \delta_1 - \beta_1 \gamma_1 \neq 0$ is the condition for nonsingularity (see Ex. 2, Sec. 1–6).

When in Eq. (5–6) the improper elements correspond, then $\alpha_1 = 0$. Then, for two corresponding pairs x_1, x_1'; $x_2 x_2'$ the relation holds:

$$\gamma_1 (x_1' - x_2') = -\beta_1 (x_1 - x_2). \quad (5–7)$$

This means that in this projectivity, if nonsingular (both $\beta_1, \gamma_1 \neq 0$), the lengths of corresponding line segments are in constant ratio. This is a *similarity transformation* or *similitude;* when $\beta_1 = \pm \gamma_1$ we speak of a *congruent transformation.*

When l and l' intersect in A, and A corresponds to itself $(A = A')$ in the projectivity, then we have a *perspectivity*, and the points on l and l' form *perspective point sets.* To this relationship we shall return in more detail.

We shall prove in Sec. 2–7 that in this case the lines connecting corresponding points all pass through one point.

1–6 Projectivities on the same line. The theory of the preceding section remains valid when l and l' coincide. Then the question arises whether there are *double points*, that is, corresponding points which coincide. Let us measure x and x', on the line, from the same origin O (Fig. 1–2), and let the nonsingular projectivity be given by Eq. (5–6) (where we drop the indices):

$$\alpha x x' + \beta x + \gamma x' + \delta = 0, \quad \alpha\delta - \beta\gamma \neq 0. \quad (6–1)$$

The double points are given by $x = x'$:

$$\alpha x^2 + (\beta + \gamma) x + \delta = 0. \quad (6–2)$$

Let us take first $\alpha \neq 0$. Then there are three cases, depending on the sign of

$$\Delta \equiv (\beta + \gamma)^2 - 4\alpha\delta.$$

Case I. $\Delta > 0$.   There are two different real roots, hence two (real) double points.   This is the *hyperbolic* case.   Let D_1 $(x = a)$, D_2 $(x = b)$ be these double points, both different from P_∞.   Then D_1, D_2 correspond to themselves, and because of Eq. (5–5) there exists for two corresponding pairs $P_1(x_1), P_1'(x_1')$; $P_2(x_2), P_2'(x_2')$ the relation

$$(D_1 D_2, P_1 P_2) = (D_1 D_2, P_1' P_2');$$

in coordinates:

$$\frac{x_1 - a}{x_1 - b} : \frac{x_2 - a}{x_2 - b} = \frac{x_1' - a}{x_1' - b} : \frac{x_2' - a}{x_2' - b},$$

or

$$\frac{x_1 - a}{x_1' - a} : \frac{x_1 - b}{x_1' - b} = \frac{x_2 - a}{x_2' - a} : \frac{x_2 - b}{x_2' - b} = k,$$

where k is a constant, evidently independent of the choice of the corresponding points:

The cross ratio of two corresponding points and the double points is constant.

A hyperbolic projectivity can therefore be written in the form:

$$\frac{x - a}{x' - a} : \frac{x - b}{x' - b} = k, \quad \text{or} \quad \frac{x' - b}{x' - a} = k \frac{x - b}{x - a}, \qquad (6\text{–}3)$$

where a, b, k are constants, $a \neq b$.   *The division ratios of two corresponding points with respect to the double points are in constant ratio.* The number k is called the *multiplier* of the projectivity.

Case II. $\Delta < 0$.   There are no real roots, hence no double points. We can write Eq. (6–3) in the same form, but a and b are now conjugate complex numbers.   This is the *elliptic case*.

Let us now consider the case $\alpha = 0$.   Then $\Delta = (\beta + \gamma)^2$, which is ≥ 0, so that Case II does not appear.   Case I is given by $\beta + \gamma \neq 0$. Equation (6–2), in this case, can be considered as a quadratic equation with one root at infinity, so that P_∞ is one of the double points, the other double point being a proper point.   Now Eq. (6–1) can be written in the form:

$$x' = -\frac{1}{\gamma}(\beta x + \delta) = c(x + c_1) \quad (c, c_1 \text{ constants}, c \neq 1)$$

or, if $x = a$ is the proper double point D,

$$x' - a = c(x - a),$$

which is a *similarity transformation*, namely, a multiplication of all segments, measured from the double point D, by the same constant $\neq 1$. This can therefore be taken as a standard form of a hyperbolic projectivity.

Here we have made use of the following theorem. *If in a quadratic equation $ax^2 + bx + c = 0$:*

(1) $a \to 0$, $b \neq 0$, *then one of the roots moves to infinity*,
(2) $a \to 0$, $b \to 0$, $c \neq 0$, *then both roots move to infinity*.

We can prove this by substituting $x = 1/y$ into the equation and letting $y \to 0$.

Case III. $\Delta = 0$. There is only one double point. This is the *parabolic case*. If $\alpha = 0$, then $\beta + \gamma = 0$, and P_∞ is the double point. The projectivity becomes a *translation:*

$$x' = x + p, \quad p \text{ constant} \neq 0, \text{ if } \delta \neq 0.$$

From this we obtain the expression for the case $\alpha \neq 0$ in the form

$$\frac{1}{x' - a} = \frac{1}{x - a} + p,$$

where $x = a$ gives the double point.

The construction of the double points of a projectivity depends, as (6–2) shows, on a quadratic equation and can thus be performed with compass and straightedge (Ex. 13, Sec. 5–4).

EXERCISES

1. Show that $\alpha\delta - \beta\gamma = 0$ is the necessary and sufficient condition that the projectivity (5–1) is singular.
2. Show that $\alpha\delta - \beta\gamma = 0$ implies $\alpha_1\delta_1 - \beta_1\gamma_1 = 0$ [see Eq. (5–6)] and conversely.
3. Show that a projectivity between two lines remains a projectivity if we define the bilinear relation between λ and μ with respect to different basic points.
4. If R corresponds on l to P'_∞ and S' on l' to P_∞, then for any two pairs of corresponding points P,P'; Q,Q', $PR \cdot P'S' = QR \cdot Q'S'$. Because of the

role they play in the theory of perspective, R and S' are called the *vanishing points* of l,l' respectively (see Sec. 11–2).

5. Prove the property of similitude (5–7) by using the relation $(PQ,RP_\infty) = (P'Q',R'P'_\infty)$ for any three pairs of corresponding points PP',QQ',RR'.

6. Find the equation of a projectivity which transforms the points with coordinates 1,2,3 on l into those with coordinates (a) 4,3,2 on l'; (b) 1,2,3 on l'; (c) $-1,-2,-3$ on l'.

7. Repeat Ex. 6 if the points with coordinates (a) $1,2,\infty$ on l pass into $5,7,\infty$ on l'; (b) $0,c,\infty$ on l into $0,b,\infty$ on l'.

8. Given a projectivity (6–1) with double points $x = a$, $x = b$. Show that

$$k = \frac{\beta a - \gamma b}{\beta b - \gamma a}.$$

9. Show that $(k^{\frac{1}{2}} + k^{-\frac{1}{2}})^2 = (\beta - \gamma)^2/(\alpha\delta - \beta\gamma)$.

10. Find the double points and the constant k of the projectivity $xx' - 4x + x' + 2 = 0$.

11. Write the elliptic transformation $xx' + a^2 = 0$ in the form (6–3), with the aid of imaginaries.

12. Show that by choice of the double points projectivities can be cast into the form

$$x' = \frac{x + \lambda}{\lambda x + 1} \text{ (hyp.)}, \quad x' = \frac{x - \lambda}{\lambda x + 1} \text{ (ell.)}, \quad x' = \frac{x}{\lambda x + 1} \text{ (par.)}.$$

13. Reduce to a canonical form:

$$x' = \frac{2x + 6}{3x - 1}.$$

14. Prove that when A and B separate P_1 and P_2 on a line (this property is sometimes written $AB//P_1P_2$), this condition is invariant under projectivities. This property plays an important role in the axiomatics of projective geometry.

15. Show that a projectivity P followed by a projectivity Q on the same line gives another projectivity. We can write this projectivity as PQ. Is $PQ = QP$?

1–7 Involutions. We return to the line. Let the points P and Q of this line, by means of a projectivity, correspond to the points P' and Q' on the same line. When we consider P' as the point Q, then Q' as a rule does not coincide with P.

When this does happen for all pairs P, P', then we call the projectivity an *involution*. An example is the reflection of a point in a fixed point Q on the line, which is given by the equation $x + x' = 0$, since x leads to x', and x' back to x.

In the general case of an involution, Eq. (6–1) must be so construed that x and x' are interchangeable. This means that $\beta = \gamma$, so that an involution on a line is given by the equation

$$\alpha x x' + 2\beta(x + x') + \delta = 0, \tag{7–1}$$

where $\beta^2 - \alpha\delta \neq 0$ in order to prevent singularity.

The relation $\beta = \gamma$ already holds if one pair of points corresponds in involution, since the equations

$$\alpha x x' + \beta x + \gamma x' + \delta = 0, \quad \alpha x x' + \beta x' + \gamma x + \delta = 0$$

lead to $(\beta - \gamma)(x - x') = 0$, or $\beta = \gamma$.

This can be expressed in the words:

A projectivity is an involution if one pair of corresponding points is in involution.

We can again distinguish between hyperbolic, elliptic, and parabolic involutions, depending on the sign of $\Delta = 4(\beta^2 - \alpha\delta)$.

The parabolic involution is always singular, and carries every point into the point for which $x = -2\beta/\alpha = -\gamma/2\beta$.

The hyperbolic involution has two double points D_1 ($x = a$) and D_2 ($x = b$) which we shall first assume to be ordinary points. Then, in Eq. (6–3), $k^2 = 1$, and since $k = 1$ gives the identity, we find in this case that

$$\frac{x' - a}{x' - b} = -\frac{x - a}{x - b}. \tag{7–2}$$

When P, P' are two corresponding points, then this equation is equivalent to

$$(D_1 D_2, P P') = -1.$$

Two corresponding points of a hyperbolic involution are harmonic with respect to the double points.

Conversely, the most general hyperbolic involution is formed by the pairs of harmonic conjugates with respect to two fixed points.

If now we assume that $D_1 = P_\infty$, then $\alpha = 0$ and the involution can be written as

$$x + x' = \text{const} = p, \qquad (7\text{-}3)$$

which is the *reflection* in the point for which $x = p/2$.

If P_∞ is not a double point, then it corresponds to an ordinary point C, the *central point*. Then

$$(D_1 D_2, C P_\infty) = -1,$$

which means that $CD_1 + CD_2 = 0$; the *central point lies halfway between the double points*. Taking C as the new origin, then $\beta = 0$ and we obtain as the equation of the involution:

$$xx' = k^2, \quad k^2 = -\delta/\alpha, \text{ a positive constant.} \qquad (7\text{-}4)$$

The product of the distances of two corresponding points to the central point is constant. A pair of corresponding points lies on the same side of C, separating D_1 and D_2 because of Eq. (7-3). Two pairs PP',QQ' do not separate each other, and if P moves to a double point in a certain sense then P' moves to the same double point, but in the opposite sense.

The elliptic involution has no double points, but we still can find a new origin for which $\beta = 0$ in Eq. (7-1), so that a real central point C still exists. Since $\Delta < 0$ we can write the involution in the form

$$xx' + m^2 = 0, \quad m^2 = \delta/\alpha, \text{ a positive constant.} \qquad (7\text{-}5)$$

The product of the distances of two corresponding points to the central point is constant. Corresponding points lie on different sides of C. Two pairs PP',QQ' separate each other, and if P moves in a certain sense on the line, then P' moves in the same sense.

For both types of involution the theorem holds:

An involution is determined by two pairs of corresponding points.

The truth of this theorem can be gathered from the fact that the ratio of α,β,δ determines Eq. (7-1). The actual proof is based on the fact that a projectivity is determined by three pairs of corresponding points, and if the given pairs of points of the involution are PP',QQ', then we have a projectivity determined by means of the pairs

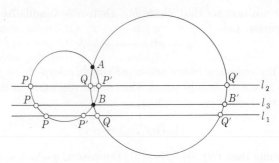

Fig. 1–9

$PP',P'P,QQ'$. The theorem that a projectivity is an involution
when one pair of points P,P' corresponds then establishes that Q and
Q' also correspond. It is therefore a remarkable property for *three*
pairs of points to lie in involution, forming a *configuration* of points.
This configuration, probably already known to Euclid, will reappear
in Ex. 3, Sec. 2–9, Fig. 2–9, and also in Ex. 6, Sec. 5–10. We say
that *the three pairs are in involution* (also form a *quadrangular* set).

We shall now show how the points of an involution can be constructed if two pairs PP',QQ' are given on a line l. Let PP' and
QQ' first lie outside each other, so that the involution is hyperbolic
(Fig. 1–9, $l = l_1$). Take a point A in a plane through l_1 outside of l_1
and construct the circles through APP' and through AQQ'. These
circles have another point B in common on the same side of l as A.
If AB intersects l in C (not shown in this figure), then, because of a
well-known property of the circle,

$$CP \cdot CP' = CQ \cdot CQ' = CB \cdot CA,$$

so that C is the central point of the involution of which the corresponding points are obtained by intersecting l_1 with the circles through A
and B. The double points are the points where l_1 is tangent to the
circles through A and B.

When PP' and QQ' separate each other, and we perform the same
construction, then B lies on a different side of l from A. Again
$CP \cdot CP' = CQ \cdot CQ'$ and the involution is elliptic (Fig. 1–9, $l = l_2$).
If the circles intersect in a line through B, we obtain a parabolic involution. Here $B = P = C = Q$ (Fig. 1–9, $l = l_3$).

Three pairs of points in involution are discussed in the 7th book of the *Mathematical Collection* of Pappus (c. 300 A.D.), in a commentary to Euclid's lost work "On Porisms." We find the pairs again in Girard Desargues' *Brouillon Project* (1639) under the name "involution à six points." Desargues (1593–1661 or '62) of Lyons was in his days a well-known architect. Although some of his contemporaries, including Descartes and Pascal, recognized his merits as a scientist, his mathematical work (often written in an obscure terminology) was well-nigh forgotten until its importance was rediscovered in the 19th century. The "Brouillon" is lost, but a copy of it, made by De la Hire in 1679, was rediscovered by Michel Chasles in 1845. It is to Chasles that we mainly owe the theory of involution in its present form: *Aperçu Historique* (Paris, 1837; 2nd ed., 1875), Note 10 (full title, Sec. 1–4). On Desargues, see R. Taton, *L'Œuvre Mathématique de G. Desargues* (Paris, 1951).

EXERCISES

1. Find the equation of the involution of which the double elements are (a) $x = 5$, $x = -7$, (b) $x = 5$, $x = \infty$.

2. Show that the transformation $x' = (7 - 3x)/(5x + 3)$ is an involution and find its double points and central point.

3. Show that a necessary and sufficient condition that three pairs of points (AA'), (BB'), (CC') are in involution F is that $(AB,CC') = (B'A',CC')$.

4. Let a projectivity on a line with fixed elements C,C' transform A into A' and B into B'. Prove that the three pairs (C,C'), (A,B'), $(A'B)$ are three pairs in involution.

5. Show that an involution is parabolic if two corresponding pairs have a point in common.

6. *Apolarity.* Two quadratic forms

$$A = a_{11}x^2 + 2a_{12}x + a_{22}, \quad B = b_{11}x^2 + 2b_{12}x + b_{22}$$

are called *apolar*, if $a_{11}b_{22} - 2a_{12}b_{12} + a_{22}b_{11} = 0$. Here B and A are not proportional $(B \neq A)$. Then all forms λA, μB (λ,μ arbitrary constants) are also apolar. Show that the necessary and sufficient condition that the points determined by $A = 0$ are harmonic with respect to those given by $B = 0$ is that A and B are apolar. What happens if A and B have a factor in common?

7. When B_1 and B_2 are quadratic forms $(B_2 \neq \mu B_1)$, then there exist quadratic forms apolar to B_1 and B_2. If one of them is A then all of them are of the form λA. Prove.

8. All quadratic forms B_1 and B_2 apolar to the quadratic form A are of the form $\lambda_1 B_1 + \lambda_2 B_2$ (λ_1, λ_2 arbitrary constants). Prove. Such a form is called a *pencil* of quadratic forms.

9. Show that *there exists at most one unique pair of points which separates harmonically each of two given pairs of points.* Hence two nonparabolic involutions on a line have one pair of corresponding points in common.

10. The points given by the pencil $\lambda_1 B_1 + \lambda_2 B_2 = 0$ (Ex. 8) for each set of values λ_1, λ_2 form an involution. Prove.

11. Show that every involution can be written in the form $\lambda_1 B_1 + \lambda_2 B_2 = 0$, where B_1 and B_2 are arbitrary quadratic forms ($B_2 \neq \mu B_1$ and λ_1, λ_2 are variable).

12. Find the pair of points which separate harmonically the pairs with coordinates $1, -3$ and $2, 6$.

13. Find the double points of the involution cut out by the pencil $\lambda(x^2 - x) + \mu(x^2 - 5x + 6) = 0$.

14. *Periodic projectivities.* An involution T followed by the same involution T gives, by definition, the identity I. We write $TT = T^2 = I$. Show that the conditions that a projectivity $P : a\lambda\mu + b\lambda + c\mu + d = 0$ satisfies the equation $P^3 = I$ is $b^2 + c^2 = ad + bc$. We call an involution a projectivity *of period* 2, and the projectivity P *of period* 3.

15. When (Ex. 14) $P^n = I$ (n positive integer), we speak of a *projectivity of period n.* Show that there are no periodic parabolic projectivities.

16. Show that every (noninvolutory) projectivity P can be obtained as an involution T followed by another T'; $P = TT'$. Is $T'T = TT'$?

17. Given a hyperbolic projectivity P, not an involution. Let a point A by repeated application of P pass into $A_1, A_2, \ldots$. Then the sequence $A, A_1, A_2, \ldots A_n$ has one of the double points as limit point, and the sequence $B, B_1, B_2, \ldots B_n$, obtained by repeated application of the inverse projectivity P^{-1}, has as its limit point the other double point. This procedure is independent of the choice of A (if not a double point itself).

1–8 Introduction of imaginary elements. The search for double points in elliptic projectivities has led to quadratic equations with imaginary or complex roots. Since we decided at the beginning of this chapter to consider — for the time being — only real values of the coordinates, we concluded that there are no double points in this case. This changes when we extend the range of numbers underlying our geometry from that of real numbers to that of complex numbers. In this case we assign to each complex number a point on the line as coordinate. The line now becomes a two-dimensional entity which can be brought into a one-to-one correspondence with the Gauss plane (complex plane) in which we are accustomed to represent complex numbers $z = x + iy$ by means of real points with coordinates (x,y). Points with real coordinates or *real points* correspond to the points on the x-axis in the Gauss plane. The Gauss plane has the same geometry as the Euclidean plane so far as the ordinary points are concerned. There is a difference when ideal elements are introduced (there is only one ideal point).

Points with imaginary or complex values are called *imaginary points*. The line on which real and imaginary points are admitted is called a line in *complex geometry*, in contrast to our previous line, which was a line in *real geometry*. *In complex geometry all nonsingular projectivities on a line have two double points, which may be real distinct, real coincident, or imaginary distinct.*

Analytic geometry arose historically from the application of sixteenth-century algebra to the geometry of the Greeks. The underlying range of numbers was therefore originally that of the positive numbers. But positive numbers do not form a *field*, which means that though they do satisfy the ordinary laws of addition and multiplication, they do not satisfy the requirement that $a + x = b$ can be solved for all a and b. Operations in analytical geometry therefore were extended by Newton and others to the real numbers, which do form a field.

Elements form a *field* if they satisfy the following laws:

I. Laws of addition:
   (a) associative law: $a + (b + c) = (a + b) + c$,
   (b) commutative law: $a + b = b + a$,
   (c) the equation: $a + x = b$ can be solved for all a and b.

II. Laws of multiplication:
   (a) associative law: $a(bc) = (ab)c$,
   (b) commutative law: $ab = ba$,
   (c) the equation: $ax = b$ can be solved for all a and b, if $a \neq 0$.

III. Distributive laws (these connect addition and multiplication):
   (a) $a(b + c) = ab + ac$,
   (b) $(b + c)a = ba + ca$.

See, for example, A. A. Albert, *Introduction to Algebraic Theories* (Chicago, 1941), p. 113.

Imaginary elements entered into geometry with the discussion of the roots of quadratic equations by Monge and his school, and notably with the work of Poncelet. Here imaginaries were mainly introduced as an auxiliary to the study of real elements. The underlying field is here that of the complex numbers. This met with some distrust at first, until it was found that geometry need not be based on one particular number field alone, but can be based on a great variety of underlying algebras.

An example of this distrust is the statement the astronomer Airy once made: "I have not the smallest confidence in any result which is essentially obtained by the use of imaginary symbols." [*Cambridge Phil. Soc. Trans.* **10** (1858), p. 327.]

Although complex geometry was gradually accepted, a systematic investigation of this geometry had to wait until more recent times — until the works of such authors as E. Cartan, Study, Fubini, and Coolidge.

See J. L. Coolidge, *Geometry of the Complex Domain* (Oxford, 1924), or E. Cartan, *Leçons sur la Géométrie Projective Complexe* (Paris, 1931). A. Todd, *Projective and Algebraic Geometry* (New York, 1946), also uses complex geometry consistently.

In our present book we shall not go beyond the intermediate position taken by Poncelet and other authors of the nineteenth century. Imaginaries will be essentially tools to facilitate the study of the real domain. Our starting point will be curves, surfaces, and transformations defined by equations with real coefficients. We could therefore have described all results by real means exclusively, as has been done consistently, for instance in H. S. M. Coxeter, *The Real Projective Plane* (New York, 1949).

We can select other number fields to provide the underlying algebra of a geometry. Particular attention has been paid to finite fields, which are fields with only a finite set of numbers. In this way we obtain *finite geometries*. One such field is the set of all integers mod n (n a positive integer). We shall later give an example of such a finite geometry in the plane.

There are important differences between real and complex geometry. As an example we prove the *theorem of Von Staudt:*

The only one-to-one correspondence between the real points on a line which preserves the harmonic relation between four points is a (nonsingular) projectivity.

To prove this theorem, let the correspondence be given by $\lambda' = f(\lambda)$, where λ and λ' do not necessarily refer to the same set of basic points (these may even be on different lines). We let three arbitrary points of one set correspond to three arbitrary points of the other set and then select the basic points such that the relations

$$f(0) = 0, \quad f(1) = 1, \quad f(\infty) = \infty$$

hold [Eq.(5–4)]. Moreover:

$$[f(\lambda_1), f(\lambda_2); f(\lambda_3), f(\lambda_4)] = -1 \text{ when } (\lambda_1\lambda_2, \lambda_3\lambda_4) = -1.$$

First take $\lambda_3 = \frac{1}{2}(\lambda_1 + \lambda_2)$, hence $\lambda_4 = \infty$. This gives

$$f\left(\frac{\lambda_1 + \lambda_2}{2}\right) = \frac{1}{2}[f(\lambda_1) + f(\lambda_2)].$$

Since $f(0) = 0$, we obtain from this

$$f\left(\frac{\lambda}{2}\right) = \frac{1}{2}f(\lambda),$$

so that the general additive relation holds:

$$f(\lambda_1 + \lambda_2) = f(\lambda_1) + f(\lambda_2). \tag{8–1}$$

This equation admits only one continuous solution, namely $f(\lambda) = \lambda$. Darboux has shown that the condition $f(\lambda) > 0$, for $\lambda > 0$, is sufficient to secure this solution. Indeed, from Eq. (8–1) we derive that for any positive and negative integer n,

$$f(n\lambda) = nf(\lambda),$$

and since $f(1) = 1$, we obtain from this by substituting $\lambda = p/n$, where p is an integer, that

$$f\left(\frac{p}{q}\right) = \frac{p}{q}$$

for all positive and negative integers p,q.

Now let, for all $\lambda > 0$, $f(\lambda) > 0$. Then, since $f(\lambda_1 - \lambda_2) = f(\lambda_1) - f(\lambda_2)$ [because $f(0) = 0$], we see that $f(\lambda_1) > f(\lambda_2)$ when $\lambda_1 > \lambda_2$. But since every irrational λ can be approached as closely as we like by a sequence of rational numbers, both from the upper and from the lower side, we see that $f(\lambda) = \lambda$ for all real values of λ.

We can now show that for real λ this condition $f(\lambda) > 0$ for $\lambda > 0$ is satisfied. This is done by means of the identity (Ex. 11, Sec. 1-3)

$$(\mu, -\mu; 1, \mu^2) = -1$$

or

$$f(\mu^2) = (f(\mu))^2.$$

Substituting $\mu = \sqrt{\lambda}$, $\lambda > 0$, we obtain the required condition and the demonstration is finished, except for the remark that $\lambda' = \lambda$ when the points $0, \infty, 1$ correspond to $0, \infty, 1$ respectively, and the correspondence $\lambda' \leftrightarrow \lambda$ is bilinear when the points $0, \infty, 1$ correspond to any other triple of points.

We thus have seen that the theorem stating that every projectivity preserves cross ratio has as its converse that every one-to-one correspondence preserving cross ratio is a projectivity.

This converse is not true for complex geometry. The correspondence $\lambda' = \bar{\lambda}$ ($\bar{\lambda}$ the complex conjugate of λ), for example, is not a projectivity, but preserves the harmonic relationship. This is an example of an *antiprojectivity*.

The theorem is found in Christian Von Staudt's *Geometrie der Lage* (1847), Sec. 9; his proof is different and not quite complete (see this book, Sec. 4-2). Later, Klein and others questioned the reasoning of Von Staudt, and saw the necessity for an assumption of continuity (see F. Klein, *Ges. Abhandl. I*, Nos. XIX, XX). Then the question was settled by G. Darboux, *Mathem. Annalen* **17** (1880), pp. 54-61. Further information can be found in *Veblen-Young* II, Chapter VI, or O. Schreier-E. Sperner, *Einführung in die Analytische Geometrie und Algebra* II (Leipzig, 1935). p. 195.

EXERCISES

1. Show that from $f(\lambda_1 + \lambda_2) = f(\lambda_1) + f(\lambda_2)$ and $f(\lambda^2) = [f(\lambda)]^2$ follows that $f(\lambda_1 \lambda_2) = f(\lambda_1) f(\lambda_2)$.

2. Show that when $f(\lambda_1 + \lambda_2) = f(\lambda_1) + f(\lambda_2)$, $f(\lambda_1 \lambda_2) = f(\lambda_1) f(\lambda_2)$ and λ is real, $f(\lambda) = \lambda$. This may be expressed by stating that the identity is the only *automorphism* of the field of real numbers.

3. Show that the condition that $f(\lambda) > 0$ for $\lambda > 0$ is equivalent to the condition that there are values of λ such that a (real) pair of points exists which separates both the points $(1, \lambda)$ and $(0, \infty)$ harmonically.

CHAPTER 2

LINE PENCILS

2–1 The Cartesian equation of a line. We have seen that it is possible to assign to a line a positive or a negative sense. We can similarly endow a plane with a sense by distinguishing between a clockwise and a counterclockwise sense. We call the clockwise sense *negative*, the other sense *positive*. The plane is now *oriented*. We stress, with an eye on later developments, that the nonoriented plane is the plane of ordinary analytic (and elementary) geometry. We call it the *Euclidean* plane.

Euclid (c. 300 B.C.), a mathematician of Alexandria in Egypt, wrote the *Elements* in 13 books, 4 of which deal with plane, and 3 with solid geometry. Our high school textbooks on geometry are all based on Euclid's *Elements*. Starting with points and lines, the *Elements* deals with triangles, circles, planes, spheres, and polyhedra, in a strictly axiomatic way. Only in recent times have substantial improvements been made in Euclid's axiomatics, mainly under the influence of the work of Moritz Pasch (1843–1930) and David Hilbert (1862–1943). See D. Hilbert, *The Foundations of Geometry* (translated by E. J. Townsend, Chicago, 1902).

In an oriented plane we can define the (directed) angle $\phi = \angle(l_1 l_2)$ between two rays l_1 and l_2 as the angle between $-\pi$ and $+\pi$ through which l_1 has to turn in order to cover l_2, counted positive if this turning is counterclockwise, and otherwise negative. Then (Figs. 2–1, 2–2)

$$\angle(l_1 l_2) + \angle(l_2 l_1) = 0. \tag{1-1}$$

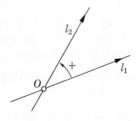

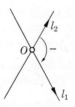

FIG. 2–1   FIG. 2–2

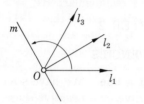

FIG. 2–3

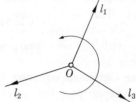

FIG. 2–4

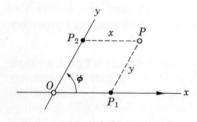

FIG. 2–5

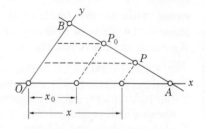

FIG. 2–6

This formula reminds us of Eq. (1–1), Chapter 1, but we must be careful with the relation similar to Eq. (1–2). For this purpose we introduce the term *half-ray* to indicate the part of an oriented line on the positive side of one of its points O. In Fig. 2–3, where the half-rays l_1, l_2, l_3 are on one side of a line m through O:

$$\angle (l_1 l_2) + \angle (l_2 l_3) + \angle (l_3 l_1) = 0, \tag{1–2}$$

but in Fig. 2–4, where there is no such line m, we find

$$\angle (l_1 l_2) + \angle (l_2 l_3) + \angle (l_3 l_1) = 2\pi. \tag{1–3}$$

We shall try to orient our lines in such a way that Eq. (1–2) holds. If not, then we can still speak of the angle of two lines, if we remember that this expression is ambiguous without further specification.

For the definition of the angle of two lines, see Sec. 4–8 and H. S. M. Coxeter, *The Real Projective Plane* (New York, 1949), pp. 8–9.

We determine a point P in the oriented plane by means of two *Cartesian coordinates* (x, y) with respect to two oriented axes OX and

OY [at angle ϕ, axes not necessarily rectangular; $PP_2 = x$, $PP_1 = y$ (Fig. 2–5)]. The positive sense on these axes is that of the increasing variable. All (ordinary) points in the plane are in one-to-one correspondence with the sets (x,y), x and y ranging from $-\infty$ to $+\infty$; for the time being we shall study real values only. For a generic point $P(x,y)$ on a (nonoriented) line intersecting OX in A and OY in B and passing through a given point $P_0(x_0,y_0)$, we find (Fig. 2–6)

$$\frac{y - y_0}{x - x_0} = -\frac{OB}{OA} = m \quad \text{(a constant)}, \tag{1-4}$$

so that the equation of the line is

$$y - y_0 = m(x - x_0). \tag{1-5}$$

This equation includes for $m = 0$ and $m = \pm\infty$ the lines parallel to the axes. It is a linear equation, because it has the form

$$Ax + By + C = 0 \quad (A,B \text{ not both zero}). \tag{1-6}$$

Conversely, every linear equation can be brought into the form (1–5) by taking an arbitrary point $P_0(x_0,y_0)$ on it:

$$Ax_0 + By_0 + C = 0, \tag{1-7}$$

subtracting Eq. (1–7) from Eq. (1–6) and dividing by B; when $B = 0$ we have the case $m = \pm\infty$. We conclude:

Every straight line is represented by a linear equation in x and y and, conversely, every such linear equation represents a straight line.

When we introduce the *intercepts* $OA = a$, $OB = b$ (Fig. 2–6), and $a,b \neq 0$, then Eq. (1–6) can be cast into the form

$$\frac{x}{a} + \frac{y}{b} = 1. \tag{1-8}$$

The line l given by Eq. (1–6) [we say for short "line (1–6)"] is not oriented. We can also determine the line by measuring on the ray through O (positive sense away from O) the distance $OH = p$ ($p > 0$); then l is at $H \perp OH$. Let α,β be the angles which OX and OY make with OH (Fig. 2–7):

$$\alpha = \angle(OX,OH), \quad \beta = \angle(OY,OH)$$

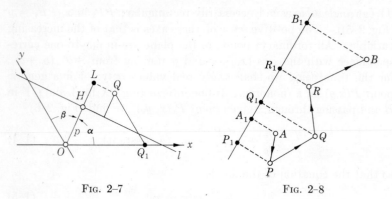

FIG. 2–7   FIG. 2–8

(in Fig. 2–7 $\angle\alpha$ is positive, $\angle\beta$ negative). Now take an arbitrary point $Q(x_1,y_1)$ in the plane and let d be its distance from l. If we now project the broken line OQ_1,Q_1Q on OH $(QQ_1 = y_1)$, and also the straight line OQ, then we obtain the relation (QL parallel to l)

$$x_1 \cos \alpha + y_1 \cos \beta = OH + LQ,$$

so that we find for the distance LQ

$$d = x_1 \cos \alpha + y_1 \cos \beta - p. \qquad (1\text{–}9)$$

Here $d = LQ$ is positive when Q and O are on different sides of l, negative when these points are on the same side of l.

In deriving Eq. (1–9) we have used the following principle:

> *When we project a broken line with straight or curved segments connecting two points A and B and oriented from A to B (in Fig. 2–8: APQRB) on a line l, then the projection of this broken line on l is equal to that of the straight line AB, provided we take all projections with the proper sign.* (In Fig. 2–8: $A_1P_1 + P_1Q_1 + Q_1R_1 + R_1B_1 = A_1B_1$.) This principle holds in space as well as in the plane.

The expression $N \equiv x \cos \alpha + y \cos \beta - p = 0$ $(p > 0)$ is therefore negative on the side of the line where the origin is, and positive on the other side. For points on the line, and for those only,

$$N \equiv x \cos \alpha + y \cos \beta - p = 0, \qquad (1\text{–}10)$$

which is a new form of the equation of the line, the *normal form*.

For rectangular axes ($\phi = 90°$) the normal form becomes

$$x \cos \alpha + y \sin \alpha - p = 0, \tag{1-11}$$

also called the *Hessian* form of the equation. When, in this case, we cast Eq. (1-11) into the form (1-5), the constant m is the *slope* of the line:

$$m = -\cot \alpha = \tan \psi, \tag{1-12}$$

where ψ is the angle between the line and the positive x-axis.

The orientation of the line is here immaterial, since

$$\tan \psi = \tan - (\pi - \psi).$$

The form (1-11) was often used by Otto Hesse (1811–1874), who, when professor at Heidelberg, wrote a textbook *Vorlesungen aus der Analytischen Geometrie* (1865), with many elegant demonstrations.

Returning to the general case of oblique axes, and taking two points $A(a_1, a_2)$ and $B(b_1, b_2)$ on the ray l, as well as a generic point $P(x, y)$, then by projecting the points of l on OX and OY, we obtain [cf. Eq. (2-2), Chapter 1]

$$x = \frac{a_1 - \lambda b_1}{1 - \lambda}, \quad y = \frac{a_2 - \lambda b_2}{1 - \lambda}, \tag{1-13}$$

where λ is the division ratio $PA : PB$. The value $\lambda = +1$ associates to l the ideal point (see Chapter 1, Sec. 1-2).

2-2 Invariance of the orientation. Our reasoning is based on the possibility of orienting the plane. It is clear that this orientation does not depend on motions of the plane. If a sense of rotation is defined in one region, then the same sense is induced in all regions of the plane. It is useful to express this fact, geometrically obvious, in algebraic form. For this we take rectangular axes and take the positive sense as that indicated in Sec. 2-1. A motion of the plane consists of a translation and a rotation, and can therefore be expressed by the equations

$$x = x' \cos \alpha - y' \sin \alpha + a, \quad y = x' \sin \alpha + y' \cos \alpha + b. \tag{2-1}$$

The orientation can be expressed by the sign of the determinant formed by the coordinates of three points $P(x_1, x_2)$, $Q(y_1, y_2)$, $R(z_1, z_2)$:

$$\Delta = \begin{vmatrix} x_1 & x_2 & 1 \\ y_1 & y_2 & 1 \\ z_1 & z_2 & 1 \end{vmatrix}, \quad -\Delta = \begin{vmatrix} x_1 & x_2 & 1 \\ z_1 & z_2 & 1 \\ y_1 & y_2 & 1 \end{vmatrix}. \tag{2-2}$$

This determinant is zero when the three points are on a line, i.e., are *collinear*. We exclude this case. Then the determinant is positive when the points are $P(0,0)$, $Q(1,0)$, $R(0,1)$. (In this order it remains >0 when P,Q,R are cyclically permuted.) This is the positive sense of the plane. The determinant is negative for the permutations PRQ, RQP, QPR.

Under the transformations (2–1) the sign of Δ remains unchanged (even Δ itself), since it is multiplied by the determinant of the transformation:

$$\begin{vmatrix} \cos \alpha & -\sin \alpha & 0 \\ \sin \alpha & \cos \alpha & 0 \\ 0 & 0 & 1 \end{vmatrix} = \begin{vmatrix} \cos \alpha & -\sin \alpha \\ \sin \alpha & \cos \alpha \end{vmatrix} = +1. \tag{2-3}$$

This is the algebraic translation of the fact that the orientation is the same for all points in the plane or for all positions of the coordinate system. [Equation (2–1) can be interpreted both as a motion of the plane and as a change of coordinates, see Chapter 4.] If, however, we take the transformation

$$x = x' \cos \alpha - y' \sin \alpha + a, \quad y = -x' \sin \alpha - y' \cos \alpha + b, \tag{2-4}$$

then the sign of Δ is changed. Equations (2–4) are obtained from Eqs. (2–1) by changing the sign of y. They can therefore be interpreted as a rotation and a reflection. But such a change of coordinates does change the orientation, since it interchanges the positive and the negative y-axis.

If the rotation and translation of the axes are coupled with a change of scale in the x- and y-axis,

$$x = ax', \quad y = by',$$

then the reasoning remains the same. When a and b have the same sign, the determinant retains its sign. When a and b differ in sign, the determinant changes its sign, and this indicates a reflection. This remark will be useful for the study of affine transformations (Chapter 4).

2-3 Pencils of lines. Two lines l_1 and l_2 with equations

$$A_1x + B_1y + C_1 = 0, \quad A_2x + B_2y + C_2 = 0 \qquad (3\text{-}1)$$

have

(a) a point of intersection, if

$$\Delta = A_1B_2 - A_2B_1 \neq 0; \qquad (3\text{-}2)$$

(b) no point of intersection, and are parallel, if

$$\Delta = 0, \quad B_1C_2 - B_2C_1 \neq 0 \quad \text{(hence also } A_1C_2 - A_2C_1 \neq 0), \qquad (3\text{-}3)$$

and hence by (3-3),

$$A_1:B_1 = A_2:B_2 \neq C_1:C_2;$$

(c) all points in common, if

$$\Delta = 0, \quad B_1C_2 - B_2C_1 = 0 \quad \text{(hence also } A_1C_2 - A_2C_1 = 0).$$

Suppose we eliminate y from Eq. (3-1). Then in Case (b), we obtain for x the equation $B_1C_2 - B_2C_1 = 0$. This (cf. Sec. 1-6) can be interpreted by saying that there is a root $x = \infty$, hence also $y = \infty$. We interpret this as meaning that *parallel lines have the point at infinity in common, or, parallel lines intersect at infinity.* This interpretation will be justified by further developments. We can express our conclusions as follows:

Two lines have a point in common, which may be ordinary or ideal. In the last case the lines are parallel.

We now introduce the *abbreviated notation*

$$L \equiv Ax + By + C, \qquad (3\text{-}4)$$

so that $L = 0$ represents a line l. Then the equation

$$L_1 - \lambda L_2 = 0, \qquad (3\text{-}5)$$

where λ is a constant and L_1, L_2 are defined by

$$L_a \equiv A_ax + B_ay + C_a \quad (a = 1,2), \qquad (3\text{-}6)$$

represents for every value of λ a line, of which the equation is always satisfied by $L_1 = 0$, $L_2 = 0$. Equation (3-5) thus represents for every λ a line through the point of intersection of the lines $L_1 = 0$,

$L_2 = 0$. Conversely, every line through a point P has an equation which can be cast into the form (3–5) with suitable λ, since the condition that a line through P passes through an arbitrarily chosen point $Q(x_0,y_0) \neq P$ of the plane is

$$\lambda = \frac{A_1 x_0 + B_1 y_0 + C}{A_2 x_0 + B_2 y_0 + C}. \tag{3–7}$$

The line $L_1 = 0$ is given by $\lambda = 0$, the line $L_2 = 0$ by $\lambda = \pm\infty$. When λ runs through all values from $-\infty$ to $+\infty$, together with $\lambda = \pm\infty$, Eq. (3–5) represents all lines through P in continuous succession. Those lines form the *pencil of lines* through P [for short: *pencil* (P)]. Equation (3–5) is the equation of the pencil, P its *vertex*. When lines $L_1 = 0$, $L_2 = 0$ are parallel, Eq. (3–5) consists of all lines parallel to these lines. In this case, we may write [cf. Eq. (3–3)]

$$A_1 x + B_1 y + C_1 + \lambda(\mu A_1 x + \mu B_1 y + C_2) = 0 \quad (C_2 \neq \mu C_1).$$

The value $\lambda = -(1/\mu)$ gives $C_1 - (1/\mu)C_2 = 0$, which can be interpreted as the equation of the *ideal line or line at infinity of the plane*. *All points at infinity of the plane lie on the line at infinity.*

The equation of a pencil can also be written in the form

$$\alpha L_1 + \beta L_2 = 0, \tag{3–8}$$

where $L_1 = 0$ is given by $\alpha = 1$, $\beta = 0$, and $L_2 = 0$ by $\alpha = 0$, $\beta = 1$.

Since the lines of a pencil depend on one parameter, we say that *there are ∞^1 lines in a pencil.* Similarly, there are ∞^1 points on a line. The complex line has ∞^2 points, since each complex number involves two real numbers. There are ∞^2 real points in the plane, ∞^3 real points in space, etc.

2–4 Three and four lines.　Let us consider three lines

$$L_i \equiv A_i x + B_i y + C_i = 0 \quad (i = 1,2,3). \tag{4–1}$$

These lines do not, as a rule, intersect in one point. If they do pass through one point, then line $L_3 = 0$ belongs to the pencil of lines formed by $L_1 = 0$, $L_2 = 0$. Then there must exist two constants α,β such that $L_3 \equiv \alpha L_1 + \beta L_2$. This property can be stated as follows:

A necessary and sufficient condition that three different lines $L_1 = 0$, $L_2 = 0$, $L_3 = 0$ *pass through a point is that nonzero constants* k_1, k_2, k_3 *exist such that*

$$k_1 L_1 + k_2 L_2 + k_3 L_3 = 0. \tag{4–2}$$

This relation is equivalent to

$$\begin{vmatrix} A_1 & B_1 & C_1 \\ A_2 & B_2 & C_2 \\ A_3 & B_3 & C_3 \end{vmatrix} = 0, \tag{4–3}$$

since the equations $L_1 = 0$, $L_2 = 0$, $L_3 = 0$ have a root (x,y) in common. Equation (4–3) can be compared with the equation $\Delta = 0$ [see Eq. (2–2)], which expresses that three points are on the same line.

Equation (4–2) can always be cast into the form

$$L_1 + L_2 + L_3 = 0 \tag{4–4}$$

by a judicious choice (normalization) of the equations of the three lines (e.g., $k_1 L_1 = 0$ instead of $L_1 = 0$, etc.).

As a first application, let us take four lines $L_1 = 0$, $L_2 = 0$, $L_3 = 0$, $L_4 = 0$, of which no three pass through one point. Such lines are called *independent*. There exists a line PQ connecting the vertex P of the pencil $L_1 - \lambda L_2 = 0$ with the vertex Q of the pencil $L_3 - L_4 = 0$. Hence the line PQ must be of the form $L_1 - \lambda L_2 = 0$ and also be of the form $L_3 - \mu L_4 = 0$. This means that a nonzero constant k exists such that

$$L_1 - \lambda L_2 \equiv k(L_3 - \mu L_4),$$

or, in other words:

If $L_1 = 0$, $L_2 = 0$, $L_3 = 0$, $L_4 = 0$ *are four independent lines in the plane, then there exist nonzero constants* m_1, m_2, m_3, m_4 *such that*

$$m_1 L_1 + m_2 L_2 + m_3 L_3 + m_4 L_4 = 0. \tag{4–5}$$

This equation, by normalization of the L, can be cast into the form

$$L_1 + L_2 + L_3 + L_4 = 0. \tag{4–6}$$

If some of the lines pass through one point, then some of the m in
Eq. (4–5) may be zero, and Eq. (4–6) does not exist.

Four or more points, of which no three lie on a line, are also called
independent.

EXERCISES

1. Show that the equation of a line passing through the two points
$(x_1 y_1)$ and $(x_2 y_2)$ is

$$\begin{vmatrix} x & y & 1 \\ x_1 & y_1 & 1 \\ x_2 & y_2 & 1 \end{vmatrix} = 0, \quad \text{or} \quad \frac{x - x_1}{x_2 - x_1} = \frac{y - y_1}{y_2 - y_1}.$$

2. Show that the angle α of two lines $L_1 = 0, L_2 = 0$ [Eq. (3–1)] is given
in rectangular axes by

$$\tan \alpha = \pm \frac{A_1 B_2 - A_2 B_1}{A_1 A_2 + B_1 B_2},$$

and derive from this formula the condition for parallelism, and for orthogonality: $A_1 A_2 + B_1 B_2 = 0$.   From this formula show that two lines $y = m_1 x$
and $y = m_2 x$ are perpendicular if $m_1 m_2 = -1$.

3. Find the normal form of the equations of the line: (a) $x + y + 4 = 0$,
(b) $3x - 4y + 5 = 0$, (c) $y = x - 3$.   The coordinate system is rectangular.

4. Find the distance from point $P(x_0, y_0)$ to the line $L \equiv 3x + 4y + 5 = 0$
and determine in which parts of the plane the expression L is positive or
negative.

5. Determine whether the following sets of three lines pass through one
point:

(a) $5x - 2y = 0$, $3x + y - 5 = 0$, $x - 3y + 7 = 0$,
(b) $3x - 4y + 5 = 0$, $2x - y + 1 = 0$, $x - 3y + 4 = 0$,
(c) $x + 2y + 7 = 0$, $2x + 4y - 1 = 0$, $3x + 6y = 0$.

6. Construct in a diagram the lines of the pencil $(x - a) - \lambda(y - b) = 0$
for the values $\lambda = 0, \infty, -1, +1$, (a) when a,b both > 0, (b) when
$a < 0, b > 0$, (c) when $a = 0, b = 0$.

7. Find the equation of the line through the point of intersection of the
lines $3x - 5y + 7 = 0$, $8x - 9y - 1 = 0$, (a) parallel to the x-axis, (b) perpendicular to the line $x - y + 5 = 0$ (take rectangular axes), (c) passing
through the origin.

8. Through the origin O of a rectangular Cartesian system we draw two
straight lines l_1 $(y = m_1 x)$ and l_2 $(y = m_2 x)$.   A line p parallel to the x-axis
intersects l_1 in P_1, l_2 in P_2.   At P_1 we erect the perpendicular to l_1, at P_2 the
perpendicular to l_2.   Show that the locus of the point of intersection of the
two perpendiculars when p is variable is a straight line through O.

9. The vertices B and C of $\triangle ABC$ are fixed, and A moves on a straight line. Show that the center of the inscribed square, of which one side lies on BC, describes a straight line.

10. Find the linear relation existing between the forms $L_1 \equiv x + y - 5$, $L_2 \equiv x - y + 7$, $L_3 \equiv 2y - 4$, $L_4 \equiv 5x + 1$.

11. The vertices A and B of a rectangular triangle ABC slide on the axes of a rectangular coordinate system, A on OX, B on OY. The hypotenuse is AB. Find the locus of C.

12. Show that the relation of Pappus (Ex. 10, Sec. 1–3) also holds when P_2 lies outside line $P_1Q_1Q_2$. This theorem for $\triangle P_2P_1Q_1$ is called the *theorem of Stewart*.

13. If $L_\alpha \equiv ax + by + c = 0$, $\alpha = 1,2,3,4,5,6$, are six lines, then the intersections of $L_1 = 0$ and $L_2 = 0$; $L_3 = 0$ and $L_4 = 0$; $L_5 = 0$ and $L_6 = 0$ are collinear if

$$\begin{vmatrix} a_1 & b_1 & c_1 & a_1 & b_1 & c_1 \\ a_2 & b_2 & c_2 & a_2 & b_2 & c_2 \\ a_3 & b_3 & c_3 & 0 & 0 & 0 \\ a_4 & b_4 & c_4 & 0 & 0 & 0 \\ 0 & 0 & 0 & a_5 & b_5 & c_5 \\ 0 & 0 & 0 & a_6 & b_6 & c_6 \end{vmatrix} = 0 \quad \text{(Cayley)}.$$

2–5 Theorem of Desargues. This theorem, which plays an important part in the axiomatics of plane geometry, can be proved as an example of the theory of pencils. It can be stated as follows.

If corresponding sides of two triangles in a plane intersect in points on a line, then the lines joining corresponding vertices pass through a point.

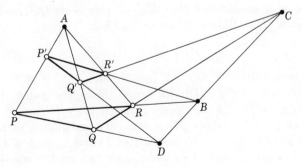

Fig. 2–9

Conversely, *if the lines joining corresponding vertices of two triangles in a plane pass through a point, then the corresponding sides intersect in points on a line.*

To prove the theorem let (Fig. 2–9) PQR and $P'Q'R'$ be the vertices of two triangles of which $PQ, P'Q'$ intersect in D; $QR, Q'R'$ in C; $RP, R'P'$ in B. We assume that no vertices or sides of the triangles are incident. Given that B, C, D lie on a line a. Let the equations of the different lines be

$$(QR):L_1 = 0, \quad (RP):L_2 = 0, \quad (PQ):L_3 = 0;$$
$$(Q'R'):L_1' = 0, \quad (R'P'):L_2' = 0, \quad (P'Q'):L_3' = 0.$$

Line a belongs to the pencil of $L_1 = 0$, $L_1' = 0$, also to that of $L_2 = 0$, $L_2' = 0$, and of $L_3 = 0$, $L_3' = 0$. Hence there exist nonzero constants α_i, α_i', $i = 1,2,3$, such that

$$\alpha_1 L_1 + \alpha_1' L_1' \equiv \alpha_2 L_2 + \alpha_2' L_2' \equiv \alpha_3 L_3 + \alpha_3' L_3'; \tag{5–1}$$

each of these forms, equated to zero, represents a. Thus there exist three linear forms M_i such that

$$\begin{aligned}
M_1 &\equiv \alpha_2 L_2 - \alpha_3 L_3 \equiv \alpha_3' L_3' - \alpha_2' L_2', \\
M_2 &\equiv \alpha_3 L_3 - \alpha_1 L_1 \equiv \alpha_1' L_1' - \alpha_3' L_3', \\
M_3 &\equiv \alpha_1 L_1 - \alpha_2 L_2 \equiv \alpha_2' L_2' - \alpha_1' L_1'.
\end{aligned} \tag{5–2}$$

The equation $M_1 = 0$ represents a line passing through the point of intersection P of $L_2 = 0$, $L_3 = 0$, and also through P', the point of intersection of $L_2' = 0, L_3' = 0$. Hence $M_1 = 0$ is the equation of PP'. We see in a similar way that $M_2 = 0$ represents QQ', and $M_3 = 0$ represents RR'. But according to Eq. (5–2),

$$M_1 + M_2 + M_3 \equiv 0, \tag{5–3}$$

which means that PP', QQ', RR' pass through a point A.

Conversely, let PP', QQ', RR' pass through a point A. Then, according to Eq. (4–4), their equations $M_i = 0$ can be made to satisfy Eq. (5–3). Since M_1 is a linear combination of L_2 and L_3 as well as of L_2' and L_3'; M_2 similarly of L_3 and L_1, and of L_3' and L_1'; M_3 of L_1 and L_2, and of L_1' and L_2', we can readily see that since neither L_1, L_2, L_3 nor L_1', L_2', L_3' can be made to satisfy an equation of type (4–2), the M can be written in the form (5–2) with appropriate α_i, α_i'. Then follows Eq. (5–1) showing that B, C, D are on a line.

The two triangles are said to be in *perspective correspondence*. Point A is the *center of perspectivity*, line a is the *axis of perspectivity*. Desargues' theorem can then be stated in the following terms:

> *If two triangles are perspective from a point, then they are also perspective from a line.*

Desargues published this theorem on perspective triangles somewhat casually in an appendix to a treatise on perspective by his friend, the well-known engraver Abraham Bosse (1648, see Desargues, *Oeuvres* I, p. 413).

Another proof can be given by an immediate appeal to the elements of space geometry. Let $APQR$ now be the representation of a tetrahedron (Fig. 2–9) intersected by a plane in the triangle $P'Q'R'$. Let B be the intersection of QR and $Q'R'$, and similarly C and D the intersections of corresponding edges. Then the planes PQR and $P'Q'R'$ intersect in a line a on which B, C, D must lie, since these points belong to both planes. The figure, as we have said, is to be considered as drawn in the common projection of solid geometry (e.g., axonometry, see Sec. 11–5), and then, considered as a plane figure, proves the theorem of Desargues. It shows the *configuration of Desargues*, $(10_3, 10_3)$, which symbol means that it is a figure of 10 points and 10 lines such that through every point pass three lines, and on every line lie three points. We often simply write (10_3). We may also consider Fig. 2–9 as the projection of a triangle with vertices 1,2,3 in space, on a plane π, taken from two different points 4,5 in a general position outside of the plane of the triangle. Then (Fig. 2–10) the lines (14),(24),(34) intersect the plane π in P, Q, R; the lines (15), (25),(35) in $P'Q'R'$. [We indicate P in the figure by (14), etc.] Point A is the intersection of (45) with π, line a the intersection of plane (123) with π. The Desargues' configuration is again the result of the fact that three planes in a general position intersect in a point, two planes in general position in a line. In other words: *If we intersect the figure formed by five independent points in space* 1,2,3,4,5, *with their ten connecting lines* (12),(13), . . . ,(45), *through each of which pass three planes* [e.g., (123),(124),(125) through (12)] *with a plane not incident with any of these lines, then the figure of intersection*

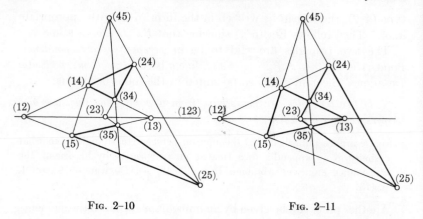

FIG. 2-10   FIG. 2-11

is a Desargues' configuration. [Since we can divide the five points in $10 = 5!/2! \, 3!$ different ways in groups of 2 and 3, a configuration of Desargues can be considered in 10 different ways as generated by two perspective triangles (cf. Figs. 2–10 and 2–11].

These proofs, based on space considerations, show that the theorem of Desargues is an immediate consequence of the space axioms on the connection of points, lines, and planes (the principal ones are the axioms which establish that two points determine a line, three noncollinear points a plane, and that two planes have a line in common if they have a point in common). It can be shown that the connection axioms for the plane alone are insufficient for the proof of Desargues' theorem. For a purely two-dimensional treatment, the theorem itself (or some equivalent proposition) has to be taken as an axiom, as Hilbert has shown. See, for example, G. de B. Robinson, *The Foundations of Geometry* (Toronto, 1940); also D. Hilbert, *The Foundations of Geometry* (English translation, Chicago, 1902), Chapter V.

An extensive investigation of configurations is found in F. Levi, *Geometrische Konfigurationen* (Leipzig, 1929).

2–6 Division ratio. The number λ in the equation $L_1 - \lambda L_2 = 0$ allows a simple geometrical interpretation. For this purpose let us consider the pencil as composed of rays, let l_1 be given by $L_1 = 0$, l_2 by $L_2 = 0$, l by $L_1 - \lambda L_2 = 0$, where the L_a, $a = 1,2$, are given by their normal forms (1–10). Take a point A on l, draw $AA_1 \perp l_1$, $AA_2 \perp l_2$. Then, according to Eqs. (3–7) and (1–9),

$$|\lambda| = \frac{|AA_1|}{|AA_2|} = \left| \frac{\sin \angle(l_1 l)}{\sin \angle(l_2 l)} \right|.$$

If O lies outside of the sector bounded by l_1 and l_2, then for all l not passing past O

$$\lambda = \frac{\sin \angle(l_1 l)}{\sin \angle(l_2 l)}. \tag{6-1}$$

We call λ the *division ratio* of l with respect to l_1 and l_2.

The lines with the equations

$$L_1 - \lambda L_2 = 0, \quad L_1 + \lambda L_2 = 0$$

are called *harmonic* with respect to l_1 and l_2; each is the *harmonic conjugate* of the other. It is clear that this property holds even if L_1 and L_2 are not in the normal form (and independent of the choice of O). It is a geometric property of the four lines. When l and m are harmonic with respect to l_1 and l_2, l_1 and l_2 are harmonic with respect to l and m.

If we take L_1 and L_2 in the normal forms, then according to Eq. (6–1), $L_1 - L_2 = 0$ and $L_1 + L_2 = 0$ represent the inner and outer (or outer and inner) bisectors of l_1 and l_2:

Two lines are harmonic with respect to their bisectors.

We shall apply this representation of the bisectors to prove the following theorem of Euclid:

The inner bisectors of a triangle pass through a point.

Indeed, let $L_1 = 0$, $L_2 = 0$, $L_3 = 0$, all taken in the normal form, represent the sides of the triangle ABC. Let the origin be inside the triangle. Then the equations of the inner bisectors are

$$L_1 - L_2 = 0, \quad L_2 - L_3 = 0, \quad L_3 - L_1 = 0.$$

The right-hand members of the equation add up to zero, which proves the theorem. Since also

$$(L_1 - L_2) + (L_2 + L_3) - (L_3 + L_1) \equiv 0,$$

we see that one inner bisector passes through the point of intersection D of the outer bisectors of the other angles.

The advantages of the abbreviated notation were first demonstrated by Julius Plücker (1801–1868) in his *Analytisch-Geometrische Entwicklungen* (1828), from which the previous example is taken. Plücker, who was a professor at Bonn during most of his life, was not only an important mathematician, but also an experimental physicist who pioneered in electrical radiation and spectroscopy.

EXERCISES

1. State the theorem of Desargues when the center of perspectivity is at infinity, and when the axis of perspectivity is at infinity.

2. State the theorem of Desargues when the center lies on the axis of perspectivity, and both are at infinity. In this case we speak sometimes of the *little theorem of Desargues*. Can you derive it from a theorem in solid geometry?

3. State what becomes of Desargues' theorem when two of the corresponding vertices, or sides, coincide.

4. Find all the 10 pairs of perspective triangles in a configuration of Desargues.

5. The points in which the inner bisectors at two vertices of a triangle intersect the opposite sides and the point in which the outer bisector at the third vertex intersects the opposite side lie on a line. Prove.

6. Let $L_1 = 0$, $L_2 = 0$, $L_3 = 0$ represent the sides of a triangle. State the theorem which can be derived from the identities

$$L_3 + (L_1 + L_2) \equiv L_1 + (L_2 + L_3) \equiv L_2 + (L_3 + L_1).$$

7. Show by the method of abbreviated notation that (a) the altitudes of a triangle pass through one point, and (b) the medians of a triangle pass through one point.

8. *Configurations.* We denote by (p_m, l_q) a figure consisting of p points and l lines such that through every point pass m lines, and on every line lie q points. When $p = l$, $m = q$, we write for the configuration (p_m). (a) Show that $pm = lq$. Give the symbol for the figure formed (b) by three points and their connecting lines, (c) four points and their connecting lines, and (d) four lines and their points of intersection.

9. Show that the only configuration of points and lines in which every point of intersection of configuration lines is also a point of the configuration is

$$\left[\left(\frac{m(m-1)}{2} \right)_2, \quad (m)_{m-1} \right].$$

Study the case $m = 3,4$ and the dual cases in which points and lines are interchanged.

2-7 Cross ratio. Consider two rays l and m of a pencil P, with division ratios λ_1 and λ_2 respectively with respect to two rays l_1 and l_2. Then the quotient of these ratios,

$$\mu = \frac{\lambda_1}{\lambda_2} = \frac{\sin \angle (ll_1)}{\sin \angle (ll_2)} : \frac{\sin \angle (ml_1)}{\sin \angle (ml_2)}, \qquad (7\text{-}1)$$

is called the *cross ratio* (or *anharmonic ratio*) of l,m with respect to l_1 and l_2. We write

$$\mu = (lm,l_1l_2) = (l_1l_2,lm).$$

The cross ratio of rays is the same as that of the corresponding lines. For this cross ratio of four lines in a pencil we can repeat most of what has been said in Sec. 1-4 about the cross ratio of four points. This relation between cross ratios of points and lines is clarified by the following theorem.

Theorem of Pappus. If four lines a_1,a_2,a_3,a_4 of a pencil P are intersected by any line (not passing through P) in four points A_1,A_2,A_3,A_4, then the cross ratio of the four lines (a_1a_2,a_3a_4) is equal to the cross ratio of the four points (A_1A_2,A_3A_4).

We orient the four lines away from P (Fig. 2-12), and we take the origin such that

$$(a_1a_2,a_3a_4) = \frac{\sin \angle (a_1a_3)}{\sin \angle (a_2a_3)} : \frac{\sin \angle (a_1a_4)}{\sin \angle (a_2a_4)}.$$

Then we find for (A_1A_2,A_3A_4):

$$\begin{aligned}
(A_1A_2,A_3A_4) &= \frac{A_1A_3}{A_2A_3} : \frac{A_1A_4}{A_2A_4} \\
&= \frac{\text{area } \triangle PA_1A_3}{\text{area } \triangle PA_2A_3} : \frac{\text{area } \triangle PA_1A_4}{\text{area } \triangle PA_2A_4} \\
&= \frac{PA_1 \cdot PA_3 \sin \angle (a_1a_3)}{PA_2 \cdot PA_3 \sin \angle (a_2a_3)} : \frac{PA_1 \cdot PA_4 \sin \angle (a_1a_4)}{PA_2 \cdot PA_4 \sin \angle (a_2a_4)} \\
&= \frac{\sin \angle (a_1a_3)}{\sin \angle (a_2a_3)} : \frac{\sin \angle (a_1a_4)}{\sin \angle (a_2a_4)} = (a_1a_2,a_3a_4).
\end{aligned}$$

This proves the theorem, and also shows that although Eq. (6-1) for the division ratio of two lines depends on the position of the origin,

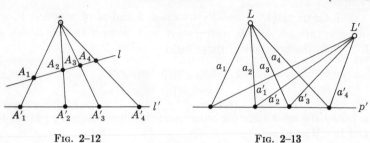

FIG. 2–12   FIG. 2–13

the cross ratio is independent of this and is also independent of the
orientation of the lines. From Pappus' theorem follow the other
theorems:

*Two lines are intersected by four lines of a pencil in points with
the same cross ratio.*

This means (Fig. 2–12) that

$$(A_1A_2, A_3A_4) = (A'_1A'_2, A'_3A'_4). \tag{7–4}$$

*Two points are connected to four points on a line by lines with
the same cross ratio.*

This means (Fig. 2–13) that

$$(a_1a_2, a_3a_4) = (a'_1a'_2, a'_3a'_4). \tag{7–5}$$

We say that the cross ratio is invariant under projection.

In particular, four harmonic lines of a pencil intersect any line,
not through the vertex, in four harmonic points, and any four lines
connecting a point not on a given line with four harmonic points on
the line are harmonic.

The theorem of Pappus can be found in the famous 7th book of the
Mathematical Collection (c. 300 A.D.), in which so many books are discussed
of which the originals have been lost. The theorem is probably much older,
since Pappus presented it as one of the lemmas useful for an understanding
of Euclid's (now lost) book *On Porisms*. The full importance of this theorem as one of the foundations of projective geometry was only recognized
in the early nineteenth century.

1. *Pappus' statement of his theorem.* If three straight lines AB, AC, AD are intersected by two straight lines through a point H such that one line intersects the three lines in B,C,D, and the other in E,F,G, respectively, then the rectangle $HE \cdot GF$ is to $HG \cdot FE$ as the rectangle $HB \cdot DC$ is to $HD \cdot BC$. Show that this theorem is equivalent to that of the invariance of cross ratios under projection.

2. *Perspective point sets.* When the corresponding points of two perspective point sets (here one set of corresponding points A_1,A_1' coincides, see Sec. 1–5) are connected by lines ($A_2A_2', A_3A_3', \ldots$), these lines pass through one point. Prove.

3. Find the cross ratios of the four lines (a) $y = 0$, $x = 0$, $x + 2y = 0$, $x + 3y = 0$; (b) $x - y + 1 = 0$, $x + 2y + 1 = 0$, the line joining the intersection of these two lines to $(1,1)$, and to $(2,1)$.

4. Show that a cross ratio of the four lines $L_1 - \lambda_i L_2 = 0$, $\mu = 1,2,3,4$ is $(\lambda_1 - \lambda_3)/(\lambda_1 - \lambda_4):(\lambda_2 - \lambda_3)/(\lambda_2 - \lambda_4)$. Check this with Ex. 3.

2–8 Duality. The theorem of Desargues deals only with the positions of points and lines, their connections and intersections. It does not deal with *metrical* relationships, that is, with distances or angles. Moreover, it has the remarkable property that if we change the terms *point* and *line* in the following way

$$(D) \quad \begin{array}{l} \text{point} \leftrightarrow \text{line} \\ \text{line} \leftrightarrow \text{point} \end{array},$$

$$(D) \quad \left\{ \begin{array}{l} \text{line connecting two points (their join)} \leftrightarrow \text{point of intersection} \\ \text{of two lines} \\ \text{point of intersection of two lines} \leftrightarrow \text{line connecting two points,} \end{array} \right.$$

then the first part of Desargues' theorem changes into the second part and conversely. Figures, theories, and theorems which pass into each other by virtue of the substitution (D) are called *dual*. The two parts of Desargues' theorem are dual; if we take the two parts together into one theorem, then this theorem is *self-dual*. A triangle can be called a self-dual figure, since it can be considered as composed of three lines with their three points of intersection as well as three points with their three connecting lines. Here are more dual figures:

Three points on a line (*collinear* points)	Three lines through a point (*concurrent* lines)
Four points and their six lines of connection (*complete quadrangle*)	Four lines and their six points of intersection (*complete quadrilateral*)
Point sets on a line	Line pencils through a point
We write for the line connecting points P and Q: (PQ), or (QP)	We write for the point of intersection of lines p and q: (pq), or (qp)
Points and lines as in Fig. 2–14	Lines and points as in Fig. 2–15

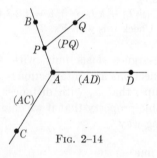

Fig. 2–14

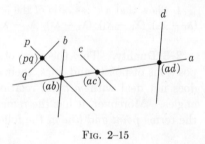

Fig. 2–15

When convenient we shall indicate points by capital letters $A, B, \ldots$, and corresponding lines by corresponding small letters $a, b, \ldots$.

The theorem of Pappus can also be stated in a dual way, if we consider the concept of cross ratio of four lines in a pencil as dual to that of the cross ratio of four points on a line. This seems at first strange, since metrical concepts enter into the definition of cross ratio, but Pappus' theorem shows that the particular combination of metrical relations which enters into the cross ratio is an invariant under the duality. We repeat the dual versions of Pappus' theorem from Sec. 2–7:

Two lines are intersected by four lines of a pencil in points with the same cross ratio.	Two points are connected to four points on a line by lines of the same cross ratio.

The dual of four harmonic points on a line is therefore four harmonic lines in a pencil.

That distances and angles are not dual can easily be seen if we try to set up the dual of a metrical theorem. For instance, three sides determine a triangle, but three angles determine a triangle only when their sum is two right angles, and even then only for a similitude. We shall later see how metrical relations can be introduced in a dual way.

There is no particular dual for parallel lines either, except as lines through a point. The reason is that we have introduced one line in an exceptional position (the ideal line), but we have not introduced one point in an exceptional position.

A consistent treatment of the concept of cross ratio without the aid of distance and angle was made by Ch. Von Staudt, in his *Geometrie der Lage* (geometry of position, 1847). It was an important contribution to the axiomatics of projective geometry. See Veblen-Young I, p. 157 (the algebra of "throws").

2–9 Complete quadrilateral and quadrangle. Let a,b,c,d be four lines, of which no three pass through one point, and $(ab),(ac), \ldots ,(cd)$ their points of intersection. This figure, we have seen, is called a *complete quadrilateral*, of which a,b,c,d are the four sides, and the six points $(ab),(ac), \ldots ,(cd)$, the vertices. The vertices can be separated into three pairs of "opposite" vertices, which are connected by the three *diagonals* p,q,r (Fig. 2–16): $[(ab)(cd)]$ by p; $[(ac)(db)]$ by q; $[(ad)(bc)]$ by r; these lines form the *diagonal triangle*.

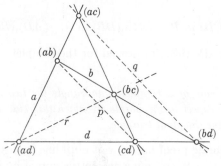

Fig. 2–16

Let the equations of the four sides a,b,c,d be $L_1 = 0$, $L_2 = 0$, $L_3 = 0$, $L_4 = 0$. Since no three of them pass through a point, we can, according to Eq. (4–6), take these equations in such a form that

$$L_1 + L_2 + L_3 + L_4 \equiv 0. \tag{9–1}$$

This shows that $L_1 + L_2 \equiv -(L_3 + L_4)$, so that the equations

$$L_1 + L_2 = 0, \quad L_3 + L_4 = 0 \tag{9–2}$$

represent the same line. This must be the diagonal p. In the same way, we find that q is represented by $L_1 + L_3 = 0$ or $L_2 + L_4 = 0$, and r by $L_1 + L_4 = 0$ or $L_2 + L_3 = 0$. Since

$$L_1 - L_2 \equiv (L_1 + L_3) - (L_2 + L_3),$$

we see that the line m given by $L_1 - L_2 = 0$ passes through (ab) and the intersection (qr). But [see Eq. (6–2)] this line $L_1 - L_2 = 0$ is the harmonic conjugate of $L_1 + L_2 = 0$ with respect to $L_1 = 0$, $L_2 = 0$, which are the lines a and b respectively, or $(ab,pm) = -1$. We thus obtain the theorem:

> *At a vertex of a complete quadrilateral the two sides are harmonic with respect to the lines connecting this vertex with the vertices of the diagonal triangle.*

The dual of the complete quadrilateral is the *complete quadrangle*, formed by four points A,B,C,D, connected by the six sides (AB), $(AC),\ldots,(CD)$. These sides can be separated into three pairs of "opposite" sides, which intersect in the three *diagonal points* P,Q,R (Fig. 2–17):

$$(AB),(CD) \text{ in } P; \quad (AC),(DB) \text{ in } Q; \quad (AD),(BC) \text{ in } R.$$

The dual of the theorem proved for the complete quadrilateral is the theorem:

> *On every side of a complete quadrangle the two vertices are harmonic with respect to the points in which this side is intersected by the sides of the diagonal triangle.*

A dual algebraic proof has to wait until line coordinates are introduced (Sec. 3–2). We obtain a geometrical proof by intersecting PR

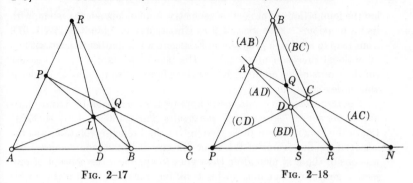

FIG. 2-17   FIG. 2-18

and BD in S (Fig. 2-17). Then, projecting the point set $ACQN$ on PR from B, we obtain with the aid of Pappus' theorem:

$$\mu = (AC,QN) = (PR,SN),$$

and projecting $PRSN$ back on AC from D,

$$\mu = (PR,SN) = (CA,QN).$$

Hence $(AC,QN) = (CA,QN) = \mu$, or $\mu = 1/\mu$. Since $\mu = +1$ is impossible, we obtain $\mu = -1$, the condition for the harmonic relationship.

These properties of the complete quadrangle and quadrilateral allow us to construct the fourth harmonic point to three given collinear points and the fourth harmonic line to three given concurrent lines *with the straightedge only*. Indeed, given (Fig. 2-18) three distinct collinear points A,B,C. Then take two points P,Q on a line through C not coinciding with AB, and let AP and BQ intersect in R. The line connecting R with the point of intersection L of AQ and BP intersects AB in the point D harmonic to C with respect to A and B. The dual construction solves the analogous problem for the pencil. (See Ex. 6.)

Von Staudt, in his *Geometrie der Lage*, defined the fourth harmonic point as the point obtained from three collinear points ABC by means of a complete quadrilateral. He was thus able to build up the theory of harmonic ratios and also of cross ratios ("Wurfe," "throws") independent of any metrical considerations taken from Euclidean geometry, and so

lay the foundations of projective geometry as an independent system, with
its own axioms. (See Sec. 3–9.) Christian von Staudt (1798–1867),
from 1835 to his death professor in Erlangen, was a mathematician with an
exceptional precision of thought. His books are hard to read because
(in the words of his admirer, Klein) their form is "so rigid as to render it
almost devoid of life."

The term *complete quadrilateral* appears first in a book by Lazare Carnot, *Essay sur la Théorie des Transversales* (Paris, 1806). Carnot (1753–
1823), the "organisateur de la victoire" of the French revolution, was the
father of the discoverer of the reversible circuit in thermodynamics. He
was one of the first men after Desargues to approach the concept of projective geometry, not only in his book on transversals, but also in his
previous *Géometrie de Position* (1803). Carnot, who remained faithful to
his republican principles, refused service under Napoleon except after
Elba, was exiled by the Bourbons, and died at Magdeburg.

EXERCISES

1. Discuss the complete quadrilateral (a) when one of the diagonals is the
line at infinity, (b) when one of the sides is the line at infinity.

2. Discuss the complete quadrangle when two of its vertices are at infinity.

3. Show that a line l is intersected by the three pairs of opposite sides of a
complete quadrangle in three pairs of points in involution. This figure led
Desargues to the concept of the "involution à six points" (see Sec. 1–7 and
Fig. 2–19, where 1,2,3,4 are the vertices of the quadrangle). State the dual
theorem.

4. On a line, two pairs of corresponding points AA', BB' of an involution
are given. (Can this be done by any labeling of four points as AA', BB'?)

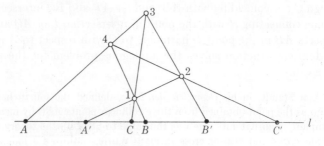

Fig. 2–19

Find, with the straightedge only, the point C' corresponding to an arbitrarily given point C on the line.

5. Show that the diagonal points of a complete quadrangle are not collinear. This theorem functions as *Fano's axiom* in the axiomatics of projective geometry.

6. Construct with the straightedge only the fourth harmonic line to three given concurrent lines.

7. If the points of intersection of five pairs of corresponding sides of two complete quadrangles with distinct vertices are collinear, then the point of intersection of the sixth pair of corresponding sides lies on the line of the other five. Prove.

8. Given four independent points P,Q,R,A. Show that there exists a complete quadrangle with A as vertex and P,Q,R as diagonal points. Also probe the dual proposition.

9. The centers of the diagonals of a complete quadrilateral lie on a line (Gauss). Prove.

10. Show that vertices and sides of a complete quadrangle form a configuration $(4_3,6_2)$. What is the dual configuration $(6_2,4_3)$? (See Ex. 9, Sec. 2-6.)

11. Four independent points in the plane determine four triangles. Show that the centers of their circumcircles and the perpendicular bisectors of the lines connecting each pair of points form a complete quadrangle.

12. Show that with five independent points the centers of the circumcircles and the perpendicular bisectors (Ex. 11) form a configuration (10_3) of Desargues.

2-10 Projectivity in a pencil. The lines $a_1,a_2,a_3,\ \ldots$ of a pencil P (Fig. 2-12) intersect a line l, not through P, in a set of points $A_1,A_2,$ $A_3,\ldots$. If a projectivity is established between the points on l, that is (see Sec. 1-6), a bilinear correspondence between the coordinates of these points, then we can establish a one-to-one correspondence between the lines of the pencil, which we also call a *projectivity*. For this we have simply to associate a_2 with a_1, etc., if A_2 is associated with A_1, etc. Since the cross ratio of four points is preserved under the projectivity on a line, the cross ratio of four lines is preserved under a projectivity in the pencil. Such a projectivity can, therefore, be expressed algebraically by a bilinear relationship between the λ, if $L_1 - \lambda L_2 = 0$ is the equation of the pencil:

$$a\lambda\lambda' + b\lambda + c\lambda' + d = 0. \tag{10-1}$$

We can now transfer our results about hyperbolic, parabolic, and elliptic projectivities to the lines of the pencil. When $b = c$, we have an *involution* in the pencil; here the lines are matched in pairs. We can distinguish again between hyperbolic, elliptic, and parabolic involutions, with corresponding theorems about harmonic sets of lines.

We now prove the theorem:

> *A pencil of lines in nonsingular involution has either one corresponding pair of perpendicular lines, or all corresponding pairs are perpendicular.*

To prove it let us refer the pencil $L_1 - \lambda L_2 = 0$ to two lines $L_1 = 0$, $L_2 = 0$, which correspond to each other in the involution. Let us take L_1 and L_2 in the normal form for rectangular coordinates:

$$L_1 \equiv x \cos \alpha_1 + y \sin \alpha_1 - p_1, \quad L_2 \equiv x \cos \alpha_2 + y \sin \alpha_2 - p_2.$$

We have to find whether there exist two values λ, λ' such that

$$\frac{\cos \alpha_1 - \lambda \cos \alpha_2}{\sin \alpha_1 - \lambda \sin \alpha_2} \cdot \frac{\cos \alpha_1 - \lambda' \cos \alpha_2}{\sin \alpha_1 - \lambda' \sin \alpha_2} = -1$$

or

$$\lambda\lambda' - (\lambda + \lambda') \cos (\alpha_1 - \alpha_2) + 1 = 0. \tag{10-2}$$

The equation of the involution $a\lambda\lambda' + b(\lambda + \lambda') + c = 0$ must be such that $\lambda = 0$ corresponds to $\lambda' = \infty$, hence $b = 0$, $a \neq 0$. The number $c \neq 0$, because the involution is nonsingular. We therefore have to find the common solutions of Eq. (10-2) and of

$$a\lambda\lambda' + c = 0, \quad a \neq 0, \quad c \neq 0.$$

There is always one solution, except when $c = a$ and $\cos (\alpha_1 - \alpha_2) = 0$, in which case all values of λ satisfy both equations. Then $\alpha_1 = \alpha_2 + \pi/2$ and the involution takes the form

$$\lambda\lambda' + 1 = 0. \tag{10-3}$$

This involution is elliptic and is formed by a right angle turning about its vertex, the two sides of the right angle forming the pair of lines in involution.

The theorem also admits of a simple geometric demonstration (see Ex. 1, below).

EXERCISES

1. If an involution in a pencil is defined by connecting point P in Fig. 1–9 with the points in involution on the line l, show from the figure that there is exactly one pair of perpendicular lines in the involution, with one exception, when all lines in the involution are perpendicular.

2. Define three pairs of lines in involution with the aid of a complete quadrilateral (see Ex. 3, Sec. 2–9).

3. *Perspective pencils.* If two pencils P and P' are in projective correspondence, and one line a_1 coincides with the corresponding line a'_1, then the pencils are *perspective*. Show that the points of intersection of corresponding lines $(a_2,a'_2),(a_3,a'_3)$, etc., lie on a line l. This is the dual to the theorem of Ex. 2, Sec. 2–7.

CHAPTER 3

LINE COORDINATES. HOMOGENEOUS COORDINATES

3–1 The "new" geometry. The beginning of the modern period in geometry is usually placed in 1822 with the appearance of the stately tome entitled *Traité des Propriétés Projectives des Figures* (treatise on the projective properties of figures). It was written by Jean Victor Poncelet (1788–1867), a pupil of the geometer Gaspard Monge of the Paris Ecole Polytechnique. Monge was the founder of modern descriptive geometry, and developed the methods of analytic geometry. Poncelet, a military engineer, served in Napoleon's *grande armée*, which invaded Russia in 1812. During this disastrous campaign Poncelet was made a prisoner of war, and was compelled to stay in Saratov on the Volga. Here, without any books or other resources, he elaborated ideas of which the germ had been laid in Monge's instruction, and discussed them with fellow polytechnicians, also prisoners. Thus he developed the theories which he eventually published in 1822. Poncelet later taught applied mathematics, first at Metz, then at Paris, and was active in public life as a military and technical specialist.

Poncelet's preface to his book was a program of the new school. Here he stressed, against the geometrical methods of the Ancients, what he called the *principle of continuity*, by which he could extend the properties of one figure to another by gradual changes, and which he even extended to the transition of the real to the imaginary. One of the principal applications of this method was the *projection* of one figure on another, from space on plane, or from plane on plane, or plane on line, especially the *central projection*. It was this idea which gave the name *projective geometry* to the new science.

Poncelet also stressed the idea that the unlimited line and the point can be considered equivalent in the projective geometry of the plane. This is the principle of duality, which in Poncelet's book is still connected with a given conic (see our Chapter 5). In its full generality (as we have introduced it in our Chapter 2) it appears in the works of Gergonne and Steiner.

Joseph Diaz Gergonne (1771–1859), an artillery officer who taught at Nîmes and Montpellier, was the publisher of the *Annales de Mathé-*

52

matiques (1810–1831), the oldest purely mathematical periodical, in which he published his own contributions and those of other outstanding mathematicians of the period. A struggle for priority embittered the lives of Gergonne and Poncelet, but now we consider these men co-founders of projective geometry.

The roots of modern geometry can be traced back to a period long before Gergonne and Poncelet. Some of the most fundamental theorems were known to the Ancients, but somehow they remained isolated facts and their general implications were not seen. In the fifteenth and sixteenth centuries we find again approaches among painters such as Piero Della Francesca and Albrecht Dürer, and in the seventeenth century we see Desargues almost penetrating to the core of the theory. But it was not until Monge (1746–1818) with his co-workers and pupils, at the Ecole Polytechnique in Paris, developed descriptive and analytic geometry, that the new algebraic and projective geometry began to flourish.

The term "analytic geometry" appears in this period also for the first time in its present sense, and seems to go back to the famous textbook writer S. F. Lacroix; the term appears in the title of J. B. Biot's *Essai de Géométrie Analytique* (1802). (See p. 146.)

By 1820, when Gergonne had been publishing his *Annales* for some time, the new ideas were "in the air." They were elaborated in rapid succession by French and German authors:

1822, J. V. Poncelet, *Traité des Propriétés Projectives des Figures.*

1827, A. F. Möbius, *Der barycentrische Calcul.*

1828–1831, J. Plücker, *Analytisch-Geometrische Entwicklungen.*

1832, J. Steiner, *Systematische Entwicklung der Abhängigkeit geometrischer Gestalten von Einander.*

1837, M. Chasles, *Aperçu Historique sur l'Origine et le Développement des Méthodes en Géométrie* (new ed. 1875, 1883).

1847, C. G. Von Staudt, *Die Geometrie der Lage.*

To these books may be added:

1844, H. Grassmann, *Die lineare Ausdehnungslehre* (revised 1862).

1852, M. Chasles, *Géométrie Supérieure* (2nd ed. 1870).

1856–1860, C. G. Von Staudt, *Beitrage zur Geometrie der Lage,* 3 vols.

Among these authors we can distinguish two different trends, which both go back to Monge. Monge's geometry was both analytic and synthetic, using algebra and calculus as much as the method of the Ancients. For Poncelet, and above all for Steiner, the method was purely geometric (synthetic), and discarded the help of algebraic-analytic developments. Poncelet, who introduced imaginary elements into geometry, was not dogmatic in this respect, but Steiner was. Plücker, on the contrary, created new algebraic methods to master the material, such as the abbreviated notation and the line coordinates (see below). We thus distinguish between synthetic geometry (Steiner) and algebraic geometry (Plücker). Projective geometry can be developed both synthetically and algebraically. In this book we stress the algebraic method, but take an occasional excursion into the synthetic method.

3–2 Line coordinates. We have been able to express duality in such terms as point-line or intersection-connection, but in the proofs of the theorems we still had to start with points as primary elements. The proofs of the theorems on complete quadrangles and quadrilaterals in Sec. 2–8 were not dual. We shall now show how to express duality algebraically also. For this purpose, let us write the equation of a line l in (oblique) Cartesian coordinates (not through O) in the form

$$ux + vy + 1 = 0 \quad (u,v \text{ constants, not both zero}). \quad (2\text{–}1)$$

If we compare this with our previous expression

$$Ax + By + C = 0, \quad (2\text{–}2)$$

we see that

$$u:v:1 = A:B:C, \quad (2\text{–}3)$$

where $C \neq 0$. When a and b are the intercepts of l on the axes, and $a,b \neq 0$, then

$$u = -\frac{1}{a}, \quad v = -\frac{1}{b}.$$

Plücker proposed to call the numbers u and v the *coordinates* of the line. We can thus speak of the point $P(x,y)$, where x and y are *point coordinates*, and of the line $l(u,v)$, where u and v are *line coordinates*.

When between (u,v) and (x,y) the relation (2–1) exists, then P lies on l, and we say that point and line are *incident*. For instance, point $P(1,1)$ and line $l(-1/2; -1/2)$ are incident. Some special cases are

(a) $u = a$ (constant, $\neq 0$). This equation is satisfied by all lines passing through a point A on the x-axis such that $OA = -1/a$.

(b) $pu - qv = 0$ (p,q constants $\neq 0$). This equation gives all lines for which, according to Eq. (2–3), $A:B = q:p$, and whose equation in point coordinates, therefore, is $qx + py + C = 0$. These lines are parallel to the line $y = -(q/p)x$.

(c) $u = 0$, $v = a$, $a \neq 0$, represents a line parallel to the x-axis; $v = 0$, $u = a$, $a \neq 0$, a line parallel to the y-axis.

(d) $u = 0$, $v = 0$ leads to $1 = 0$, which can be interpreted as the line at infinity ($a \to \infty$, $b \to \infty$) (the ideal line) of the plane.

(e) So far we have excluded the case that $C = 0$. When $A,B \neq 0$, $C \to 0$, u and v both tend to ∞. All lines through the origin are therefore given by $u = \infty$, $v = \infty$ and can be distinguished only by their ratio v/u [see (b)].

Equation (2–1) represents, for fixed (u,v), a relation between the coordinates of an infinite number of points (x,y) which lie on the straight line (u,v). We call Eq. (2–1) the *equation of the line (in point coordinates)*. Now consider (x,y) as fixed. Then Eq. (2–1) represents a relation between the coordinates of an infinite number of lines (u,v) all passing through the point (x,y). We therefore call Eq. (2–1) the *equation of the point (in line coordinates)*. For instance, the equation $7u - 9v + 2 = 0$ is the equation of the point $(7/2, -9/2)$, just as $5x - 4y + 8 = 0$ is the equation of the line $(5/8, -4/8)$.

Returning to the particular cases, we see (a) that $u = a$ ($a \neq 0$) is the equation of the point $(-1/a, 0)$, while $v = b$ ($b \neq 0$) is that of the point $(0, -1/b)$. From (b) we see that $pu - qv = 0$ is the equation of the ideal point in the direction of the line $qx + py = 0$. Since $u = 0$, $v = 0$, representing the line at infinity, satisfy $pu - qv = 0$, we see that *the ideal points of all lines in the plane lie on the ideal line of the plane*.

3–3 Duality in point and line coordinates.

We can now express the geometric duality of point and line also in algebraic terms. Here are some examples.

1. Point with coordinates (x,y).

$1'$. Line with coordinates (u,v).

2. Line not through O: $ux + vy + 1 = 0$ (u,v fixed).

$2'$. Point not at infinity: $ux + xy + 1 = 0$ (x,y fixed).

3. $Ax + By + C = 0$: line with $u = A/C$, $v = B/C$ ($C \neq 0$).

$3'$. $Au + Bv + C = 0$: point with $x = A/C$, $y = B/C$ ($C \neq 0$).

4. Origin: $x = 0$, $y = 0$.

$4'$. Line at infinity: $u = 0$, $v = 0$.

5. $Ax + By = 0$: line through O.

$5'$. $Au + Bv = 0$: point at infinity.

6. Two lines $\begin{cases} A_1x + B_1y + C_1 = 0 \\ A_2x + B_2y + C_2 = 0 \end{cases}$
determine a point
$$x:y:1 = \begin{vmatrix} B_1C_1 \\ B_2C_2 \end{vmatrix} : \begin{vmatrix} C_1A_1 \\ C_2A_2 \end{vmatrix} : \begin{vmatrix} A_1B_1 \\ A_2B_2 \end{vmatrix},$$
which is an ideal point, if
$$\begin{vmatrix} A_1B_1 \\ A_2B_2 \end{vmatrix} = 0, \quad \begin{vmatrix} B_1C_1 \\ B_2C_2 \end{vmatrix} \neq 0.$$

$6'$. Two points $\begin{cases} A_1u+B_1v+C_1=0 \\ A_2u+B_2v+C_2=0 \end{cases}$
determine a line
$$u:v:1 = \begin{vmatrix} B_1C_1 \\ B_2C_2 \end{vmatrix} : \begin{vmatrix} C_1A_1 \\ C_2A_2 \end{vmatrix} : \begin{vmatrix} A_1B_1 \\ A_2B_2 \end{vmatrix},$$
which passes through the origin,
if $\begin{vmatrix} A_1B_1 \\ A_2B_2 \end{vmatrix} = 0, \quad \begin{vmatrix} B_1C_1 \\ B_2C_2 \end{vmatrix} \neq 0.$

7. Pencil of lines: $L_1 - \lambda L_2 = 0$, $L_a \equiv A_ax + B_ay + C_a$, $a = 1,2$.

$7'$. Points on a line ("pencil of points") $P_1 - \lambda P_2 = 0$, $P_a \equiv A_au + B_av + C_a$, $a = 1,2$.

8. Three concurrent lines $L_i = 0$, $i = 1,2,3$:
$$\begin{vmatrix} A_1 & B_1 & C_1 \\ A_2 & B_2 & C_2 \\ A_3 & B_3 & C_3 \end{vmatrix} = 0,$$
or (by appropriate normalization)
$$L_1 + L_2 + L_3 = 0.$$

$8'$. Three collinear points $P_i = 0$, $i = 1,2,3$:
$$\begin{vmatrix} A_1 & B_1 & C_1 \\ A_2 & B_2 & C_2 \\ A_3 & B_3 & C_3 \end{vmatrix} = 0,$$
or (by appropriate normalization)
$$P_1 + P_2 + P_3 = 0.$$

9. Point (x,y) on line through points $A(a_1,a_2)$, $B(b_1,b_2)$:
$$x = \frac{a_1 - \mu a_2}{1 - \mu}, \quad y = \frac{a_2 - \mu b_2}{1 - \mu},$$
where $\mu =$ division ratio, proportional to the λ of $7'$,
$$\left(\mu = \lambda \frac{C_2}{C_1}\right).$$

$9'$. Line (u,v) through point of intersection of lines $l(a_1,a_2)$, $m(b_1,b_2)$:
$$u = \frac{a_1 - \mu a_2}{1 - \mu}, \quad v = \frac{b_1 - \mu b_2}{1 - \mu},$$
where μ is proportional to the λ of 7,
$$\left(\mu = \lambda \frac{C_2}{C_1}\right),$$
both proportional to division ratio.

10. Two points with division ratios μ_1, μ_2 have a cross ratio μ_1/μ_2 with respect to A and B. This cross ratio is also equal to λ_1/λ_2 (the λ of 7'). If $\mu_1 + \mu_2 = 0$, or $\lambda_1 + \lambda_2 = 0$, the points are harmonic conjugates with respect to A and B.

10'. Two lines with two values μ_1, μ_2 (9) or λ_1, λ_2 (7) have a cross ratio $\mu_1/\mu_2 = \lambda_1/\lambda_2$ with respect to l and m. If $\mu_1 + \mu_2 = 0$, or $\lambda_1 + \lambda_2 = 0$, the lines are harmonic conjugates with respect to l and m.

The duality between point and line is now fully expressed in the algebraic symbolism. Moreover, a duality between origin and line at infinity is also established.

The lack of duality in the metrical relations is apparent from the following table, where a rectangular Cartesian coordinate system (itself at this stage not dualizable) is presupposed.

11. Angle α of lines $L_1 = 0$, $L_2 = 0$:
$$\tan \alpha = \pm \frac{A_1 B_2 - A_2 B_1}{A_1 A_2 + B_1 B_2}.$$

11'. Distance of points $P_1 = 0$, $P_2 = 0$:
$$\frac{1}{c_1 c_2} \sqrt{(A_1 C_2 - A_2 C_1)^2 + (B_1 C_2 - B_2 C_1)^2}.$$

12. Distance of points (x_1, y_1), (x_2, y_2):
$$\sqrt{(x_1 - x_2)^2 + (y_1 - y_2)^2}.$$

12'. Angle α of lines (u_1, v_1), (u_2, v_2):
$$\tan \alpha = \pm \frac{u_1 v_2 - u_2 v_1}{u_1 u_2 + v_1 v_2}.$$

We also present here the formula for the distance d of a point (x, y) to a line (u, v):

13. From point (x_0, y_0) to line $Ax_0 + By_0 + C = 0$:
$$d = \frac{Ax_0 + By_0 + C}{\pm \sqrt{A^2 + B^2}}.$$

13'. From point $Au + Bv + C = 0$ to line (u_0, v_0):
$$d = \frac{Au_0 + Bv_0 + C}{\pm C \sqrt{u_0^2 + v_0^2}}.$$

If the line, or point, is given by $ux + vy + 1 = 0$, these two formulas can be replaced by the single one:

$$d = \pm \frac{ux + vy + 1}{\sqrt{u^2 + v^2}}.$$

EXERCISES

1. Find the point coordinates of the points given by (a) $5u - 2v + 3 = 0$, (b) $u - v = 0$, (c) $v = 8$.

2. Find the condition for parallelism and for orthogonality of the lines (u_1,v_1) and (u_2,v_2) in a rectangular system.

3. Find the coordinates of the line connecting the points

$$3u - 5v + 2 = 0, \quad 7u + 3v - 1 = 0$$

and find its equation in point coordinates.

4. Find the coordinates of the point in which the line joining the points (x_1,y_1) and (x_2,y_2) intersects the line (u,v).

5. Prove the statements 6', 9, 9', 10, 10', 11, 11', 12', 13' of this section.

6. Prove algebraically that on every side of a complete quadrangle the two vertices are harmonic with respect to the points in which this side is intersected by the sides of the diagonal triangle. Use line coordinates. Do it in a way dual to that used to prove the corresponding theorem on a complete quadrilateral (see Sec. 2–8).

7. Give a geometrical interpretation of the identity

$$(P_1 + P_2) + (P_3 + P_4) \equiv (P_1 + P_3) + (P_2 + P_4)$$
$$\equiv (P_1 + P_4) + (P_2 + P_3),$$

where $P_\lambda = A_\lambda u + B_\lambda v + C_\lambda$, $\lambda = 1,2,3,4$. (Take $C_\lambda = 1$.)

3–4 Homogeneous Cartesian coordinates. There are still exceptional elements in our coordinate system. They are the ideal points and the ideal line in point coordinates, the origin and the lines through it in line coordinates. This awkward touch can be removed by the use of *homogeneous* coordinates. For this purpose, we write

$$x = \frac{x_1}{x_3}, \quad y = \frac{x_2}{x_3} \tag{4–1}$$

and call $(x_1:x_2:x_3)$, or simply (x_1,x_2,x_3) or (x_i), $i = 1,2,3$, the *homogeneous Cartesian coordinates* of a point P in the plane. The point is determined by the *ratio* of its homogeneous coordinates:

$$x_1:x_2:x_3 = x:y:1, \tag{4–2}$$

so that point $P(5,6,-3)$ is identical with point $P(10,12,-6)$ or $P(-5,-6,+3)$; it is the point with ordinary (nonhomogeneous) coordinates $x = -5/3$, $y = -2$. Points on the x-axis are characterized by $x_2 = 0$, on the y-axis by $x_1 = 0$. The points at infinity are obtained by taking $x_3 = 0$, so that *the line at infinity l_∞ is given by the equation $x_3 = 0$* (and no longer by the awkward $C = 0$, $C \neq 0$). The

origin has the coordinates $(0:0:1)$ or $(0:0:a)$, $a \neq 0$. The equation
of a straight line is

$$A_1x_1 + A_2x_2 + A_3x_3 = 0, \quad \text{or} \quad (Ax) = 0 \text{ for short}$$
$$(A_1, A_2, A_3 \text{ not all zero}), \quad (4\text{–}3)$$

which is a homogeneous equation of the first order. An ideal point
has the coordinates $(a:b:0)$; it is the point at infinity of the line
$y:x = b:a$. Every set (x_i) represents a point, with one exception:
$(0:0:0)$. "The point $(0:0:0)$" is without definite meaning.

Let us write Eq. (4–3) in the form

$$u_1x_1 + u_2x_2 + u_3x_3 = (ux) = 0. \quad (4\text{–}4)$$

We now call $(u_1:u_2:u_3)$ the *homogeneous (Cartesian) coordinates* of
the line (4–4). We pass to ordinary (nonhomogeneous) line coordinates by means of the equation:

$$u_1:u_2:u_3 = u:v:1. \quad (4\text{–}5)$$

Equation (4–4) expresses the incidence of point (x_i) and line (u_i).
The equation $u_1 = 0$ represents the special point on the x-axis, $u_2 = 0$
that on the y-axis, and *the origin is now given by $u_3 = 0$*. A line
$(a:b:0)$ is a line through the origin, the line $(0:1:0)$ is the x-axis, the
line $(0:0:1)$ the line at infinity, l_∞ (Figs. 3–1, 3–2). The duality
between point and line now assumes the following form:

1. Line: $(ux) = 0$ (u_i constants, not all zero).

1′. Point: $(ux) = 0$ (x_i constants, not all zero).

2. Line through O: $u_1x_1 + u_2x_2 = 0$.

2′. Point on l_∞: $u_1x_1 + u_2x_2 = 0$.

3. Line parallel to y-axis:
$$u_1x_1 + u_3x_3 = 0.$$

3′. Point on x-axis: $u_1x_1 + u_3x_3 = 0$.

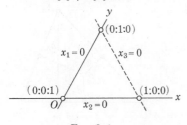

Fig. 3–1

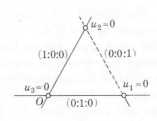

Fig. 3–2

4. Point on line connecting points $A(a_i)$ and $B(b_i)$:

$(\lambda a_1 + \mu b_1):(\lambda a_2 + \mu b_2):(\lambda a_3 + \mu b_3)$,

where $-\dfrac{\mu}{\lambda}\dfrac{a_3}{b_3}$ is the division ratio.

5. Two points P,Q for which the λ,μ in the previous equation are (λ_1,μ_1), (λ_2,μ_2), determine a cross ratio

$$(PQ,AB) = \frac{\mu_1}{\lambda_1} : \frac{\mu_2}{\lambda_2}.$$

6. Three points $(a_i),(b_i),(c_i)$ on a line:

$$(abc) = \begin{vmatrix} a_1 & a_2 & a_3 \\ b_1 & b_2 & b_3 \\ c_1 & c_2 & c_3 \end{vmatrix} = 0.$$

4′. Line through intersection of lines (a_i) and $m(b_i)$:

$(\lambda a_1 + \mu b_1):(\lambda a_2 + \mu b_2):(\lambda a_3 + \mu b_3)$,

where $-\mu/\lambda$ is proportional to the division ratio.

5′. Two lines p,q for which the λ,μ in the previous equation are (λ_1,μ_1), (λ_2,μ_2), determine a cross ratio

$$(pq,ab) = \frac{\mu_1}{\lambda_1} : \frac{\mu_2}{\lambda_2}.$$

6′. Three lines $(a_i),(b_i),(c_i)$ through a point:

$$(abc) = 0.$$

3–5 Other homogeneous coordinates.

We have been led to a *basic triangle* formed by the elements $(1:0:0)$, $(0:1:0)$, and $(0:0:1)$, consisting of ordinary and of ideal elements. The question arises whether homogeneous coordinates can be found with a basic triangle consisting exclusively of ordinary sides and vertices. Such a system was introduced by Möbius in his book on the barycentric calculus (see Sec. 1–1). Möbius proposed a basic triangle $A_1A_2A_3$ (Fig. 3–3) with altitudes h_1,h_2,h_3. If a point P is at distance d_1,d_2,d_3 of the three sides of the triangle, all positive for a point inside the triangle, then the *barycentric coordinates* of $P(x_i)$ satisfy the equation

$$x_1:x_2:x_3 = \text{area } \triangle PA_2A_3:\text{area } \triangle PA_3A_1:\text{area } \triangle PA_1A_2$$

$$= \frac{d_1}{h_1} : \frac{d_2}{h_2} : \frac{d_3}{h_3}. \qquad (5\text{--}1)$$

The sides of the basic triangle are given by $x_1 = 0$, $x_2 = 0$, $x_3 = 0$. The point where the medians intersect (the center of gravity, or centroid, or barycentrum) has the coordinates $(1:1:1)$; we call it U, the *unit point*. Since the d_i are linear expressions in the Cartesian

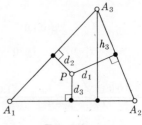

Fig. 3–3

coordinates of P (cf., for example, formula 13, Sec. 3–3) with respect to an arbitrary system of Cartesian axes, Eq. (5–1) can be written

$$\begin{aligned} \rho x_1 &= A_1 x + B_1 y + C_1, \\ \rho x_2 &= A_2 x + B_2 y + C_2, \\ \rho x_3 &= A_3 x + B_3 y + C_3, \end{aligned} \qquad (5\text{–}2)$$

where ρ is a proportionality factor ($\neq 0$) and the lines $A_i x + B_i y + C_i = 0$ represent the sides of the triangle. The determinant (ABC) of the A_i, B_i, C_i is $\neq 0$, since the sides of the triangle do not meet in one point. The x and y can therefore also be solved in terms of x_1/x_3 and x_2/x_3 (see Ex. 1, Sec. 3–7). This means that a straight line in barycentric coordinates has the equation

$$(ux) = u_1 x_1 + u_2 x_2 + u_3 x_3 = 0 \quad (u_1, u_2, u_3 \text{ constants, not all zero}). \quad (5\text{–}3)$$

Equation (5–3) allows us to introduce $u_1 : u_2 : u_3$ as *barycentric line coordinates*. Then Eq. (5–3) is the condition for the incidence of point (x_i) and line (u_i).

Möbius, in 1828, obtained his coordinates by placing (positive or negative) masses m_i in the points A_i. To the center of gravity P of these masses he assigned the coordinates m_i. If the Cartesian coordinates of the A_i are (a_i, b_i), then those of P are, according to a well-known theorem of statics,

$$x = \frac{m_1 a_1 + m_2 a_2 + m_3 a_3}{m_1 + m_2 + m_3}, \quad y = \frac{m_1 b_1 + m_2 b_2 + m_3 b_3}{m_1 + m_2 + m_3}. \qquad (5\text{–}4)$$

Equation (5–1) follows from the equations

$$\frac{d_1}{h_1} = \frac{m_1}{m_1 + m_2 + m_3}, \quad \frac{d_2}{h_2} = \frac{m_2}{m_1 + m_2 + m_3}, \quad \frac{d_3}{h_3} = \frac{m_3}{m_1 + m_2 + m_3},$$

which can readily be derived from the properties of the center of gravity. Möbius' barycentric coordinates are the m_i and not their ratio, so that in his system a point has a weight. The values d_i/h_i of Eq. (5–1) were introduced as the coordinates of a point by K. W. Feuerbach, *Grundriss zu analytischen Untersuchungen der dreieckigen Pyramide* (1827). If in this case we write $x_i = d_i/h_i$, then we have obtained *areal coordinates*. Here

$$x_1 + x_2 + x_3 = 1.$$

The homogeneous coordinates for which

$$x_1 : x_2 : x_3 = d_1 : d_2 : d_3 \qquad (5\text{–}5)$$

are called *trilinear coordinates*.   Their unit point is the center of the inscribed circle of the basic triangle (the so-called *incenter*).

We see that in this and similar ways we can introduce all kinds of homogeneous coordinates, and as long as they are proportional to the d_i the equation of a straight line is always linear.

Those readers interested in trilinear coordinates can find a detailed exposition in W. A. Whitworth, *Trilinear Coordinates* (Cambridge, 1866), or may consult Chapter XIII of C. Smith, *An Elementary Treatise on Conic Sections*, 2nd ed. (London, 1883).   On barycentric coordinates and their relation to graphostatics, see H. Weber-J. Wellstein, *Encyklopädie der Elementar-Mathematik* III (Leipzig, 1917), Chapter XIII.   On areal coordinates see also E. A. Weiss, *Jahresber. Deutsch. Math. Verein.* **51** (1941), p. 9 (italics).

3–6 Projective coordinates.   We shall now consider the general case in which the x_i are defined as proportional to the d_i with *arbitrary* proportionality factors k_i ($\neq 0$):

$$x_1:x_2:x_3 = k_1 d_1 : k_2 d_2 : k_3 d_3. \tag{6–1}$$

Such coordinates are called either *general homogeneous coordinates* or *projective coordinates*.   For the unit point $(1:1:1)$,

$$k_1:k_2:k_3 = \frac{1}{d_1} : \frac{1}{d_2} : \frac{1}{d_3}, \tag{6–2}$$

where the d_i are the distances from the unit point to the sides of the basic triangle.   Hence *any* point in the plane not on the sides of the basic triangle can be taken as the unit point.   The choice of the unit point determines the ratio of the k_i, so that a *system of projective coordinates is uniquely determined by four independent points*.   Any three of these points can be taken as the basic points A_i; the remaining one can then function as unit point U.

In the same way as in Eq. (5–2), we find for the formulas of transition from homogeneous Cartesian coordinates (x,y,z) to projective coordinates x_i,

$$\rho x_i = A_i x + B_i y + C_i z \quad (i = 1,2,3), \tag{6–3}$$

or, with a change of notation,

$$\rho x_i = a_{i1} x + a_{i2} y + a_{i3} z \quad (i = 1,2,3),$$

with determinant

$$(abc) = \begin{vmatrix} a_{11} & a_{12} & a_{13} \\ a_{21} & a_{22} & a_{23} \\ a_{31} & a_{32} & a_{33} \end{vmatrix} = \text{Det } (a_{ij}) \quad (i,j = 1,2,3), \qquad (6\text{-}4)$$

different from zero, and ρ an arbitrary factor of proportionality ($\neq 0$). The straight line again has the equation

$$(ux) = u_1x_1 + u_2x_2 + u_3x_3 = 0. \qquad (6\text{-}5)$$

The choice of the basic points determines the right-hand side of Eq. (6-3), but for a factor different for each of the x_i. This factor is determined by the choice of U. The ratio of the nine constants a_{ij} is indeed determined by the $4 \times 2 = 8$ ordinary Cartesian coordinates of the basic and unit points, since these points are independent.

The coefficients u_i in Eq. (6-5) can be considered as the *projective coordinates of the line*. There is a line u $(1:1:1)$, the *unit line*, determined by the choice of the A_i, U. The unit point does not lie on the unit line because the condition for incidence is $(ux) = 0$.

The geometrical interpretation of projective line coordinates follows from formula 13′, which shows that the distance from a point to a line $l(u,v)$ is linear in (u,v). By reasoning similar to that followed in the case of point coordinates, we find that

$$u_1:u_2:u_3 = l_1p_1:l_2p_2:l_3p_3 \quad (l_i \text{ constants, not all zero}), \qquad (6\text{-}5)$$

where p_i is the distance from point A_i to line l (Fig. 3-4).

General projective coordinates were first introduced by J. Plücker, *Crelle's Journal* **5** (1829), pp. 1–36, reprinted in *Ges. Mathem. Abh.* (1895), pp. 124–158.

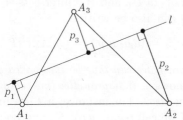

FIG. 3-4

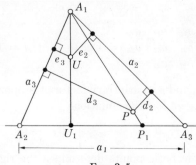

Fig. 3–5

3–7 Properties of projective coordinates.   Let e_i (Fig. 3–5) be the distances from the unit point U, and d_i again be those from an arbitrary point P to the sides of the basic triangle, all positive when U and P lie inside this triangle. Then, according to Eqs. (6–1) and (6–2),

$$\frac{k_2 e_2}{k_3 e_3} = 1, \quad \frac{x_2}{x_3} = \frac{k_2 d_2}{k_3 d_3} = \frac{e_3 d_2}{e_2 d_2} = \frac{d_2}{d_3} : \frac{e_2}{e_3}.$$

If we give all lines through A_1 a sense away from A, then

$$\frac{e_2}{e_3} = -\frac{\sin \angle (A_1 U, A_1 A_2)}{\sin \angle (A_1 U, A_1 A_3)}, \quad \frac{d_2}{d_3} = -\frac{\sin \angle (A_1 P, A_1 A_2)}{\sin \angle (A_1 P, A_1 A_3)},$$

and when we denote $A_1 A_2$ by a_3, $A_3 A_1$ by a_2, $A_1 U$ by u_1, $A_1 P$ by p_1:

$$\frac{x_2}{x_3} = \frac{\sin \angle (p_1 a_3)}{\sin \angle (p_1 a_2)} : \frac{\sin \angle (u_1 a_3)}{\sin \angle (u_1 a_2)} = (p_1 u_1, a_3 a_2) = (a_2 a_3, u_1 p_1). \quad (7\text{–}1)$$

If AU intersects $A_2 A_3$ in U_1, and AP intersects $A_2 A_3$ in P_1, then we find that Eq. (7–1) can also be written

$$x_2 : x_3 = (a_2 a_3, u_1 p_1) = (A_2 A_3, U_1 P_1). \quad (7\text{–}2)$$

Projective point coordinates can thus be interpreted as cross ratios.   A similar reasoning shows us that *projective line coordinates can be interpreted as cross ratios also.*   For instance, if l is a line (u_i), u the unit line $(1:1:1)$, and if we call point (ua_1), E_1, and point (la_1), L_1, then

$$u_2 : u_3 = (A_2 A_3, E_1 L_1). \quad (7\text{–}3)$$

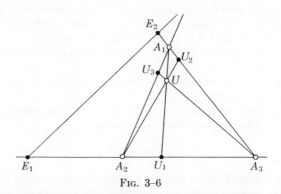

FIG. 3–6

The table at the end of Sec. 3–4, set up for barycentric coordinates, also holds for projective coordinates in general.

As an application, let us find the relative position of unit point $(1:1:1)$ and unit line $x_1 + x_2 + x_3 = 0$. This line intersects the side $x_1 = 0$ in a point E_1 for which $x_2 + x_3 = 0$, hence E_1 $(0:-1:1)$. The line A_1U (Fig. 3–6) passes through A_1 $(1:0:0)$ and U $(1:1:1)$ and hence (Ex. 20, below) has the equation $x_2 - x_3 = 0$. It therefore intersects $x_1 = 0$ in a point U_1 $(0:1:1)$. Hence E_1, U_1 are harmonic with respect to A_2, A_3. We thus find, reasoning in a similar way for the other sides: *The unit line intersects the sides of the basic triangle in three points E_i. Each point E_i is harmonic to point U_i with respect to the vertices of the basic triangle on side a_i, where U_i is the point where A_iU intersects the side a_i.*

When we call U and u *harmonic* with respect to the triangle, then we see that to every point belongs a line, and to every line a point, such that point and line are harmonic with respect to a given triangle (see Ex. 3, below). Exceptions are the vertices and sides of the triangle, as well as the points on the sides and the lines through the vertices.

EXERCISES

1. Solve Eq. (5–2) for x and y in terms of x_1/x_3 and x_2/x_3.

2. Carry out the reasoning leading to Eq. (6–5).

3. A point P is given, not on the sides of a triangle ABC. Let AP, BP, and CP intersect the sides BC, CA, and AB in A_1, B_1, C_1 respectively. Let A_2, B_2, C_2 be the harmonic conjugates of A_1, B_1, C_1 respectively, with respect to the vertices of the triangle on which these points are situated. Show that $A_2 B_2 C_2$ lie on a straight line. State the dual theorem.

4. Show that the unit line of the system of barycentric coordinates is the line at infinity.

5. Find the condition that two lines $(ax) = 0$, $(bx) = 0$, in barycentric coordinates, are parallel.

6. Show that the point dividing the line connecting points (a_i) and (b_i) in ratio of $\lambda : \mu$ has the barycentric coordinates

$$\mu \frac{a_i}{\Sigma a_i} + \lambda \frac{b_i}{\Sigma b_i}.$$

7. Let a point P in the plane of a triangle be projected in the directions of the three medians on the corresponding sides, and let the projections be P_1, P_2, P_3. Show that the center of gravity of $\triangle P_1 P_2 P_3$ lies midway between P and the center of gravity of the given triangle (E. Schoenhardt, *Deutsche Math.* **3**, 1937, 446).

8. Given four points $(x_i), (y_i), (z_i), (t_i)$ in the plane. Show that we can always choose these coordinates such that $x_i + y_i + z_i + t_i = 0$.

9. *The theorem of Pappus-Pascal.* Three points A_1, A_2, and A_3 lie on a line l, and three points B_1, B_2, B_3 lie on another line m. Let $A_1 B_2$ and $A_2 B_1$ meet in P; $A_1 B_3$ and $A_3 B_1$ in Q; $A_2 B_3$ and $A_3 B_2$ in R. Prove that P, Q, R lie on a straight line (Fig. 3–7). This theorem, found in Pappus, and perhaps known to Euclid, is often called *Pascal's theorem:* it is a special case of Pascal's theorem on conics (see Sec. 5–10). [It is important in axiomatics; see G. De B. Robinson, *The Foundations of Geometry* (Toronto, 1940), Chapter III; see also Ex. 18.]

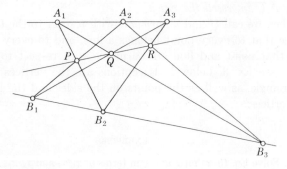

Fig. 3–7

10. State the dual theorem of that of Ex. 8, and show that Pascal's theorem is self-dual, and determines a configuration $(9_3,9_3)$. [It is not the only (9_3), as is shown in Fig. 3-8.]

11. A Pascal configuration is a (9_3), a Desargues configuration is a (10_3). Show that a (k_3) does not exist for $k \leqq 7$. (It can be shown that the case $k = 8$ is also not possible in the real domain, although it is possible in the complex domain.)

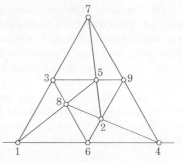

Fig. 3-8

12. Show that the line PQR in Ex. 12 passes through the point of intersection C of l and m if and only if A_1B_1, A_2B_2, A_3B_3 are concurrent.

13. Use Pascal's theorem of Ex. 9 to construct, with the ruler only, a line through a point P and a nonaccessible point of intersection of two given lines not through P. *This construction is useful in geometric drawing.*

14. On the three sides A_1A_2, A_2A_3, A_3A_1 of an oriented triangle take three points B_3, B_1, B_2 respectively. Let A_1B_1, A_2B_2, A_3B_3 form the triangle $P_1P_2P_3$, where P_1 is the intersection of A_2B_2 and A_3B_3, P_2 of A_3B_3 and A_1B_1, P_3 of A_1B_1 and A_2B_2. Prove

$$(A_1B_1, P_2P_3) = (A_2B_2, P_3P_1) = (A_3B_3, P_1P_2)$$
$$= -\frac{A_1B_3 \cdot A_2B_1 \cdot A_3B_2}{A_2B_3 \cdot A_3B_1 \cdot A_1B_2}.$$

15. *Theorem of Ceva.* If the points B_1, B_2, B_3 lie on the sides A_2A_3, A_3A_1, A_1A_2 of an oriented triangle $A_1A_2A_3$, and A_1B_1, A_2B_2, A_3B_3 pass through one point, then $A_1B_3 \cdot A_2B_1 \cdot A_3B_2 = -A_2B_3 \cdot A_3B_1 \cdot A_1B_2$ (G. Ceva, 1678).

16. *Theorem of Menelaus.* If a line intersects the sides of an oriented triangle A_1A_2, A_2A_3, A_3A_1 in B_3, B_2, B_1, then

$$A_1B_3 \cdot A_2B_1 \cdot A_3B_2 = +A_2B_3 \cdot A_3B_1 \cdot A_1B_2$$

(Menelaus, c. 100 A.D.). Such a line $B_1B_2B_3$ is called a *transversal* of the triangle. This concept played an important role in L. N. M. Carnot's *Essai sur la Théorie des Transversales*, Paris, 1806 (see Sec. 2-9).

17. Prove the theorem of Sec. 2-9 on the complete quadrangle by using projective point coordinates, as in Ex. 8.

18. Prove Desargues' theorem by means of Pascal's theorem (Ex. 9). If, therefore, Pascal's theorem is accepted as an axiom, in addition to the axioms of connection in the plane, Desargues' theorem can be proved (G. Hessenberg, *Math. Ann.* **61**).

19. A triangle PQR is so placed that its vertices are on the sides BC, CA, and AB respectively of a fixed triangle. Its sides PR and QR pass through two fixed points on a fixed line through A. Show that PQ passes through a fixed point, and state the dual theorem.

20. The equation of the straight line passing through the points (a_i) and (b_i) is $(xab) = 0$. Prove.

21. Show that the equation of the point of intersection of line (u_i) with the line connecting the points (a_i) and (b_i) is $(ua)b_i - (ub)a_i = 0$, and that the equation of the line joining point (a_i) to the intersection of the lines joining the points $(b_i),(c_i)$ and $(d_i),(e_i)$ is .

$$(abc)(xde) - (adc)(xbe) = 0.$$

22. Show that in barycentric coordinates the equation of the circumscribed circle (the "circumcircle") of the fundamental triangle is

$$a_1^2 x_2 x_3 + a_2^2 x_3 x_1 + a_3^2 x_1 x_2 = 0,$$

when the a_i are the sides of this triangle. For this purpose, use the theorem (proved by elementary geometry) that the perpendiculars dropped from a point P on the circumcircle on the three sides intersect these sides in three points L,M,N on a straight line, the *line of Simson* (better: *line of Wallace*). See Ex. 14, Sec. 6–6.

23. To a point P with homogeneous coordinates a_i we associate the *complementary* point $P'(a_i')$ such that $a_1':a_2':a_3' = (a_2 + a_3):(a_3 + a_1):(a_1 + a_2)$. Show that (a) the unit point U and the points on the unit line u are self-complementary, (b) that the points P,P',U are collinear and $(PP',UU_1) = -2$, where U_1 is the point in which PP' intersects u (E. Vigarié, *Mathésis* **7** (1887), pp. 6–12).

24. Using barycentric coordinates in Ex. 23, prove that in a triangle ABC the centroid trisects the line joining the circumcenter to the orthocenter. This is the *line of Euler*.

3–8 Transformation of projective coordinates.

What happens to the projective coordinates of a point P if we pass from one set of basic triangle and unit points (a *reference system*) to another set? Since the new coordinates of P, as well as the old ones, can be derived from Cartesian coordinates by means of an equation of the form (6–3), the new (x_i') are linear homogeneous functions of the old (x_i):

$$\begin{aligned}
\sigma x_1' &= c_{11}x_1 + c_{12}x_2 + c_{13}x_3, \\
\sigma x_2' &= c_{21}x_1 + c_{22}x_2 + c_{23}x_3, \quad \text{or} \quad x_i' = \sum_{j=1}^{3} c_{ij}x_j \quad (i = 1,2,3). \quad (8\text{--}1) \\
\sigma x_3' &= c_{31}x_1 + c_{32}x_2 + c_{33}x_3,
\end{aligned}$$

We introduce the following *summation convention: When in a term an index appears twice, we must sum on this index.* Equations (8–1) can then be written

$$\sigma x_i' = c_{ij}x_j \quad (i,j = 1,2,3). \tag{8-2}$$

This means therefore that we must sum on j, but not on i, since i does not appear twice in the same term. This dropping of the Σ signs was first suggested by Einstein in order to simplify the notation of the tensor calculus.

The number σ ($\neq 0$) is an arbitrary proportionality factor and the c_{ij} are constants for which the determinant

$$C = \text{Det } (c_{ij}) \tag{8-3}$$

is $\neq 0$, because we must be able to solve the equations (8–2) for the x_i. We can readily see that *every* set of equations of the form (8–2) between x_i and x_i' with $C \neq 0$ represents a change of reference system. Indeed, if the sides of the basic triangle $x_i' = 0$ are given by the three equations

$$d_{ij}x_j = 0 \quad [d_{ij} \text{ constants}, \text{ Det } (d_{ij}) \neq 0],$$

then according to Eq. (8–2) the c_{1j}, c_{2j}, c_{3j} are proportional to the d_{1j}, d_{2j}, d_{3j} with arbitrary proportionality factors $\lambda_1, \lambda_2, \lambda_3$ respectively. When the new unit point U' ($c_1:c_2:c_3$) is given, then

$$\lambda_1(d_{1j}c_j):\lambda_2(d_{2j}c_j):\lambda_3(d_{3j}c_j) = 1:1:1,$$

from which the ratio of the λ_i can be found.

Equations (8–1) and (8–2) constitute the *most general linear transformation of three homogeneous variables.* They are called *projective transformations.* It is exactly because of the fact that the transformations from one set of projective coordinates to another set are general linear homogeneous transformations that these projective coordinates are so important.

To obtain the transformation of the x_i, we write

$$\gamma_{ij} = \text{Cofactor of } c_{ij} \text{ in } C \quad (C \neq 0). \tag{8-4}$$

Then the x_i are expressed in the x_i' by means of the equations

$$\sigma_1 x_i = \gamma_{ji}x_j' \quad (\sigma_1 \text{ a proportionality factor}) \tag{8-5}$$

(notice that it is γ_{ji}, not γ_{ij})

The corresponding transformations of the u_i in terms of the u_i' and conversely follow from the fact that a straight line $(ux) = u_i x_i = 0$ has $(u'x') = u_i' x_i' = 0$ as its equation in the new system. Hence (σ_2 is a proportionality factor),

$$u_i' x_i' = u_i' c_{ij} x_j = \sigma_2 u_j x_j,$$

which must hold for an infinite set of values of x_i. Hence,

$$\sigma_2 u_i = c_{ji} u_j' \tag{8–6}$$

[in Eq. (8–2) it is c_{ij}; here it is c_{ji}], and

$$\sigma_3 u_i' = \gamma_{ij} u_j \quad (\sigma_3 \text{ a proportionality factor}). \tag{8–7}$$

The determinants of all four transformations (8–2), (8–5), (8–6), and (8–7) are $\neq 0$ (see Ex. 2, Sec. 3–10). They have different *transformation matrices:*

$$\|c_{ij}\|, \quad \|\gamma_{ji}\|, \quad \|c_{ji}\|, \quad \|\gamma_{ij}\|. \tag{8–8}$$

We write

$$\|c_{ij}\| = \begin{Vmatrix} c_{11} & c_{12} & c_{13} \\ c_{21} & c_{22} & c_{23} \\ c_{31} & c_{32} & c_{33} \end{Vmatrix} \tag{8–9}$$

for the set of nine numbers c_{ij} in the same square array in which they appear in the transformation (8–2). Such an array is called a *square matrix*, or *matrix* for short. C is the determinant of the matrix. C is one number, while the matrix (8–9) consists of nine numbers.

The matrix $\|c_{ji}\|$ is called the *transpose* of $\|c_{ij}\|$; it is obtained by reflecting all terms of $\|c_{ij}\|$ in its main diagonal. The matrix $\|\gamma_{ji}\|$ is called the *adjoint* matrix of $\|c_{ij}\|$.

Transformations with the same matrix $\|c_{ij}\|$ are called *cogredient*, for example, $x_i' = c_{ij} x_j$, $y_i' = c_{ij} y_j$.

We have so far only discussed projective transformations with $C \neq 0$. Transformations (8–2) with $C = 0$ are called *singular*. They determine the ratio of the x_i' uniquely in terms of the x_i, but not conversely. We can readily see that in this case all transformed points (x_i') lie in a plane or on a line. Indeed, if $C = 0$, then there exists at least one set of constants A_i (not all zero) such that $A_i c_{ij} x_j = 0$, hence $(Ax') = 0$, which represents a plane. If the rank of C is two, the (x_j') do not lie on a line; if the rank of C is one, the

(x'_j) lie on a line. Such transformations are therefore of no use as coordinate transformations. We shall encounter them again in descriptive geometry, but then as active transformations (Sec. 4–1).

Given a matrix $\|c_{ij}\|$, $i,j = 1,2, \ldots, n$. When the determinant $C = |c_{ij}| \neq 0$, then the matrix and C are of *rank n*. If not only $|c_{ij}|$, but also all cofactors of order k, $k = n - 1, \ldots, r + 1$, are zero, but not all cofactors of order r, then the matrix and C have *rank r*. When $r = 1$ at least one of the $c_{ij} \neq 0$; when $r = 0$ all c_{ij} vanish.

When $r < n$, then we can find r rows c_j, $j = 1,2, \ldots, n$, $\alpha = 1,2, \ldots, r$ (appropriately ordered so as to be the first r rows of the matrix), which are *independent*, that is, there exists no relation of the form $k_1 c_{1j} + k_2 c_{2j} + \cdots + k_r c_{rj} = 0$ (not all the constants k_α zero). The same holds for r columns. But we can always find a linear relation between $r + 1$ rows (or columns), and $n - r$ independent linear relations between the n rows (or columns).

Hence if $y_i = c_{ij}x_j$ and C is of rank r, then there exist $n - r$ linearly independent relations of the form $A_{\alpha i}y_i = 0$, with appropriate constants $A_{\alpha i}$. It is this property we used above.

Given a set of n linear homogeneous equations in x_i, $i = 1,2, \ldots, n$,

$$c_{ij}x_j = 0,$$

then it has the only solution $x_i = 0$ when $r = n$. When $r = n - 1$ then the solution is

$$x_1 : x_2 : \ldots : x_n = \gamma_{i1} : \gamma_{i2} : \ldots : \gamma_{in},$$

where γ_{ij} is the cofactor of c_{ij} in $|c_{ij}|$ and we can take any value of i for which the γ_{ij} are not all zero. In general, for $r < n$, there is an infinity of solutions, of which $n - r + 1$ are always linearly dependent. Here it is always possible to find a set of linearly independent solutions $x'_i, x''_i, \ldots, x_i^{(n-r)}$ such that any solution can be cast into the form

$$c_1 x'_i + c_2 x''_i + \cdots + c_{n-r} x_i^{(n-r)},$$

with appropriate constants c_p, $p = 1, \ldots, n - r$. We express this by saying that the $x_i^{(p)}$ form a *vector space* of $n - r$ dimensions (see Sec. 4–6).

An elementary introduction into this field is T. L. Wade, *The Algebra of Vectors and Matrices*, Cambridge, Mass. (1951); more advanced are H. W. Turnbull, *The Theory of Determinants, Matrices and Invariants*, London (1929), C. C. MacDuffee, *The Theory of Matrices*, New York (1946), or S. Perlis, *Theory of Matrices*, Cambridge, Mass. (1952). See also, M. Bôcher, *Introduction to Higher Algebra* (1907).

3-9 The projective plane. In the course of our discussion we have had the opportunity to modify the character of the plane in which we were operating. By introducing coordinates, we assigned orientation, were led to ideal lines and points, and occasionally changed the underlying field of numbers. Finally, we have obtained a plane in which a point is determined by the ratio of three numbers x_i (not all zero), a line by a relation $(ux) = 0$, and in which there are no ideal elements. In it the following simple properties hold:

> Two points determine a line.
> Two lines determine a point.

To these rules there is no exception, *there is full duality between points and lines.* There are no metrical relationships; the only numerical relationship is that of cross ratio between four collinear points and four concurrent lines, and although in this text we have used metrical concepts to define cross ratio, it has already been remarked (Sec. 2-9) that numerical values can be assigned to cross ratios independently of metrical concepts (by using the harmonic relationships of the complete quadrangle, following von Staudt [see, e.g., H. S. M. Coxeter, *The Real Projective Plane* (1949), Chapter 12]. Homogeneous coordinates can be introduced by means of cross ratios alone (see Sec. 3-7), and thus also independently of metrical concepts.

This plane, thus obtained, is called the *projective plane.* It can be determined by a set of axioms as an independent type of geometry.

Such a set of axioms has been given by A. N. Whitehead, *The Axioms of Projective Geometry,* Cambridge (1906); see also Veblen-Young II, Chapter I. Projective geometry was historically developed as a part of Euclidean geometry, and only in the second half of the 19th century was it realized that it allowed an independent foundation. Von Staudt, for instance, still needed the parallel axiom in his study of the foundations of projective geometry. Klein, in his work on non-Euclidean geometry, established the independence of projective geometry from the theory of parallels (see, e.g., *Ges. Abh.* I, p. 250, paper of 1871). This opened the possibility of an independent foundation for projective geometry. The pioneer work was done by Moritz Pasch [see his *Vorlesungen über neuere Geometrie* (1882), 2nd ed., with an appendix by M. Dehn on the foundations of geometry in historical development (Berlin, 1926)].

The projective plane differs in several respects from the Euclidean plane. We have already seen that a line in this plane is closed, and that the coordinates of its points can be made to pass continuously into each other when we move on the line. Another difference results from the fact that we can assign to the Euclidean plane a clockwise or counterclockwise orientation, which does not change under any motions of the plane. This is analytically expressed in the fact that the sign of the determinant of rotations is positive. Reasoning in a similar way with the equations $\rho x_i' = c_{ij}x_j$, Det $(c_{ij}) \neq 0$, we see that we cannot assign a sign to the determinant, since the multiplication of the x_i by a factor σ results in the multiplication of the determinant by σ^3. This shows that *it is impossible to assign an orientation to the projective plane.* The projective plane is a *nonorientable* surface.

This property is due to the fact that σ is raised to an odd power and explains why it is possible to assign a sense to the projective line; this sense can be kept under all transformations for which Det $(c_{ij}) > 0$. For this purpose we can take three points ABC arbitrarily, then sense $(ABC) =$ sense $(BCA) =$ sense $(CAB) = -$sense $(ACB) = \dots$.

The nonorientability of the projective plane is related to the following theorem. Let us take the figure formed by three lines l,m,n intersecting in A,B,C (Fig. 3–9). Then line l is divided by B and C into two parts, that between B and C labeled 1, and between C and B labeled 1'. In the same way we have on m the parts 2,2' and on n the parts 3 and 3'. The plane is now divided not into *seven triangular regions,* as the Euclidean plane, *but into four,* namely those bounded by 123,1'2'3,1'23',12'3', labeled I, II, III, IV. We can define these regions by stating that no two points P,Q in one region are separated by any pair of points in which the line PQ meets the lines l,m,n, while any points P,R of different regions are separated by two of the points in which the line PR meets the lines l,n,m.

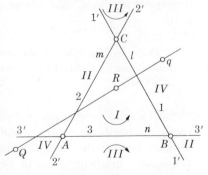

Fig. 3–9

An exact proof of this statement can be found in Veblen-Young II, pp. 52–53.

We can give an orientation to triangle 123, but this does not induce an orientation in any other of the triangular regions, since the sense $2'31' = 1'2'3$ of region II appears different at n and at C.

A simple model of a projective plane can be obtained by taking the family F of all ∞^2 planes and ∞^2 lines through a point P in space, calling the lines "points" and the planes "lines." Every projective property of the plane can be interpreted as a property of the elements of F; for instance, the fact that two lines in the plane always have a point in common means in F that two planes through P always have a line in common. [We can readily prove that the cross ratio properties can also be transferred from the projective plane to F (cf. Sec. 8–1).]

If we express a line through P in space by the Cartesian equations $x:y:z = x_1:y_1:z_1$, then (x_1,y_1,z_1) can be considered as the homogeneous coordinates of a point in a plane not passing through P. This is an alternate way of introducing homogeneous coordinates.

Let us now intersect F with a sphere of center P. Then there is a one-to-one correspondence between a plane of F and a great circle of the sphere, and between a line of F and two diametrically opposite points of the sphere. *We thus obtain a one-to-one correspondence of the projective plane with the surface of a sphere, in which the great circles correspond to "lines" and a pair of antipodal points to a point* (Fig. 3–10).

The nonorientability of the projective plane was discovered in a correspondence by F. Klein and L. Schläfli [Klein, *Ges. Math. Abh.* II (1874), pp. 64, 65].

Such a sphere can again be replaced by a hemisphere, of which we count the points only once except those on the boundary, of which we must identify diametrically opposed points. We now deform the hemisphere gradually without tearing or connecting parts of the boundary. Then we obtain figures which retain the one-to-one con-

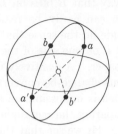

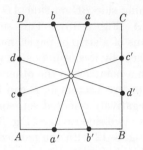

Fig. 3-10

Fig. 3-11

tinuous point correspondence with the original figure. We call such figures *topologically equivalent*. By deforming the hemisphere into the interior and boundary of the circle, we find that the projective plane is topologically equivalent to a circle of which all interior points count as "points," and the diametrically opposed points on the circumference are identified. The circle may be any simply connected region, the identified points need not be diametrically opposed; it is sufficient that a unique identification of pairs on the boundary exists. The circle may, for instance, be changed into a square, for the points on whose perimeter a crosswise pairing exists (Fig. 3-11). This pairwise identification illustrates in all these cases that the projective plane is closed, and how it is closed.

3-10 Orientable and nonorientable surfaces. The first example of a nonorientable surface was given by Möbius. He described a *one-sided* surface obtained by taking a rectangle *ABCD* (Fig. 3-12) and

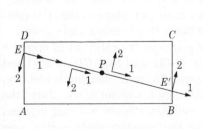

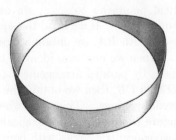

Fig. 3-12

Fig. 3-13

turning side BC on side AD in such a way that B falls on D and C on A (Fig. 3–13). This surface, which can easily be realized by means of a strip of paper, has only one side, in the sense that we can connect by a continuous curve any point P on one side of the surface with a point P' on the other side of the paper. A positively oriented set of two vectors at P can by continuous change be converted into a negatively oriented set, something which is impossible on an ordinary, two-sided plane (Fig. 3–12). Comparing the rectangle $ABCD$ of Fig. 3–12 with the part $cdc'd'$ of Fig. 3–11, we see that the neighborhood of a line in the projective plane is precisely a Möbius strip.

Is it possible to represent the projective plane topologically as a closed, one-sided surface in ordinary space? Let us somewhat more systematically study the different surfaces which are topologically equivalent to a square $ABCD$ with possible identification of points on the boundary. The interior of the square itself, without any identification of points on the perimeter, is a one-to-one continuous representation of the Euclidean plane (just as a line segment by means of a function such as $y = \tan^{-1} x$ can be a one-to-one continuous correspondence of an infinite Euclidean line). To see this, map the plane on the surface of a sphere by stereographic projection (central projection from one point of the sphere, on the tangent plane at the diametrically opposite point). This makes the sphere minus one point the topological equivalent of the Euclidean plane. Widening the sphere at this point, we obtain a sphere with one opening, and this figure can be changed into the interior of a circle and this again into the interior of a square. Let us now identify those points on the sides BA and CD which lie on lines parallel to the other sides (parallel arrangement, Fig. 3–14). Turning CD on BA, superimposing identical points $aa',bb', \ldots$, we obtain a cylinder with two boundary curves p,p'. If we bend the square in its own plane so that CD coincides with BA, we obtain a figure like a ring between two circles.

When we now also identify the points on the other set of opposite sides by parallel arrangement (Fig. 3–15), and turn CD on BA, and DA on CB, then we obtain the figure of a torus (doughnut, lifebuoy, wedding ring). This is a two-sided figure without a boundary; the figure is closed. A topologically equivalent figure is a ring between two concentric circles with points on the boundary circles on the same radius identified.

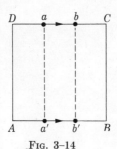

Fig. 3–14

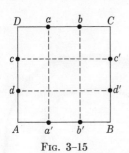

Fig. 3–15

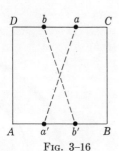

Fig. 3–16

If we now identify the points on AB and CD by a crosswise arrangement and then let the points of CD be identified with those on AB, we must turn CD 180° in space before we connect it with AB. We obtain a one-sided figure, the Möbius strip (Fig. 3–16).

Let us now close the Möbius strip by identifying the other pair of opposite sides of the square of Fig. 3–16 by parallel arrangement (Fig. 3–17); when we superimpose the identified points we now obtain a surface which intersects itself. First, by identification of CB and DA, we obtain a cylinder. The boundary curves q and q' of this cylinder, which have to be connected, have opposite sense. We obtain the connection by letting q shrink somewhat, stretching the cylinder at q and bending it through the surface of the cylinder until q is opposite q', now with the same sense (Fig. 3–18), and widening q

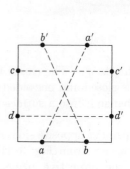

Fig. 3–17

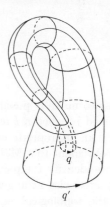

Fig. 3–18

Fig. 3–19

again so as to make it possible to attach q to q'. The closed figure thus obtained is called a *Klein bottle;* it is closed and one-sided (Fig. 3–19). By an appropriate cut we can change it into a surface topologically equivalent to a Möbius strip.

When we identify the points on both pairs of opposite sides of the square by crosswise arrangement, then we see from Fig. 3–11 that we have the topological equivalent of the projective plane. We can change it into a closed surface by first deforming the square

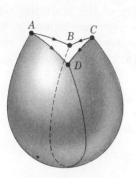

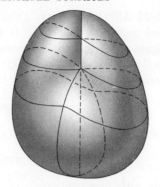

FIG. 3–20   FIG. 3–21

into a sphere with a skew quadrangular part cut out in which A,C are
higher than BD (Fig. 3–20). Then we let A and C approach each
other as well as B and D. The result is a closed one-sided surface
(Fig. 3–21) which penetrates itself along the line $ABCD$. It can also
be obtained by closing the Möbius strip by a surface through its
boundary.

This exposition follows that in D. Hilbert and S. Cohn-Vossen, *An-
schauliche Geometrie* #47 (Berlin, 1932), English transl.: *Geometry and the
Imagination* (New York, 1951). See also Veblen-Young II, pp. 67–69.
Möbius discovered his surface in 1858 (posthumously publ.: *Ges. Werke II*,
p. 519); it was discovered at about the same time by J. B. Listing at
Göttingen, published *Abh. Ges. Wiss. Göttingen Abh.* 10 (1861), pp. 97–
180. On one-sided surfaces see also F. Klein, *Elementary Mathematics
from an Advanced Point of View II, Geometry* [transl. by E. R. Hedrick and
C. A. Noble (New York, 1939), Chapter I.]* The model of Fig. 3–21 has
two singular points and can be represented by the locus of the osculating
circles of all normal sections at the point of a surface, hence by the inverse
of a cylindroid [see Struik, *Differential Geometry* (1950), p. 93]. In 1901
Boy constructed a model without a singular point; it crosses itself along a
curve. For polyhedral models of the projective plane, see T. A. Behrend,
Journal and Proc. Roy. Soc., New South Wales, **77** (1943), pp. 20–23.

---

* An example of a one-sided surface of rotation has been given by
R. Hoppe, *Grunert Arch. f. Mathem.* **57** (1876), pp. 328–334. Its equation
in parametric form is $x = \cos u \cos 2v$, $y = \cos u \sin 2v$, $z = \sin u(\cos v -
\cos u \sin v)$.

3-11 Affine geometry. The geometry of the projective plane is called *projective geometry*. It finds its algebraic expression by the assignment of the homogeneous coordinates (x_i) to a point and (u_i) to a line; incidence is then given by $(ux) = 0$. Two lines $(u_1),(v_i)$ determine the point

$$x_1:x_2:x_3 = (u_2v_3 - u_3v_2):(u_3v_1 - u_1v_3):(u_1v_2 - u_2v_1)$$

without exception; two points $(x_i),(y_i)$ determine the line

$$u_1:u_2:u_3 = (x_2y_3 - x_3y_2):(x_3y_1 - x_1y_3):(x_1y_2 - x_2y_1),$$

again without exception.

Let us now single out one line in the projective plane, and call it the *ideal line*. For this line we select $x_3 = 0$. We require that this line be invariant under the transformations (8-1), or $x_3 = 0 \to x_3' = 0$. Then $c_{31} = c_{32} = 0$. If now we introduce x,y and x',y' by means of the equations

$$x:y:1 = x_1:x_2:x_3, \quad x':y':1 = x_1':x_2':x_3', \tag{10-1}$$

then Eq. (8-1) with $C \neq 0$ (Eq. 8-3) passes into

$$\begin{aligned} x' &= c_{11}x + c_{12}y + c_{13}, \\ y' &= c_{21}x + c_{22}y + c_{23}, \end{aligned} \quad \begin{vmatrix} c_{11} & c_{12} \\ c_{21} & c_{22} \end{vmatrix} \neq 0, \tag{10-2}$$

where we have written $c_{33} = 1$, which can be done without loss of generality. This implies that under these transformations the line $x_3 = 0$, remaining unchanged, has become the line at infinity of the plane. Lines which in the projective plane intersect on $x_3 = 0$ now have become parallel lines. The plane thus obtained is called the *affine plane*. Points can be defined in this plane by (x,y) and coordinate transformations by Eq. (10-2). The plane can be oriented and is two-sided. Since for four collinear points A,B,C,P_∞, where P_∞ is a point on $x_3 = 0$,

$$(AB,CP_\infty) = AC:BC, \tag{10-3}$$

we obtain the division ratio as an affine concept. A segment can therefore be divided in a given ratio. If we compute this ratio for the points on the axis $x_2 = 0$:

$$A_3\,(0:0:1), \quad P\,(a:0:1), \quad Q\,(b:0:1), \quad P_\infty\,(1:0:0),$$

we find $a/b = x_P/x_Q$, where x_P and x_Q are the coordinates of P and Q found in accordance with Eq. (10–1). Equation (10–2) can therefore be interpreted as the transformation from one system of nonhomogeneous Cartesian coordinates to another with another origin, in which we still may multiply the unit of measure in the x'- and y'-directions by a constant factor (cf. the reasoning in Sec. 3–8). Where in the projective plane we speak of two points on a line *separating* two others, in the affine plane we speak of one point on a line *between* two others.

In the axiomatic foundation of projective and affine geometry the relations of separation and betweenness are introduced by the axioms of order. It was on these axioms of order that the foundation of geometry by Euclid was most deficient, since Euclid took the order concepts for granted. Modern axiomatics, beginning with M. Pasch (Sec. 3–9), has shown the fundamental character of the axioms of order.

We obtain an *isomorphic representation* of the affine plane on the projective plane by taking any line as the ideal line, calling two lines parallel when they intersect on this line, and defining the division ratio by means of Eq. (10–3) with P_∞ as the point on the ideal line. All properties of the affine plane can then be interpreted as projective properties. We call this the *projective interpretation* of affine geometry.

As an example, let us consider the theorem that the diagonals of a parallelogram 1234 divide each other into equal parts at their point of intersection R. This property holds in the affine plane, since it deals with parallel lines and division ratios but with no other metrical concepts. In the projective interpretation of this theorem, we replace the parallel lines 14 and 23 by two lines meeting in P, 43 and 12 by two lines meeting in Q; PQ is the projective interpretation of the line at infinity. The fact that R lies halfway between 1 and 3 means that R is the harmonic conjugate of the point at infinity S of line 13 with respect to 1 and 3. We thus obtain a complete quadrangle 1234, of which P, Q and R are the diagonal points, and the theorem that R and S are harmonic with respect to 1 and 3. The theory of the complete quadrangle is thus a projective interpretation of the theory of the parallelogram with its diagonals.

We can go further, and take the dual of the complete quadrangle in the projective plane. This leads to the theory of the complete quadrilateral; in particular, r and s are harmonic with respect to 1 and 3. Now we can consider one of the lines of the complete quadrilateral as the line at infinity of the affine plane. If we take line 4 as the line at infinity, then we have as an *affine interpretation* of our theorem that in the triangle formed by the lines 1,2,3 the median at vertex (13) is the harmonic conjugate with respect to 1 and 3 of the line through point (13) parallel to side 2, which (see Ex. 3, Sec. 3–7) implies that the medians of a triangle pass through one point. This theorem can, in its turn, be taken as a starting point to obtain the theorem of Ex. 3, Sec. 3–7, and so we can go on building chains of related theorems (see Ex. 1 below). This ability to relate theorems to each other, and to do this in many ways, is perhaps the most important difference between our approach to geometry and that of the Ancients of the classical Greek school. For those geometricians each theorem was, far more than with us, a fact by itself and for itself, each time to be demonstrated by an appeal to the axioms.

In making this last statement, we must be on our guard against exaggeration. The geometry of the Ancients was not without some general principles, and the fact that we find in Pappus some of the fundamental theorems of projective geometry in what purports to be a commentary on a (now lost) book by Euclid may lead to the suspicion that the presentation of the theorems in their traditional form has obscured the spirit in which they were discovered. In the case of Archimedes we do have his own statement that his presentation differed from the method used in the actual discovery. And in the discussion of what we now call the Pappus (or Guldin) theorems on centers of gravity of figures of rotation, we find in Pappus' *Mathematical Collection* an appraisal of these theorems as embracing "a multitude of theorems of all kinds on curves, surfaces, and solids, all demonstrable at once by a single proof." However, such a statement is exceptional in the geometry of the Greeks.*

---

* It is even of unknown authorship, since the whole passage in Book VII of Pappus' *Mathematical Collection* dealing with this particular theorem on surfaces of revolution seems to be an interpolation [see P. Ver Eecke, *Pappus d'Alexandrie* (1933), p. XCIV].

EXERCISES

1. Give a projective interpretation of the theorems (a) the medians of a triangle pass through one point, (b) a line parallel to a side of a triangle cuts the other sides in segments of equal ratio.

2. Give an affine interpretation of Desargues' theorem (cf. Ex. 1, 2 of Sec. 2–6) and of the Pappus-Pascal theorem (Sec. 3–7).

3. Prove that if $C \neq 0$ [Eq. (8–3)], the determinants of the transformation (8–5), (8–6), (8–7) are also different from zero.

4. Introduce projective coordinates on a line (hence two basic points and one unit point) and show that their transformation by change of the reference system is the general linear homogeneous transformation.

5. Show that n lines in a general position divide the Euclidean (or affine) plane into $1 + n + n(n - 1)/2$ regions and the projective plane into $1 + n(n - 1)/2$ regions.

6. Find the theorems obtained by restating Gauss' theorem on the centers of the diagonals of a complete quadrilateral (Ex. 9, Sec. 2–9) by taking as the line at infinity (a) a side, (b) a diagonal.

CHAPTER 4

TRANSFORMATIONS OF THE PLANE

4–1 Active and passive transformations. Transformations of co-ordinates, such as $\rho x_i' = c_{ij} x_j$, have appeared in the previous chapter as the expression of changes of reference systems. But they also admit an entirely different interpretation. They can be considered as transformations by which a point $P(x_i)$ passes into *another* point $P'(x_i')$ *without a change of reference system*. For instance, taking an example from the plane, the equations

$$x' = x \cos \alpha + y \sin \alpha,$$
$$y' = -x \sin \alpha + y \cos \alpha \qquad (1\text{--}1)$$

admit two interpretations. They may represent a counterclockwise rotation of the rectangular axes OX, OY about an angle α (Fig. 4–1), under which the points P of the plane remain in place. They may also represent a clockwise rotation of the points P about an angle α at O, measured in the same coordinate system (Fig. 4–2).

Transformations of points with fixed reference system are called *active*, transformations of reference systems with fixed points of the plane are called *passive*. We shall here consider active transformations.

Wits have occasionally compared the passive point of view to the *alias*, where a person changes his name, and the active point of view to the *alibi* of certain mystery stories, where the same name is carried by different persons (or where the same person appears in different places).

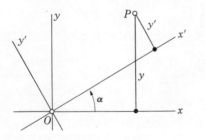

Fig. 4–1

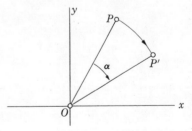

Fig. 4–2

4-2 Collineations. A projective transformation is determined by the equations

$$\rho x_i' = c_{ij}x_j \quad (i,j = 1,2,3), \tag{2-1}$$

where the x_i, x_i' are the projective coordinates of two points in the plane. As an active operation it is also called a *collineation*, since a linear relation between points $(ux) = 0$ passes into a linear relation, and hence lines pass into lines, points of intersection of lines passing into points of intersection of the corresponding lines. The transformations (2–1) induce the transformations of lines:

$$\sigma u_i' = \gamma_{ij}u_j \quad [\gamma_{ij} = \text{cofactor of } c_{ij} \text{ in } C = \text{Det } (c_{ij})]. \tag{2-2}$$

When $C = 0$ the collineation is *singular* (see the remark in Sec. 3–8).

The cross ratio of four collinear points and of four concurrent lines is invariant under collineations. This follows immediately from the equation

$$\rho(x_i' + \lambda y_i') = c_{ij}(x_i + \lambda y_i)$$

for the points on the line connecting $P(x_i)$ and $Q(y_i)$, using the interpretation of cross ratio given in Sec. 3–4. It also follows from the fact that a complete quadrangle corresponds to a complete quadrilateral, and hence the harmonic relationship is preserved. Von Staudt's theorem then proves that a projectivity exists between corresponding points on corresponding lines (see Sec. 1–8). By means of this theorem, we can also prove the theorem:

Every one-to-one relationship (without exception) between the points of a plane, in which lines pass into lines, is a collineation.

Von Staudt's proof was geometrical, and used the so-called *Möbius net*. Let the four independent points 1,2,3,4 correspond to the independent points 1′,2′,3′,4′ respectively [Figs. 4–3(a) and (b)]. Then the six lines connecting them also correspond, as well as their points of intersection, e.g., the diagonal points 5,6 with 5′6′. Then the intersection 7 of (56) and (34) corresponds to the intersection 7′ of (5′6′) and (3′4′). But 2376 and 2′3′7′6′ also form corresponding complete quadrangles, and we can repeat the process of finding new corresponding points (8,8′),(9,9′) on (34),(3′4′) respectively, and similarly on other lines. The plane, in this way, is covered more and more with a net of corresponding lines and points. This is the Möbius net. The cross ratios defining the new points in terms of those already found are all rational. The problem now arises to prove

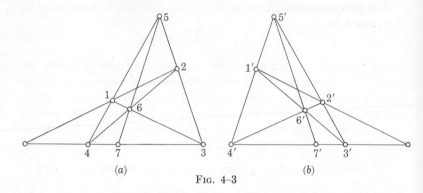

Fig. 4–3

that *all* points of the plane can be made to correspond. Every point can be approached as closely as we like with "rational" points. That the limits correspond uniquely can then be proved without any further assumption, if we use Darboux's remark (Sec. 1–8). See Pasch-Dehn (Sec. 3–9), and Godeaux-Rozet, *Géométrie Projective* (Liège, 1952), Ch. VI. The theorem, as we know, only holds for the real plane, not for the complex plane.

We can now also readily understand the theorem:

A collineation is uniquely determined when four pairs of corresponding independent points are given.

The proof follows closely that given for the case where Eqs. (2–1) mean coordinate transformations; it is made plausible by the fact that four such pairs give eight conditions for the nine ratios of the c_{ij}. Instead of four pairs of independent points, we can also give four pairs of independent lines.

The Möbius net construction described above also shows that four pairs of points determine a collineation.

We can also define a collineation (2–1) between the points of two different planes. The x_i and x_i' are then referred to different reference systems. The above theorems also hold for this case.

4–3 Classification of collineations. Collineations in the same plane are classified by means of their *double* or *fixed elements*, that is, the points and lines which correspond to themselves. We find the double points by substituting $x_i' = \lambda x_i$ into Eq. (2–1). The resulting equations then admit a solution if values of λ can be found such that

$$\begin{vmatrix} c_{11} - \lambda & c_{12} & c_{13} \\ c_{21} & c_{22} - \lambda & c_{23} \\ c_{31} & c_{32} & c_{33} - \lambda \end{vmatrix} = 0. \qquad (3\text{–}1)$$

This is also the equation for the fixed lines, since we can write Eq. (2–2) in the form $\sigma_1 u_i = c_{ji} u_j'$. *Hence there are as many fixed points as there are fixed lines.* From the properties of projectivities on a line and in a pencil (Chapters 1 and 2), we can also conclude that (in the real domain), *on every fixed line not consisting of all fixed points there are at most two fixed points,* as well as the dual proposition. The line connecting two fixed points is itself a fixed line; the intersection of two fixed lines is a fixed point.

Equation (3–1) has three roots, of which one is certainly real. If these roots are real and different there are three double points and three double lines, and when they are independent we can select them as the basic points A_1, A_2, A_3. The basic lines then pass through these points. In this case the collineation can be expressed by the equations

$$\rho x_1' = ax_1, \ \rho x_2' = bx_2, \ \rho x_3' = cx_3 \ (a,b,c \text{ all different, none zero}). \qquad (3\text{–}2)$$

The sides of the basic triangle are invariant, although only the basic points are themselves invariant. The a,b,c are determined if we know one more pair P,P' of corresponding points.

Equation (3–1) has three roots, while a collineation is determined by four pairs of points. This indicates that the study of the roots of Eq. (3–1) alone is not sufficient for a classification of collineations. For this we need the whole matrix of which Eq. (3–1) is the determinant. The classification of such λ-*matrices* depends on their *invariant factors* (see below). It can be shown that there are five different arrangements of these factors, each corresponding to one type of collineation, if we do not discriminate between real and imaginary double points. Equation (3–2) represents one of these types. We discuss one other, the so-called *homology,* which belongs to those collineations for which Eq. (3–1) has a double root. It is obtained from Eq. (3–2) by writing $a = b$:

$$\rho x_1' = ax_1, \ \rho x_2' = ax_2, \ \rho x_3' = cx_3 \ (a \neq c; a,c \neq 0). \qquad (3\text{–}3)$$

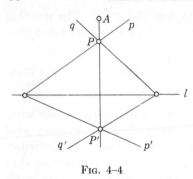

FIG. 4–4

There is one fixed point A $(0:0:1)$, and one fixed line l of which all points are also invariant, namely, $x_3 = 0$. Since $px_1 + qx_2 = 0$ passes into $px_1' + qx_2' = 0$, all lines m through A are invariant, although only A and the intersection of m with l are invariant points. Every point P passes into a point P' on AP. The choice of one pair P,P' determines the homology. Lines $p,q, \ldots$ through P correspond to lines $p',q' \ldots$ through P' which intersect on l (Fig. 4–4). Two triangles in homology are perspective (Desargues) triangles (cf. Sec. 2–5).

The equivalence of λ-matrices under projective transformations — that is, the possibility of transforming them into each other — depends, as we have said, on the *invariant factors*. To find them we must take, for every number m, $1 \leq m \leq r$ (r is the rank of the matrix), the greatest common divisor $D_m(\lambda)$ of all cofactors of m rows and m columns. We assign to the highest power of λ in $D_m(\lambda)$ the value 1. Then it can be shown that $D_m(\lambda)$ is either equal to $D_{m+1}(\lambda)$ or a factor of it. The polynomials $E_m(\lambda)$ such that

$$D_m(\lambda) = E_m(\lambda)D_{m-1}(\lambda) \quad (1 \leq m \leq r),$$

are called the *invariant factors* of the λ-matrix, except when they are constants and hence $= 1$. From this follows

$$D_m(\lambda) = E_m(\lambda)E_{m-1}(\lambda) \ldots E_1(\lambda).$$

Two λ-matrices can be transformed into each other by projective transformations when and only when their corresponding invariant factors E_m are the same. This can also be expressed by the use of the theorem that each E_m is equal to or a factor of E_{m+1}. Hence, if E_r has the factors $\lambda - \lambda_1$, $\lambda - \lambda_2, \ldots, \lambda - \lambda_k$, then the factors of the other E_m occur among these with the same or smaller exponents. Let e_{ji} (also written $e_{j,i}$) be the multiplicity of $\lambda - \lambda_j$ in $E_i(\lambda)$ [these e_{ji} may be zero]. Then $e_{ji} \geq e_{j,i-1}$. The factors $(\lambda - \lambda_j)^{e_{ji}}$ which are not constants are called the *elementary divisors* of the λ-matrix. They determine uniquely the invariant factors, and are themselves uniquely determined by them. *Hence two λ-matrices are equivalent when and only when they have the same corresponding ele-*

mentary divisors. We often characterize the λ-matrices by the scheme of the e_{ji} alone, omitting the specific factors $\lambda - \lambda_j$, and write

$$[(e_{11}e_{12} \ldots e_{1k}),(e_{21}e_{22} \ldots e_{2k}), \ldots ,(e_{r1}e_{r2} \ldots e_{rk})].$$

We can omit all those e_{ji} which are zero, and also omit the parentheses when they enclose only one number. The sum of all e_{ji} is r. In the case of $r = 3$ we have the schemes [1,1,1], [2,1], [3], [(11),1], [(111)]. It can be shown that every scheme can be realized. These schemes suffice for the classification of collineations, since the particular values of the λ_j are here immaterial. This theory does not discriminate between collineations with real or complex double points.

The collineation (3–2) is the type [1,1,1]; the homology is the type [(11),1]. The type [(111)] is the identity. All types are studied in F. S. Woods, *Higher Geometry* (Boston, 1922), p. 85.

On elementary divisors, see M. Bôcher, *Introduction to Higher Algebra* (1907), or J. A. Todd, *Projective and Analytical Geometry* (New York, 1946). The theory is due to K. Weierstrass, *Ges. Werke II* (1868), p. 19.

4–4 Correlations. The linear transformation

$$\rho u'_i = c_{ij}x_j \qquad (4\text{--}1)$$

associates with a point P a line p'. We take $C \neq 0$. This transformation can be solved for x_i:

$$\sigma_1 x_i = \gamma_{ji}u'_j.$$

Then with every line p' a point P is associated. Points on the line $(ux) = 0$ then correspond to the lines through the point

$$\sigma x'_i = \gamma_{ij}u_j. \qquad (4\text{--}2)$$

The transformation thus associates the line u_i with the point x'_i and with the point x'_i the line u_i. The equation (4–2) can again be solved for u_i:

$$\rho_1 u_i = c_{ji}x'_j. \qquad (4\text{--}3)$$

Every straight line u'_i is therefore the transform of a point, and every point x'_i is the transform of a line such that points on a line pass into lines through a point, and conversely. Such a transformation is called a (nonsingular) *correlation*. A correlation followed by a correlation results in a collineation; if a correlation is repeated, we obtain a collineation called the *square* of the correlation. This square may be the identity, which happens, e.g., in the case of a polarity (Sec. 5–7). If four independent points $P_1 \ldots P_4$ and four independent lines $p_1 \ldots p_4$ are given, then there exists a correlation by means of which P_i is transformed into p_i as p_i' and there also exists a correlation by means of which p_i is transformed into P_i as P_i'.

The property that the square of the correlation is a collineation may be used for classification of correlations (see further Sec. 8–9).

EXERCISES

1. A collineation C_1 followed by another, C_2, is again a collineation. Show that the determinant of C_1C_2 is the product of the determinants of C_1 and of C_2. Is $C_1C_2 = C_2C_1$?

2. Show that the collineation

$$\rho x_1' = ax_1 + x_2, \quad \rho x_2' = ax_2, \quad \rho x_3' = bx_3, \qquad (a \neq b, \quad a,b \neq 0),$$

has two fixed points and two fixed lines, and describe their relation.

3. Show that the collineation obtained from that of Ex. 2 by taking $a = b$ has a line l of fixed points and a pencil of fixed lines with its vertex on l. This is called an *elation*.

4. Show that the collineation

$$\rho x_1' = ax_1 + x_2, \quad \rho x_2' = ax_2 + x_3, \quad \rho x_3' = ax_3$$

has only one fixed point P and one fixed line through P.

5. Show that the collineation

$$\rho x_1' = x_1, \quad \rho x_2' = ax_2, \quad \rho x_3' = 0 \quad (a \neq 0)$$

is singular, and has one singular point P (for which the transformed point is indeterminate), one fixed line l not through P, and two fixed points on l.

6. Show that the scheme of elementary divisors in the cases of Exs. 2, 3, 4 is [2,1], [(21)], [3] respectively, and in the case of Ex. 5 [1,1,0], where 0 stands for the zero root of Eq. (3–1).

7. Discuss the projective transformations on a line l; viz., $\rho x_a' = c_{ab}x_b$, $a,b = 1,2$. Compare with Sec. 1–6.

8. Show that when *the points of a plane π in space are projected on the points of a plane π' by central projection, the planes are in projective correspondence.* By central projection we mean that the line connecting the corresponding points P of π and P' of π' passes through a fixed point in space not on π or π'. (See further Sec. 11–2.)

9. Show that when a point and a line are harmonic with respect to a triangle (Sec. 3–7), their relationship is not a correlation.

4–5 Affine transformations.   An affine transformation or *affinity* is, as we have seen in Sec. 3–11, given by the equation

$$\begin{aligned} x' &= c_{11}x + c_{12}y + c_{13}, \\ y' &= c_{21}x + c_{22}y + c_{23}, \end{aligned} \tag{5-1}$$

where the (x,y), (x',y') are the (oblique) Cartesian coordinates of the point P and of the transformed point P' (but for an arbitrary measuring unit in each coordinate direction).   Contrary to Sec. 3–11, we now keep the coordinate system fixed and transform the points in the plane.   For a nonsingular transformation,

$$C = c_{11}c_{22} - c_{12}c_{21} \neq 0.$$

We can consider such a transformation as a collineation with a fixed special line, the line at infinity, and this can give us a method of classifying affinities.   We shall not attempt such a classification, but instead shall satisfy ourselves by the remark that an affinity (5–1) is a nondual type of collineation.   We obtain a self-dual collineation when we also keep the origin fixed and thus discard the translation expressed by c_{13}, c_{23}:

$$x' = c_{11}x + c_{12}y, \quad y' = c_{21}x + c_{22}y. \tag{5-2}$$

We then obtain the *centro-affine* transformations.

*Affinities do not only change points into points, lines into lines, and preserve incidence, but they also preserve parallelism and the division ratio of three points on a line.   Moreover, they preserve the ratio of areas.   We shall prove this for the centro-affine transformations (5–2).   The area A of a directed triangle OPQ, with $P(x_1,y_1)$, $Q(x_2,y_2)$, can be defined (cf. Ex. 9, Sec. 4–9) by

$$A = k \begin{vmatrix} x_1 & x_2 \\ y_1 & y_2 \end{vmatrix}, \tag{5-3}$$

where k is a constant which is equal to $\frac{1}{2}\sin\phi$, $\phi = \angle XOY$ in the Euclidean interpretation of affinities (we can also take $-k$).   After transformation (5–2) we find for the area A' of the transformed triangle $OP'Q'$, with $P'(x_1',y_1')$, $Q'(x_2',y_2')$:

$$A' = k \begin{vmatrix} x_1' & x_2' \\ y_1' & y_2' \end{vmatrix} = k \begin{vmatrix} x_1 & x_2 \\ y_1 & y_2 \end{vmatrix} \begin{vmatrix} c_{11} & c_{12} \\ c_{21} & c_{22} \end{vmatrix} = kC_1A.$$

By a passage to the limit, we can extend this result to the area of any figure in the plane. The ratio A/B of two areas is therefore an *affine* invariant. When $C_1 > 0$ the sense OPQ is preserved, when $C_1 < 0$ it is inverted, and the same holds for the sense of rotation attached to any area.

Affinities with $C_1 = \pm 1$ preserve area (but for the sign); they are called *equiareal*. Those with $C = +1$ preserve both area and orientation and are called *special affine*.

4–6 Vectors in affine geometry. Let two points $P(x_1, y_1)$, $Q(x_2, y_2)$ transform into $P'(x_1', y_1')$, $Q'(x_2', y_2')$ under the general affine transformation (5–1). Then the numbers

$$v_1 = x_2 - x_1, \quad v_2 = y_2 - y_1, \quad v_1' = x_2' - x_1', \quad v_2' = y_2' - y_1' \quad (6\text{–}1)$$

transform under (5–1) like (5–2):

$$v_1' = c_{11} v_1 + c_{12} v_2, \quad v_2' = c_{21} v_1 + c_{22} v_2. \quad (6\text{–}2)$$

These quantities v_a depend only on the relative positions of P and Q and not on the particular position of P. Moreover, not only $(\lambda v_1, \lambda v_2)$, but also $(\lambda v_1 + \mu w_1, \lambda v_2 + \mu w_2)$ transform like (6–2), when λ, μ are arbitrary constants and (w_1, w_2) is obtained from the coordinates of any other pair of points in the same way that (v_1, v_2) is obtained from those of P and Q. The sets (v, v_2), (w_1, w_2) therefore are *vectors*. The numbers (v_1, v_2) are the *coordinates* of the vector.

We define an n-dimensional *vector space* S_n as the totality of all ordered sequences v_i, $i = 1, 2, \ldots, n$, or $\mathbf{v}$ for short, taken from a field F (here that of real numbers) with the properties that

(1) with $\mathbf{v}$, $\alpha \mathbf{v}$ also belongs to S_n, where α is a number of a given field, here F,

(2) with two elements $\mathbf{v}, \mathbf{w}$, their sum $\mathbf{v} + \mathbf{w}$, which is the sequence $v_i + w_i$, also belongs to S.

The $\mathbf{v}$ are called *vectors*, the v_i their *coordinates* (often also called components, although it is better to preserve the name component for vectors, and not use it for numbers).

Then, by taking n *basic vectors* $\mathbf{e}_1(1, 0, \ldots, 0)$, $\mathbf{e}_2(0, 1, 0, \ldots, 0), \ldots, \mathbf{e}_n$ $(0, 0, \ldots, 0, 1)$, we can express every vector of S_n in the form $\mathbf{v} = v_1 \mathbf{e}_1 + v_2 \mathbf{e}_2 + \cdots + v_n \mathbf{e}_n = v_i \mathbf{e}_i$.

Vectors are *independent* when between them no linear relation with non-zero coefficients from F exists. In S_n, $n + 1$ vectors are always dependent. Instead of the n vectors e_i, we can take any set of n independent vectors as basic vectors.

We write $\mathbf{v}$ for the combination (v_1, v_2), $\mathbf{w}$ for (w_1, w_2). The vector $\mathbf{v}$ can be represented by an *arrow* (that is, a line segment with sense) from P to Q, but equally well by any parallel arrow with the same sense. We call $\mathbf{v}$ therefore a *free vector* (Fig. 4–5). Free vectors $\mathbf{v}$, we learn from (6–2), are preserved under affinities, that is, free vectors pass into free vectors, and so do the vectors $\alpha\mathbf{v}$, $\alpha\mathbf{v} + \beta\mathbf{w}$, where α, β are (real) numbers. For the addition of vectors we can use the

Fig. 4–5

parallelogram construction, which is also an *affine invariant*. When the sense PQ changes into QP, $\mathbf{v}$ changes into $-\mathbf{v}$, and this gives us the geometrical construction for subtraction, namely, $\mathbf{v} - \mathbf{w} = \mathbf{v} + (-\mathbf{w})$.

We should not consider these arrow-vectors as quantities having length, since length is not an affine invariant. The only thing we can say is that the ratio of two vectors in the same direction, $\mathbf{v}$ and $\alpha\mathbf{v}$, is α.

We have seen that no full duality between lines and points exists under the transformations (5–1), but it does exist under (5–2), if we consider origin and line at infinity as dual. A line $ux + vy + 1 = 0$ is transformed, under (5–2), into $u'x' + v'y' + 1 = 0$, where

$$u' = C_{11}u + C_{12}v, \quad v' = C_{21}u + C_{22}v, \qquad (6\text{–}3)$$

in which formulas

$$C_{ij} = \gamma_{ij}/C. \qquad (6\text{–}4)$$

We see that the (u, v) again form vectors, but the vector character is preserved under another set of transformations than that to which (x, y) is subjected. For this reason we call the vectors $\mathbf{v}$ which transform according to (6–2) *contravariant vectors*, while the vectors transforming according to (6–3) are called *covariant vectors*. A covariant

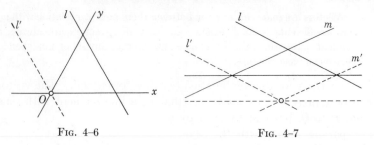

FIG. 4–6   FIG. 4–7

vector (u,v) can therefore be represented by a line $ux + vy + 1 = 0$, the covariant vector $(\alpha u, \alpha v)$ by the line $\alpha ux + \alpha vy + 1 = 0$, which is parallel to the first but α times closer to the origin. The combination of line l and origin O can be taken as the pictorial representation of a covariant vector; we can replace the origin O by a line l' through it parallel to l (Fig. 4–6) and obtain a *doublet*. Figure 4–7 gives a representation of the addition of two doublets given by (l,l') and (m,m'). This construction can be verified by taking l and m along the x- and y-axes.

It is customary to express the difference between contravariant and covariant vectors in the notation. We place the indices up in the case of contravariant vectors: v^i, and down in the case of covariant vectors: u_i. The combination $u_i v^i$ is an *invariant*, since after transformation,

$$u_i' v^{i'} = (C_{11}u_1 + C_{12}u_2)(c_{11}v^1 + c_{12}v^2) + (C_{21}u_1 + C_{22}u_2)(c_{21}v^1 + c_{22}v^2)$$
$$= u_1v^1 \cdot 1 + u_1v^2 \cdot 0 + u_2v^1 \cdot 0 + u_2v^2 = u_i v^i. \qquad (6\text{–}5)$$

We have here used the properties of determinants [cf. Eq. (6–4)]:

$$c_{11}C_{11} + c_{12}C_{12} = 1, \quad c_{11}C_{12} + c_{21}C_{22} = 0, \text{ etc.} \qquad (6\text{–}6)$$

The combination $u_i v^i$ is distributive with respect to addition:

$$u_i(v^i + w^i) = u_i v^i + u_i w^i, \quad (u_i + w_i)v^i = u_i v^i + w_i v^i, \quad (6\text{–}7)$$

and is therefore called a *product*. We call it the *inner product* of the vectors u_i and v^i.

The concept of affinity was first introduced by Euler (*Introductio in Analysin Infinitorum*, 1748, Vol. 2, Chapter 18), where also the term *affine* appears. The first systematic investigation of affinities can be found in Möbius' *Barycentischer Calcul.* Affinities are basic to the elementary theory of elasticity (although in a metrical setting; see Sec. 4-7) as well as to the tensor calculus. Despite its importance, affine geometry has received less systematic attention than projective or Euclidean geometry, although the trend has changed in recent years, beginning with L. Heffter-C. Koehler, *Lehrbuch der analytischen Geometrie* (Karlsruhe 1905, 2nd ed. 1927). Recent books giving adequate attention to affine geometry are H. S. M. Coxeter, *The Real Projective Plane* (New York, 1949), as well as the Russian text of S. P. Finikov, *Analytical Geometry* (Moscow, 1949). An axiomatic study is given in E. Artin, *Rep. Mathem. Coll. Notre Dame* (2) **2** (1940), pp. 15–20; an elementary introduction in F. Klein, *Elementary Mathematics from an Advanced Standpoint* II (translated by E. R. Hedrick-C. A. Noble, New York, 1939).

EXERCISES

1. Prove the distributive law (6–7).

2. Show in a figure the subtraction of covariant vectors.

3. Prove that $u_i v^i = 0$ means that the line representing u_i and the arrow representing v^i are parallel.

4. Give a geometrical interpretation of $u_i v^i$ when $u_i v^i \neq 0$.

5. Show that an affinity is determined by three pairs of corresponding points, forming two corresponding basic triangles.

6. After the basic triangles are given (Ex. 5), show how to find the point corresponding to a given point.

7. Study the affinity

$$x' = 7x - 4y + 1, \quad y' = 3x + 2y - 1$$

and find two basic triangles, invariant elements, new and old coordinate axes.

8. Show that an affine transformation A followed by an affine transformation B is again an affine transformation. Is $AB = BA$?

9. Find the affinities obtained by specializing $x_3 = 0$ as the line at infinity in the collineations of Sec. 4-3. How do we obtain the translation?

10. Show that *when the points of a plane π in space are projected on the points of a plane π' by parallel projection, the two planes are in affine correspondence.*

11. If parallels through the vertices of $\triangle ABC$ intersect the opposite sides in the points A_1, B_1, C_1, then area $\triangle A_1 B_1 C_1$ is twice the area $\triangle ABC$. [Theorem of Malet, see Thébault, *Annales Soc. Scient.*, Bruxelles **60** (1946), p. 84.]

12. Describe the geometrical character of the affine transformation (5–2) if $C = 0$.

13. Given the affinity

$$x' = 5x, \quad y' = 2x + 3y$$

and the coordinates of a vector (1,2). Find the new coordinates of this vector under the given affinity (a) when the vector is contravariant, v^i, (b) when it is covariant, w_i. Show that $v^i w_i$ is invariant under the transformation.

4–7 Affine transformations as deformations. We now consider affine transformations (5–1), but in a given Euclidean plane. The (x,y) will then be considered as rectangular Cartesian coordinates. Both angles and distances are, as a rule, distorted under (5–1). Are there perhaps some perpendicular directions preserved? In order to find this out, let us consider the centro-affine transformations (5–2). Then there must be values, or a value, of λ such that the lines $y' = \lambda x'$, $\lambda y' = -x$ are the transforms of two lines

$$\begin{aligned}
(c_{21} - \lambda c_{11})x + (c_{22} - \lambda c_{12})y &= 0, \\
(\lambda c_{21} + c_{11})x + (\lambda c_{22} + c_{12})y &= 0,
\end{aligned} \tag{7-1}$$

which are perpendicular. This is the case when

$$(\lambda c_{21} + c_{11})(c_{21} - \lambda c_{11}) + (c_{22} - \lambda c_{12})(\lambda c_{22} + c_{12}) = 0$$

or

$$\lambda^2(c_{11}c_{21} + c_{12}c_{22}) - \lambda(c_{21}^2 + c_{22}^2 - c_{11}^2 - c_{12}^2) - (c_{11}c_{21} + c_{12}c_{22}) = 0. \tag{7-2}$$

When the coefficients of this equation are not all zero, then the equation has two roots which are real and have the product -1. Hence *there exists in general one and only one set of perpendicular lines which is the affine transform of a set of perpendicular lines.* When we take this set to be the x- and y-axes, then the roots of Eq. (7–2) are 0 and ∞, and

$$c_{11}c_{21} + c_{12}c_{22} = 0, \quad c_{21}^2 + c_{22}^2 \neq c_{11}^2 + c_{12}^2. \tag{7-3}$$

By now writing $c_{11}/c_{12} = -c_{22}/c_{21} = \cot \alpha$, we see that the equation of the affinity can be cast into the form

$$\begin{aligned}
x' &= a(x \cos \alpha + y \sin \alpha), \\
y' &= b(-x \sin \alpha + y \cos \alpha),
\end{aligned} \quad (a^2 \neq b^2, ab \neq 0). \tag{7-4}$$

When, however,

$$c_{11}c_{21} + c_{12}c_{22} = 0, \quad c_{21}^2 + c_{22}^2 = c_{11}^2 + c_{12}^2, \tag{7-5}$$

then the only exception to our theorem occurs.   In this case *all perpendicular directions remain perpendicular*.   Within the field of the real numbers this means that in Eq. (7–4) either $a = b$ or $a = -b$. In the first case we have a rotation followed by a similitude, in the second case a reflection followed by a similitude.   The general case (7–4) represents a rotation followed by a multiplication in the *x*-direction and a different multiplication in the *y*-direction.   When in this case $\alpha = 0$, the affinity takes the form

$$x' = ax, \quad y' = by \quad (a^2 \neq b^2, ab \neq 0). \tag{7–6}$$

This is a *pure strain*.   There may be contraction or extension in the *x*- and *y*-directions according to the sign of a and b.   We thus have found the following theorem:

> *An affinity can be decomposed into a translation, a rotation, and a pure strain, each of which may be an identity.   Under a centro-affine transformation (where translation = identity) either one set of perpendicular lines remains perpendicular, or all perpendicular sets remain perpendicular.   In this last case, the homogeneous strain is a similitude.*

Figure 4–8 shows how in a case (7–4) with $a,b > 0$, a square is deformed into a rectangle.   Figure 4–9 expresses the same case in terms of vectors.   It is understood that both OX,OY and OX',OY' are special directions for the affinity.   When the square is selected arbitrarily, it is in general changed into a parallelogram.

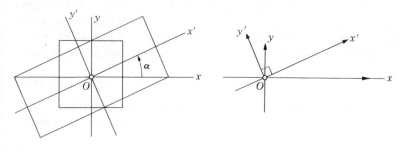

FIG. 4–8   FIG. 4–9

This metrical discussion of affinities is essential for elementary elasticity. See, for example, A. E. H. Love, *A Treatise on the Mathematical Theory of Elasticity* (1927, republished 1944), pp. 42–43, or A. G. Webster, *The Dynamics of Particles and of Rigid, Elastic, and Fluid Bodies* (2nd ed., Leipzig, 1912), Chapter IX. The theorem on the invariance of perpendicular directions under centro-affine transformations is known in surface theory as Tissot's theorem, see, e.g., Struik, *Differential Geometry* (Cambridge, 1950), p. 180.

EXERCISES

1. Find the directions which stay invariant under a centro-affine transformation and the condition that they are orthogonal. Show that in this case of orthogonality they are real.

2. From this result deduce that a centro-affine transformation with $c_{12} = c_{21}$ is a pure strain.

3. Given the affinity

$$x' = 5x + y\sqrt{3}, \quad y' = x\sqrt{3} + 3y.$$

Find a square which is transformed into a rectangle.

4. Show that the conditions that a centro-affine transformation is a rotation (with or without reflection) can be written either in the form

$$c_{11}c_{21} + c_{12}c_{22} = 0, \quad c_{11}^2 + c_{12}^2 = c_{21}^2 + c_{22}^2 = 1$$

or

$$c_{11}c_{12} + c_{21}c_{22} = 0, \quad c_{11}^2 + c_{21}^2 = c_{12}^2 + c_{22}^2 = 1.$$

4–8 Orthogonal transformations. In Sec. 4–7 we have already placed the affine transformations in a Euclidean plane. Let us return to the previous sections of this chapter, in which we worked in the projective plane and defined affine transformations as projective transformations which leave a (special) line invariant. Let us again take this special line as $x_3 = 0$, and *also postulate that two points on this line will be invariant.* They can be given as the double points I,J of the involution $ax_1x_1' + bx_2x_2' = 0$, $x_3 = 0$, that is, by the equations

$$ax_1^2 + bx_2^2 = 0, \quad x_3 = 0. \tag{8-1}$$

The projective transformations which leave these points invariant change $ax_1^2 + bx_2^2$ into $\sigma(ax_1'^2 + bx_2'^2)$, and x_3 into $\sigma_1 x_3'$, and thus satisfy the conditions $c_{31} = c_{32} = 0$ as well as

$$\sigma^{-1}a = ac_{11}^2 + bc_{21}^2, \quad \sigma^{-1}b = ac_{12}^2 + bc_{22}^2, \quad 0 = ac_{11}c_{12} + bc_{21}c_{22}. \tag{8-2}$$

By selecting the axes $x_1 = 0$, $x_2 = 0$ such that they intersect the special line $x_3 = 0$ in points which are harmonic with respect to I and J, we can make $a = -b$ when the points are real. However, *we select them in such a way that they are imaginary*, and we therefore take $a = b$. Then Eqs. (8–2) pass into

$$c_{11}^2 + c_{21}^2 = c_{12}^2 + c_{22}^2 = 1, \quad c_{11}c_{12} + c_{21}c_{22} = 0, \qquad (8\text{–}3)$$

in which we recognize Eq. (7–5) for the case $a = b$ in Eq. (7–4). Passing to nonhomogeneous coordinates, we thus find that the transformations can be written either in the form

$$\begin{aligned} x' &= x \cos \phi + y \sin \phi + a, \\ y' &= -x \sin \phi + y \cos \phi + b, \end{aligned} \qquad (8\text{–}4)$$

or in the form obtained by changing y' into $-y$. We shall now call two directions *orthogonal* when they intersect $x_3 = 0$, the line at infinity, in points harmonic to I and J. Equations (8–4) then represent the most general transformations which preserve sense and change an orthogonal system of axes into another one. When $a = b = 0$, we call these transformations *rotations*. The number ϕ is called the *angle* between the new x'-axis and the old x-axis.

This angle ϕ is here interpreted by means of projective concepts. We owe to Laguerre an explicit projective expression for ϕ. To obtain it, let us find the cross ratio (XX',IJ) formed by I and J and the points X and X' in which the old and new x-axes intersect the line $x_3 = 0$. Since $X\,(1{:}0{:}0)$, $X'\,(c_{11}{:}c_{21}{:}0)$, $I\,(i{:}1{:}0)$, $J\,(-i{:}1{:}0)$, we find

$$(XX',IJ) = \dfrac{\dfrac{0}{1} - \dfrac{1}{i}}{\dfrac{0}{1} + \dfrac{1}{i}} : \dfrac{\dfrac{c_{21}}{c_{11}} - \dfrac{1}{i}}{\dfrac{c_{21}}{c_{11}} + \dfrac{1}{i}} = \dfrac{c_{11} - ic_{21}}{c_{11} + ic_{21}} = \dfrac{\cos \phi - i \sin \phi}{\cos \phi + i \sin \phi} = e^{2i\phi},$$

or

$$\phi = \frac{i}{2} \ln (XX',IJ). \qquad (8\text{–}5)$$

We use here the formula $e^{i\alpha} = \cos \alpha + i \sin \alpha$, known as Euler's formula, derived in most texts on complex variables.*

----

* See, for instance, P. Franklin, *A Treatise on Advanced Calculus* (New York, 1940), Art. 103.

The expression (8-5) depends on the order in which we take I and J. It therefore presupposes a sense of rotation in the plane. When I and J are interchanged this sense changes. With a given sense of rotation in the plane, ϕ is determined by Eq. (8-5), but for multiples of 2π. This definition (8-5) of angle therefore differs somewhat from that defined in Sec. 2-1. Indeed, the ϕ of Sec. 2-1 is defined for rays, while ϕ is here defined for lines. The ϕ of Eq. (8-5) satisfies the property that for three lines OX, OX', OX'', except for multiples of π,

$$\angle(OX, OX') + \angle(OX', OX'') = \angle(OX, OX'').$$

Since OX and OX' can be taken as arbitrary lines in the plane, we find that *the angle of two lines is equal to $\pm i/2$ times the logarithm of the cross ratio formed by these two lines and the lines to I and J.*

When we define the *distance* D between two points $P(\xi_1, \eta_1)$, $Q(\xi_2, \eta_2)$ or $P(x_1:x_2:x_3)$, $Q(y_1:y_2:y_3)$ as

$$D = \sqrt{(\xi_1 - \xi_2)^2 + (\eta_1 - \eta_2)^2} = \frac{\sqrt{(x_1 y_3 - x_3 y_1)^2 + (x_2 y_3 - x_3 y_2)^2}}{x_3 y_3},$$
$$(8-6)$$

we find that D is invariant under Eq. (8-5). We may take D positive for real points, but we can also assume for D the Möbius convention of Sec. 1-1. In this case, we have for three points P_1, P_2, P_3 on a line

$$P_1 P_2 + P_2 P_3 + P_3 P_1 = 0,$$

if $P_i P_j = $ the distance between points P_i and P_j. For real points we have also $P_i P_j = 0$ if and only if $P_i = P_j$.

The quantities ϕ and D thus introduced have all the properties of angle and distance in the Euclidean plane. Indeed, we have found a formal apparatus which is identical with that of ordinary plane analytic geometry. In other words:

Plane Euclidean geometry can be made isomorphic with plane projective geometry, in which two conjugate imaginary points are singled out as ideal points.

Two conjugate imaginary points always lie on a real line (Ex. 11, Sec. 4-9).

From now on we can simply use the nomenclature of Euclidean geometry. Equation (8–4) with $a = b = 0$ and y' changed into $-y'$ represents a rotation with a reflection, which is itself a reflection (Ex. 12, Sec. 4–9). It does not affect distances, but changes ϕ into $-\phi$.

The projective interpretation of angle is due to E. Laguerre (*Nouv. Ann. de Mathém.* **12**, 1853, p. 64, *Œuvres* 2, pp. 9–13) who took notice of it, but in no more than a passing remark. It was F. Klein who pointed out the fundamental importance of Laguerre's formula. We can avoid imaginaries by replacing I and J by the elliptic involution of which they are the double points. A consistent axiomatic discussion on this principle can be found in H. S. M. Coxeter, *The Real Projective Plane* (New York, 1949), Chapter 9.

The points I and J are called the *isotropic points* of the plane (also *circular points at infinity*). The lines connecting a point (a,b) with I and J have the equation

$$y - b = \pm i(x - a),$$

and are called the *isotropic lines* through (a,b). For two points on such a line the expression D of Eq. (8–6) equals 0, which can be expressed by saying that the *distance between two points on an isotropic line is zero*.

The term *isotropic* is also due to Laguerre (1870). It expresses the property that the two sets of "isotropic" lines in the plane pass into themselves by motions, hence do not change their "direction" (Greek *isos* = equal, *tropein* = to turn). Another name for isotropic lines is *minimal lines*.

4–9 Vectors in Euclidean geometry. Let us consider the Euclidean plane as a special case of the affine plane, and confine our attention to rotations of rectangular axes only. Then the transformation of a contravariant vector (v_1,v_2) can be written [see Eq. (6–2)]

$$v_1' = v_1 \cos \phi + v_2 \sin \phi, \quad v_2' = -v_1 \sin \phi + v_2 \cos \phi. \qquad (9-1)$$

If we consider (v_1,v_2) as the coordinates of a covariant vector, then according to Eq. (6–3) [take $C = 1$ in Eq. (6–4)]:

$$C_{11} = \cos \phi, \quad C_{12} = \sin \phi, \quad C_{21} = -\sin \phi, \quad C_{22} = \cos \phi.$$

These coordinates transform in accordance with Eq. (6–1); there is no difference between covariant and contravariant coordinates. Hence:

> *The difference between covariant and contravariant vectors disappears in Euclidean geometry.*

We can simply speak of *vectors*, $\mathbf{v}$, of which the coordinates transform under rotations according to Eq. (6–1).

A vector $\mathbf{v}(v_1,v_2)$ has an invariant, its *length*, $v_1^2 + v_2^2$, always taken positive. Two vectors $\mathbf{v}(v_1,v_2)$, $\mathbf{w}(w_1,w_2)$ have an invariant

$$\mathbf{v} \cdot \mathbf{w} = v_1 w_1 + v_2 w_2 \tag{9–2}$$

which is the *scalar product*, since it satisfies the distributive property with respect to addition. The angle ϕ of two vectors is given by

$$\cos \phi = \frac{\mathbf{v} \cdot \mathbf{w}}{vw}, \tag{9–3}$$

where $v = \sqrt{\mathbf{v} \cdot \mathbf{v}}$, $w = \sqrt{\mathbf{w} \cdot \mathbf{w}}$ are the lengths of $\mathbf{v}$ and $\mathbf{w}$. By taking $\mathbf{v}$ and $\mathbf{w}$ along the x- and x'-axes we can readily verify that this angle is identical with that defined in the previous section by means of Laguerre's method.

A vector can thus be indicated by an arrow, and its length is given by the length of the arrow. This may be called the contravariant representation. Since the line $v_1 x + v_2 y + 1 = 0$ is perpendicular to the arrow given by (v_1,v_2), we find as the covariant representation of a vector a doublet of two parallel lines perpendicular to the arrow. By taking the arrow along the x-axis, we verify that the distance between the parallel lines is $1/\sqrt{\mathbf{v} \cdot \mathbf{v}}$. When the arrow is multiplied by the factor λ the distance between the parallel lines is multiplied by λ^{-1}. When we admit reflections there appears a difference between covariant and contravariant vectors. We shall study this in more detail in space (Sec. 8–7).

When we take the components of a vector with respect to oblique axes, there appears a difference between covariant and contravariant coordinates. Hence, *although in the Euclidean plane there is no difference between contravariant and covariant vectors, we can discriminate between contravariant and covariant coordinates when we take oblique axes.*

We have here derived ordinary plane vector analysis, which can be studied in more detail in textbooks such as L. Brand, *Vector and Tensor Analysis* (New York, 1947).

From two vectors $\mathbf{v},\mathbf{w}$ we can also derive the expression $v_1w_2 - v_2w_1$, which transforms under (9–1) as follows:

$$v_1'w_2' - v_2'w_1' = v_1w_2 - v_2w_1, \tag{9–4}$$

but, unlike the scalar product, changes its sign when reflections are admitted and when the order of $\mathbf{v}$ and $\mathbf{w}$ is changed. It is called the *rotor scalar* of the vectors and can be written $\mathbf{v} \times \mathbf{w} = -\mathbf{w} \times \mathbf{v}$. It has the properties of a product. It is equal to the oriented area of the parallelogram formed by $\mathbf{v}$ and $\mathbf{w}$, and can be represented either by this parallelogram or by any other closed oriented figure having the same area (see, e.g., Ex. 9 below).

EXERCISES

1. Show that transformations about O in which two real points on the line at infinity are invariant can be written as follows:

$$x' = a(x \cosh \phi + y \sinh \phi), \quad y' = a(x \sinh \phi + y \cosh \phi).$$

This geometry, with $a = 1$, is called *Minkowskian geometry* and underlies the theory of special relativity. (See p. 165.)

2. Show that the angle of an isotropic line with itself is indeterminate. This is sometimes expressed, in a more restricted (and dramatic) way, as *an isotropic line is perpendicular to itself.* How can this be expressed in terms of the properties of the involutions on the line at infinity of which the isotropic points are the double points?

3. Show that the isotropic lines through a point are invariant under rotations about this point.

4. Given two vectors $\mathbf{v},\mathbf{w}$. The vectors $\mathbf{v} + t\mathbf{w}$ represent for variable t a set of vectors. What is the locus of their ends if all vectors start at one point O (we can write $\overrightarrow{OP} = \mathbf{v}$, etc.)?

5. Repeat Ex. 4 for the vectors $\mathbf{i} \cos \phi + \mathbf{j} \sin \phi$, if (a) $\mathbf{i}$ and $\mathbf{j}$ are mutually perpendicular unit vectors ($\mathbf{i} \cdot \mathbf{i} = 1$, $\mathbf{j} \cdot \mathbf{j} = 1$) and ϕ is a variable parameter; and also (b) when $\mathbf{i}$ and $\mathbf{j}$ are arbitrary vectors of different directions.

6. Given two vectors $\overrightarrow{OP} = \mathbf{v}$, $\overrightarrow{OQ} = \mathbf{w}$. On PQ a point R is taken such that $PR:RQ = \lambda_1:\lambda_2$. Find vector $\overrightarrow{OR}$.

7. Given $\overrightarrow{OP} = \mathbf{v}$, $\overrightarrow{OQ} = \mathbf{w}$, $\overrightarrow{OR} = \mathbf{u}$. Show that P,Q,R lie on a line if three nonzero constants p,q,r can be found such that $p\mathbf{v} + q\mathbf{w} + r\mathbf{u} = 0$, $p + q + r = 0$.

8. Prove the theorem of Desargues on perspective triangles by taking $\overrightarrow{AP} = \mathbf{v}_1$, $\overrightarrow{AQ} = \mathbf{v}_2$, $\overrightarrow{AR} = \mathbf{v}_3$ in Fig. 2–10.

9. Show that the area of triangle OAB with $A(v_1,v_2)$, $B(w_1,w_2)$ is $\frac{1}{2}|v_1w_2 - v_2w_1|$. What is the meaning of the sign of $(v_1w_2 - v_2w_1)$?

10. Find the area of triangle ABC if $\overrightarrow{OA} = \mathbf{v}$, $\overrightarrow{OB} = \mathbf{w}$, $\overrightarrow{OC} = \mathbf{u}$.

11. Show that two conjugate imaginary points lie on a real line, two conjugate imaginary lines intersect a real point.

12. Show that a rotation about O followed by a reflection in a line through O is equivalent to a reflection in another line through O.

4–10 Groups. It has already been remarked (in Ex. 1, Sec. 4–3 and Ex. 8, Sec. 4–6) that both affine and projective transformations have the property that a transformation of either kind, followed by one of the same kind, leads to a transformation of the same kind: projective transformations, followed by projective ones, lead again to projective transformations; affine transformations followed by affine ones, lead again to affine transformations. This same property holds when these transformations are restricted to nonsingular ones.

This is due to the following property. If two linear transformations are given by the equations

$$\sigma_1 x_i' = c_{ij}x_j, \quad \sigma_2 x_i'' = c_{ij}'x_j' \quad (i,j \text{ may run from } 1 \ldots n)$$

with determinants

$$C = \text{Det}(c_{ij}), \quad C' = \text{Det}(c_{ij}')$$

then the resulting transformation

$$\sigma_3 x_i'' = c_{ij}''x_j = c_{ik}'c_{kj}x_j$$

is also linear and has as its determinant the product CC'. This is a direct result of the law of multiplication of determinants.

When a set of transformations T has the property that the performance of one transformation T_1 of the set, followed by that of another transformation T_2, leads again to a transformation of the set, $T_1T_2 = T_3$, then we say that this set has the *essential group property*. More precisely, we call a set of transformations T a *group*, if it satisfies the following two conditions:

1. the essential group property: $T_1T_2 = T_3$;

2. to every transformation T belongs a unique transformation T' of the set such that $TT' = T'T = I$, where I is the identity. We write for T' the symbol T^{-1}, so that $TT^{-1} = T^{-1}T = I$. We call T^{-1} the *inverse* transformation of T.

We may add that for groups of transformations the *associative* property also holds:

$$(T_1T_2)T_3 = T_1(T_2T_3) = T_1T_2T_3.$$

When we define an *abstract* group, the associative property must be explicitly postulated.

We can see that the nonsingular projective and affine transformations form a group, but the singular ones do not, since they do not allow an inverse transformation. Linear transformations with determinant ± 1 form a group, and so do those with determinant $+1$, but not those with determinant -1 or determinant 5.

We distinguish between *continuous* groups of transformations, of which the transformations depend on parameters which allow continuous change, and *discontinuous* groups, which consist of a discrete set of transformations. Nonsingular projective transformations in the plane form a continuous group, and since they depend on eight independent parameters (the ratio of the c_{ij}), we call it an *8-parameter group G_8*. Nonsingular affine transformations form a group G_6, nonsingular centro-affine transformations a group G_4, centro-affine transformations with determinant 1 form a group G_3. The rotations of a plane around the origin form a continuous group G_1, the one parameter being the angle ϕ of rotation:

$$x' = x \cos \phi + y \sin \phi, \quad y' = -x \sin \phi + y \cos \phi,$$

but when $\phi = n\pi/3$ ($n = 0, \pm 1, \pm 2$, etc.), the group is discontinuous and consists of 6 operations, which can be indicated by T, T^2, T^3, T^4, T^5 and $T^6 = I$. Another discontinuous group is that of the rotations which turn a regular tetrahedron, or a cube, into itself, the transformations by which one of the different cross ratios of four points on a line passes into the other five, or those collineations which change a Desargues' configuration into itself (Sec. 2–5).

If, among the transformations of a group, there are transformations which also form a group, they form a *subgroup*. The rotations about a point of the plane form a subgroup G_1 of the G_3 of all rotations and translations of the plane. The group with transformation T for which $T^6 = I$ has a subgroup $T^2, T^4, T^6 = I$ consisting of all rotations for which $\phi = 2n\pi/3$ ($n = 0, \pm 1, \pm 2$, etc.). If we take all projective transformations of the plane which leave the line $x_3 = 0$ invariant, then we obtain from the projective G_8 the affine subgroup G_6. If we take those transformations of the G_8 which leave another line invariant, then we have another subgroup G_6 of which the transformations, with their laws of composition, can be brought into a one-to-one correspondence with the group of affine transformations. Such groups are called *isomorphic*. The group of transformations by which we can pass from one of the different cross ratios of four points on a line to the others is isomorphic with the operations by which we can pass from one of the numbers μ, $1/\mu$, $1 - \mu$, $1/(1 - \mu)$, $\mu/(1 - \mu)$, $(1 - \mu)/\mu$ to the others, and this group is also isomorphic with the permutations of three different elements.

4-11 The Erlangen program. Felix Klein, when inaugurated as professor of mathematics at the University of Erlangen in 1872, was the first to show how the concept of continuous groups of transformations can be used to classify the different forms of geometry. Every group of transformations defined on some manifold (e.g., the manifold of real number triples) has elements (figures, numbers, or configurations of them) which are *invariant* under the operations of this group. For instance, the group G_8 of nonsingular projective transformations in the plane, or the *projective group*, changes all points of the plane into all points, all lines into all lines, incident points and lines into incident points and lines, and the cross ratio of four points on a line, or of four lines through a point, into the same cross ratio of the corresponding points or lines. Such elements are *projective invariants*. Klein expressed his principle by stating that *projective geometry is the theory of projective invariants*. And, more general, he gave the following definition of the study of a geometry:

Given a manifold and in it a group of transformations: investigate the elements of this manifold with respect to those properties which are invariant under the transformation of the group.

Thus, to do affine geometry means to study all invariants of the group G_6 of affine transformations. This geometry therefore includes the study of free vectors, their addition and subtraction and multiplication with a constant (but not their lengths and angles), and the study of division ratios of points on a line and of parallel lines. *And in ordinary plane Euclidean geometry we study the invariants of the G_3 of all translations and rotations of the plane.* However, ordinary plane geometry usually deals with invariants of a larger group. When it states that a triangle is determined by its three sides, it makes no difference between two symmetric triangles. This means that the underlying group includes reflections in a line. Moreover, absolute size plays no role in ordinary plane geometry; there is no linear measure, which means that the properties of ordinary plane geometry are invariant under similitudes. We must therefore conclude that ordinary elementary plane geometry is the theory of invariants under an *enlarged* group, the G_4 of rotations, translations, reflections, and similitudes, while the geometry of the oriented plane, introduced in Chapter 2, is the study of the G_4 of rotations, translations, and similitudes.

In elementary solid geometry we usually do distinguish between symmetrical figures, guided by the physical experience that although we can place one of two symmetrical plane figures on top of the other by taking it out of the plane and replacing it upside down, we cannot make a left-hand glove congruent with a right-hand one, since the world of solid bodies has no fourth dimension. Entertaining material on this subject is found in H. P. Manning, *The Fourth Dimension Simply Explained* (New York, 1910), 251 pp.

Suppose that the group under which a geometry is defined is replaced by a more comprehensive group, then only a part of the geometrical properties remain invariant. The other properties no longer appear as the properties of the geometrical entities themselves, but only as properties of that system which we obtain when we add to this geometry a special element. This element is defined such that, if we think it fixed, it allows in the plane or space of the comprehensive group only the transformations of the original group. For instance, the theorem of Euclidean geometry that the medians of a triangle pass through one point remains a theorem of affine geometry, but the similar property of the altitudes is not a property of affine geometry proper, but of affine geometry with a pair of imaginary directions singled out. And affine geometry itself can be considered as the geometry of all projective transformations which leave a line invariant. Centro-affine geometry is the geometry of all projective transformations which leave a nonincident point and line invariant. Every theorem of Euclidean geometry can be described in projective coordinates, with the aid of the expression for the isotropic points in those coordinates.

We can define new geometries by starting with different continuous transformation groups. This was the task outlined by Klein in 1872 and known as the *Erlangen program*. A great number of new geometries have since been made the object of special investigations. One of the best known is topology, the study of the invariants of all continuous transformations, of which we have presented an example in the chapter on the projective plane. We can also select finite groups and obtain so-called finite geometries, consisting of only a finite number of elements.

The concept of group first appears explicitly in the letter to a friend which young Evariste Galois (1811–1832) wrote on the eve of his death in a duel. See his *Œuvres*, pp. 25–32 (English translation in D. E. Smith, *Source Book of Mathematics*, pp. 278–285). L. Infeld has made Galois the hero of his book, *Whom the Gods Love* (New York, Whittlesey House, 1948). See also J. Sommerfield, *The Adversaries* (London, Heinemann, 1952). Galois derived the notion of a (finite) group from the study of the $n!$ permutations of the n roots of an algebraic equation. Klein's program is in his *Ges. Mathem. Abhandlungen* I, pp. 460–497 [English translation in *Bull. New York Math. Soc.* (1) **2** (1892–93), pp. 215–249]; see also Klein, *Elementary Mathematics from an Advanced Point of View II*, Section 3. Requirements of modern geometry have placed the Erlangen program into the framework of the theory of the so-called geometric object. See, for example, J. A. Schouten-D. van Dantzig, *Proc. London Math. Soc.* **42** (1936), pp. 356–376.

EXERCISES

1. Show that the nonsingular projective transformations on a line

$$x_1' = c_{11}x_1 + c_{12}x_2, \quad x_2' = c_{21}x_1 + c_{22}x_2, \quad C = c_{11}c_{22} - c_{12}^2 \neq 0$$

form a group. Also show that those transformations for which $C > 0$ form a group. What about the transformations with $C < 0$?

2. Show that the nonsingular projective transformations in the plane (2–1) form a group. Show that we cannot make a difference between transformations with $C > 0$ and $C < 0$. This difference in the case of line and plane corresponds to the orientability of a line and the nonorientability of the plane.

3. Find the group of motions in the plane under which a given (a) square, (b) regular hexagon, (c) rectangle remains invariant. What happens when we allow rotations in space of the plane into itself about a line in the plane?

4. Given a pattern of squares filling the plane. Find the group of motions under which this pattern is invariant. Do the same for a pattern of regular hexagons.

CHAPTER 5

PROJECTIVE THEORY OF CONICS

5–1 Curves of the second order. We consider in this chapter the projective plane. Its points, according to Sec. 3–9, are given by their homogeneous coordinates x_i, $i = 1,2,3$. We take two pencils of lines with vertices A,B:

$$\alpha_1 L_1 - \alpha_2 L_2 = 0 \;(\text{pencil } A); \quad \alpha_3 L_3 - \alpha_4 L_4 = 0 \;(\text{pencil } B), \quad (1\text{–}1)$$

where

$$L_\mu = A_\mu x_1 + B_\mu x_2 + C_\mu x_3, \quad \mu = 1,2,3,4. \quad (1\text{–}2)$$

For the sake of simplicity, we write $\lambda = \alpha_2/\alpha_1$, $\mu = \alpha_4/\alpha_3$, so that λ and μ may have the value $\pm\infty$.

A nonsingular bilinear relation between λ and μ,

$$a\lambda\mu + b\lambda + c\mu + d = 0, \quad ad - bc \neq 0, \quad (1\text{–}3)$$

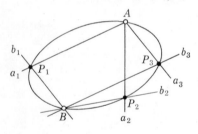

establishes a one-to-one correspondence between the lines of pencil A and of pencil B. To each line a of pencil A corresponds a line b of pencil B and conversely. This establishes a *projectivity* between the lines of the pencils, and we speak of *projective pencils.* Two corresponding lines have a point P in common. When a moves

Fig. 5–1

through the lines $a_1, a_2, a_3, \ldots$ of pencil A, then b moves through the lines $b_1, b_2, b_3, \ldots$ of pencil B, and the point of intersection P of a and b moves through the points $P_1, P_2, P_3, \ldots$ (Fig. 5–1). The locus of P is obtained by eliminating λ and μ from Eqs. (1–3) and (1–1):

$$aL_1 L_3 + bL_1 L_4 + cL_2 L_3 + dL_4 L_1 = 0, \quad (1\text{–}4)$$

which is a homogeneous equation of the second degree, and therefore of the form

$$a_{11}x_1^2 + 2a_{12}x_1 x_2 + a_{22}x_2^2 + 2a_{13}x_1 x_3 + 2a_{23}x_2 x_3 + a_{33}x_3^2 = 0, \quad (1\text{–}5)$$

or, for short,

$$a_{ij}x_ix_j = 0, \quad a_{ij} = a_{ji} \quad (i,j = 1,2,3). \tag{1-6}$$

We can assume $a_{ij} = a_{ji}$. If we write Eq. (1-6) out in full, we find a term $a_{12}x_1x_2$ and a term $a_{21}x_2x_1$, which add up to the $2a_{12}x_1x_2$ in Eq. (1-5) if we take $a_{21} = a_{12}$.

This equation (1-6) represents a *curve of the second order O_2* or a *point conic*. Since Eq. (1-4) is satisfied by $L_1 = 0$, $L_2 = 0$, and also by $L_3 = 0$, $L_4 = 0$, we see that the points A and B themselves lie on the curve O_2.

Hence we have found the theorem:

The locus of the points of intersection of the corresponding lines of two projective line pencils is a point conic.

If we intersect this point conic with a straight line p, such as $(ux) = u_ix_i = 0$, then by elimination of x_3 we obtain a homogeneous quadratic equation in x_1,x_2 which has two roots x_1/x_2 (these roots may be real and different, coincident real, or imaginary). We shall admit also these imaginary values. *The a_{ij}, however, shall always be real.* We can then state the theorem:

A curve of the second order is intersected by a line in two points, which may be different and real, coincident real, or imaginary.

It was Jacob Steiner (1796–1863) who founded projective geometry on · the projective relationship of point sets, line pencils, and plane pencils, especially in his book *Systematische Entwicklung der Abhangigkeit Geometrischer Gestalten von Einander* (1832, *Ges. Werke I*). Here he tried to discover "the organism by means of which the most different phenomena in the world of space are connected with each other — there exists a small number of very elementary fundamental relations which express the schematic structure by which the remaining mass of theorems is correctly and without any difficulty developed." It was in Steiner's purely geometrical world — Steiner abhorred analytical developments, which for him obscured clear geometrical insight — that projective geometry reached the harmony and simplicity which since then has characterized it. Its admirers sometimes exaggerated this simplicity and played with the idea that this projective geometry might be the long sought for "royal road to geometry," which bypasses the axiomatic difficulties typical of Euclidean geometry. We now know that this was an illusion; projective geometry also has its axiomatic difficulties.

5–2 Singular curves of the second order. It is possible that the left side of Eq. (1–5) is the product of two linear forms. A necessary and sufficient condition for this to happen is that $D_3 = 0$, where

$$D_3 = \begin{vmatrix} a_{11} & a_{12} & a_{13} \\ a_{12} & a_{22} & a_{23} \\ a_{13} & a_{23} & a_{33} \end{vmatrix} = \text{Det } (a_{ij}).$$

This can be shown by writing $x = x_1/x_3$, $y = x_2/x_3$, and solving the equation for x:

$$a_{11}x^2 + 2x(a_{12}y + a_{13}) + (a_{22}y^2 + 2a_{23}y + a_{33}) = 0$$

(take $a_{11} \neq 0$; if $a_{11} = 0$, take $a_{22} \neq 0$ and solve for y, if $a_{11} = a_{22} = 0$ the proposition is obvious). The discriminant of this equation in x is

$$(a_{12}y + a_{13})^2 - (a_{22}y^2 + 2a_{23}y + a_{33})a_{11}.$$

The condition that $D_3 = 0$ is equivalent to the necessary and sufficient condition that this discriminant is a perfect square, in which case, and in which case alone, the form $a_{ij}x_ix_j$ is the product of two real or imaginary linear forms.

The number D_3 is called the *discriminant* of the form $a_{ij}x_ix_j$. In the case that $D_3 = 0$, we call the point conic O_2 *singular* (or *degenerate*); it then consists of two lines, which may be distinct or coincident (in the latter case $a_{ij}x_ix_j$ is a perfect square and the rank of D_3 is 1). Since A and B (Fig. 5–1) satisfy Eq. (1–5), one of the straight lines passes through A and B. The locus of the points P is therefore another straight line which must be different from (AB), since two coinciding straight lines cannot appear as the locus of intersection of corresponding lines of two pencils, and the points of intersection of corresponding lines are collinear. The pencils A and B have one line AB in common. We say that they are *perspective* (see Ex. 3, Sec. 2–9).

The points of intersection of the corresponding lines of two perspective pencils lie on a line not passing through the vertices of these pencils.

5–3 Curves of the second class. We repeat the argument of Sec. 5–1 by replacing point coordinates by line coordinates u_i, and considering the connecting lines of the corresponding points A_1, A_2, A_3, ... B_1, B_2, B_3, ... of two projective point sets on lines a and b,

$$\alpha_1 P_1 - \alpha_2 P_2 = 0, \quad \alpha_3 P_3 - \alpha_4 P_4 = 0, \quad \lambda = \alpha_1/\alpha_2, \quad \mu = \alpha_3/\alpha_4,$$
$$P_\mu = A_\mu u_1 + B_\mu u_2 + C_\mu u_3 \quad (\mu = 1,2,3,4) \tag{3-1}$$
$$a\lambda\mu + b\lambda + c\mu + d = 0.$$

The connecting lines satisfy the equation

$$aP_1 P_3 + bP_1 P_4 + cP_2 P_3 + dP_2 P_4 = 0,$$

which is of the form

$$b_{ij} u_i u_j = 0, \quad b_{ij} = b_{ji} \quad (i,j = 1,2,3). \tag{3-2}$$

We shall always take the b_{ij} real.

An infinite number of points, defined as in $a_{ij} x_i x_j = 0$, generate as their locus a curve [Fig. 5-2(a)]. In Eq. (3-2) we have an infinite number of lines. These lines *envelop* a curve, which we consider as generated by these lines as their *envelope* (or locus) [Fig. 5-2(b)]. The lines are tangent to the curve. In the specific case of Eq. (3-2), we say that the envelope of the lines is a *curve of the second class* or *class conic* C_2. The lines $A_1 B_1, A_2 B_2, \ldots$ are tangent to this curve, and so are a and b (Fig. 5-3). The equation of a point $P : (ux) = u_i x_i = 0$ has two (different real, coincident real, imaginary) values u_i in common with Eq. (3-2). We thus have found the theorems:

The envelope of the lines connecting the corresponding points of two projective point ranges is a class conic.

A curve of the second class admits two tangents through a point, which may be real and different, coincident real, or imaginary.

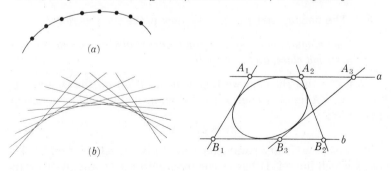

FIG. 5-2   FIG. 5-3

By comparing the case of coincident roots for the O_2 and the C_2, we see that in the case of the O_2 a tangent is obtained as the limit of the line of intersection of two points, when one moves closer and closer to the other along the curve. In the case of the C_2 a point of contact is obtained as the limit of the point of intersection of two tangents, when one moves closer and closer to the other along the curve. We often express this fact by stating that a tangent is the connecting line of two consecutive points, and a point of contact is the point of intersection of two consecutive tangents. This statement holds not only for curves O_2 and C_2, but for all differentiable curves.

When $D_3' = 0$:

$$D_3' = \begin{vmatrix} b_{11} & b_{12} & b_{13} \\ b_{12} & b_{22} & b_{23} \\ b_{13} & b_{23} & b_{33} \end{vmatrix} = \text{Det } (b_{ij}),$$

the class conic is *singular*. It consists of the lines passing through two points, or, for short, it consists of two points. These points may be separated or coincident. In the case that the C_2 is generated by projective point sets, we can only obtain two separate points; in this case the point sets have one pair of corresponding points in common; they are *perspective*. The curve of the second class consists of the point P in which all lines $A_1B_1, A_2B_2, \ldots$ intersect, and in the point of intersection $A_3 = B_3$ of a and b. (See Ex. 3, Sec. 2–6.)

The lines connecting corresponding points of two perspective point sets pass through a point not lying on the lines of these point sets.

Instead of *class conic*, we also use the term *line conic*.

5–4 The nonsingular conic.
We now prove the theorem:

A nonsingular curve of the second order is also a nonsingular curve of the second class, and conversely.

To prove this theorem we take a point $P(b_i)$ on the O_2 given by Eq. (1–5). A line l through P has its points determined by equations of the form

$$x_i = b_i + \lambda c_i, \tag{4–1}$$

where λ is an arbitrary parameter and (c_i) is a fixed point on l. The points which line (4–1) has in common with the O_2 are given by the values of λ satisfying the quadratic equation

$$a_{ij}(b_i + \lambda c_i)(b_j + \lambda c_j) = 0 \tag{4-2}$$

of which the constant term $a_{ij}b_ib_j$ is equal to zero, since $P(b_i)$ lies on O_2. Line l is tangent to O_2 at P, if Eq. (4-2) has two roots zero, that is, if $a_{ij}b_ic_j = 0$, provided that $a_{ij}c_ic_j$ is not also zero. Since (c_i) is any point on l, this second condition means that the O_2 is singular. Excluding this case, we find for *the equation of the tangent line* to a nonsingular O_2 at $P(b_i)$,

$$a_{ij}b_ix_j = 0, \tag{4-3a}$$

or, written out in full,

$$(a_{11}b_1 + a_{12}b_2 + a_{13}b_3)x_1 + (a_{12}b_1 + a_{22}b_2 + a_{23}b_3)x_2$$
$$+ (a_{13}b_1 + a_{23}b_2 + a_{33}b_3)x_3 = 0. \tag{4-3b}$$

The line coordinates of the tangent line are therefore

$$u_j = a_{ij}b_i. \tag{4-4}$$

Since we want the equation of O_2 in line coordinates, we need the relation between the u_i of Eq. (4-4) independent of the b_i, when the b_i satisfy the equation $b_iu_i = a_{ij}b_ib_j = 0$. We thus have to eliminate the b from the four equations

$$\begin{aligned}
u_1 &= a_{11}b_1 + a_{12}b_2 + a_{13}b_3, \\
u_2 &= a_{12}b_1 + a_{22}b_2 + a_{23}b_3, \\
u_3 &= a_{13}b_1 + a_{23}b_2 + a_{33}b_3, \\
0 &= u_1b_1 + u_2b_2 + u_3b_3.
\end{aligned} \tag{4-5}$$

The equation of the O_2, in point coordinates $a_{ij}x_ix_j = 0$, is therefore, in line coordinates,

$$\begin{vmatrix} a_{11} & a_{12} & a_{13} & u_1 \\ a_{12} & a_{22} & a_{23} & u_2 \\ a_{13} & a_{23} & a_{33} & u_3 \\ u_1 & u_2 & u_3 & 0 \end{vmatrix} = 0, \tag{4-6a}$$

which is a homogeneous quadratic expression in the u:

$$\alpha_{ij}u_iu_j = 0, \tag{4-6b}$$

where α_{ij} is the cofactor of a_{ij} in the determinant D_3. The determinant of the $\alpha_{ij} \neq 0$, because according to a well-known property of determinants*

---

*See, for example, A. Dresden, *Solid Analytical Geometry and Determinants* (New York, London, 1930), p. 29.

$$\text{Det } (\alpha_{ij}) = (D_3)^2$$

and D_3 is supposed to be $\neq 0$. A nonsingular O_2 is therefore a nonsingular C_2. When we solve Eq. (4–4) for b_i, we obtain $\sigma b_j = \alpha_{ij}u_i$, so that Eq. (4–6b) appears as the condition for the tangent (u_j) to pass through the point of contact (b_j).

If we start with a nonsingular C_2 given by $b_{ij}u_iu_j = 0$, $D_3' \neq 0$, then we find by an argument similar to the previous one that its equation in point coordinates is

$$\beta_{ij}x_ix_j = 0, \tag{4–7}$$

where β_{ij} is the cofactor of b_{ij} in $D_3' = \text{Det } (b_{ij})$. Thus the identity of nonsingular C_2 and O_2 is established. We call such a curve a *nonsingular conic*. Apart from nonsingular conics there are singular point conics consisting of two lines, and singular class conics consisting of two points.

EXERCISES

1. Find the equation of the point conic determined by

$$x_i - \lambda x_3 = 0 \quad \text{and} \quad x_2 - \mu x_3 = 0,$$

if $\lambda + \mu = 1$.

2. Find the value of λ for which

$$x_2^2 + \lambda x_1x_2 + 2x_1^2 + x_1x_3 + x_2x_3 - 6x_3^2 = 0$$

represents two straight lines, and find these lines.

3. Set up a perspectivity between two line pencils, one with vertex $(1:0:0)$, the other with vertex $(0:1:0)$ and find the equation of the singular point conic they generate.

4. Find (if possible) the equation in line coordinates of the conics
   (a) $x_1^2 + x_2^2 - 5x_3^2 = 0$,
   (b) $x_1x_2 + x_2x_3 + x_3x_1 = 0$,
   (c) $x_1^2 - 2x_1x_2 + x_2^2 - x_3^2 = 0$.

5. Show that the class conic of which the point equation is $x_1x_3 - x_2^2 = 0$ is $4u_1u_3 - u_2^2 = 0$, and that the point conic with line equation $u_1u_3 - u_2^2 = 0$ is $4x_1x_3 - x_2^2 = 0$.

6. If in two projective pencils (A) and (B) line a_1 corresponds to $b_1 = (BA)$, and line b_2 corresponds to $a_2 = (AB)$, then a_1 and b_2 are tangent lines to the point conic generated by the pencil. What is the dual theorem?

7. Show that for a singular point conic consisting of two distinct lines intersecting at a point P the class equation (4–6) represents the pencil with

its vertex at P counted twice. If the conic consists of two coincident lines, Eq. (4–6) is identically zero. State the dual theorem.

8. Given four independent points A,B,C,D in the plane. Find the locus of the points P such that the cross ratio $(PA,PB; PC,PD)$ has a given value. This problem is of value in photogrammetry (Special Ex. 17).

9. Construct a triangle circumscribed to a given triangle and inscribed to another triangle.

10. Show that in a collineation (non)singular conics correspond to (non)-singular conics. What happens in a correlation?

11. *Projectivity on a conic.* A collineation which preserves a nonsingular conic C establishes a one-to-one correspondence of the points on C. This is called a *projectivity* on C. Show that a projectivity is uniquely determined by three pairs of corresponding points on the conic. Also establish the dual projectivity.

12. Prove if AA',BB',CC', ... are corresponding points in a projectivity on a conic, the points obtained by intersecting $A'B$ and AB', $A'C$ and AC', ..., are on a line. This is the *axis* of the projectivity.

13. Given a projectivity on a line l by three corresponding point pairs $(AA'),(BB'),(CC')$ and a conic K in the plane. Take a point P on K, not on l, and project ABC as well as $A'B'C'$ on K. Show that the lines of the pencil (P) determine a projectivity on K (Ex. 11) and construct the double points of the projectivity on l by intersecting K with the axis of the projectivity on K (Ex. 12). We can take for K a circle (*Construction of Steiner*, 1833). [The paper in which Steiner published this result has been translated by M. S. Stark: *Geometrical Constructions with a Ruler Given a Fixed Circle with Its Center* (New York, 1940). It contains many historical notes by R. C. Archibald.]

5–5 Poles and polars.

We consider a nonsingular conic with equation $a_{ij}x_ix_j = 0$ and two arbitrary points $B(b_i)$ and $C(c_i)$ in the plane. A point on (BC) can be given by $x_i = b_i - \lambda c_i$. The points of intersection of (BC) and the conic are determined by the equation $a_{ij}(b_i - \lambda c_i)(b_j - \lambda c_j) = 0$, which is a quadratic equation of the form

$$P\lambda^2 + 2Q\lambda + R = 0, \qquad (5–1)$$

where

$$P = a_{ij}c_ic_j, \quad A = a_{ij}b_ic_j, \quad R = a_{ij}b_ib_j.$$

This equation (5–1) cannot have double roots for all values of b_i and c_i, since this means that $PR - Q^2 \equiv 0$ and this again means that all expressions $a_{ij}a_{kl} - a_{ik}a_{jl}$, $i,j,k,l = 1,2,3$ vanish, hence $D_3 = 0$. There are therefore two values of λ satisfying Eq. (5–1) and therefore two real or imaginary points of intersection of BC and the conic, which may in special cases be coincident.

These points of intersection are harmonic with respect to B and C, if the sum $\lambda_1 + \lambda_2$ of the roots of Eq. (5–1) is zero. In this case, $Q = 0$, or

$$a_{ij}b_ic_j = 0. \tag{5–2}$$

Points B and C, which satisfy Eq. (5–2), are called *conjugate* with respect to the conic. The line through B and C intersects the conic in two points harmonic to B and C.

We now keep $B(b_i)$ fixed, and consider all lines l through B. Then the locus of the points $C(x_i)$ which are conjugate to B is a straight line with equation

$$a_{ij}b_ix_j = 0, \tag{5–3}$$

or, in words (Fig. 5–4),

If on every line through a point its conjugate point is taken with respect to the conic, then the locus of these points is a line.

This line is the *polar line* or *polar* of the point with respect to the conic, and the point is called its *pole*. When the point lies on the conic its polar is the tangent line at that point, as can be understood not only from geometric considerations, but also by comparing Eq. (5–3) with Eq. (4–3). Moreover, if a point is such that two tangents can be drawn to the conic, then the polar line passes through the points of contact T_1, T_2 (Fig. 5–4), since from $(BC,PQ) = -1$ follows that $C = P$, when $P = Q$. When the polar line does not intersect the conic, then we can consider its (conjugate) imaginary points of intersection with the conic as the points of tangency.

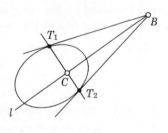

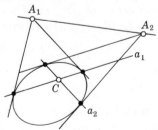

Fig. 5–4   Fig. 5–5

Let now a line $u_i x_i = 0$ be given. Then the equations

$$\rho u_i = a_{ij} b_j \tag{5-4}$$

determine one and only one ratio $(b_1 : b_2 : b_3)$, since $D_3 \neq 0$. Hence it follows from Eq. (5–3), that *to every line belongs one pole.* The pole of a tangent is its point of contact.

Two points A_1 and A_2 have two polars a_1, a_2, which intersect at C (Fig. 5–5). This point C has the property that both C, A_1 and C, A_2 are harmonic to the points of intersection of CA_1 and CA_2 with the conic. The line $A_1 A_2$ is therefore the polar c of C:

> *When a point A moves on a line c, the polar a of A turns about the pole C of c. Conversely, when a line turns about a point, its pole moves as the polar of the point.*

This theorem shows how to construct the polar of a point C (Fig. 5–5) from which no real tangents can be drawn (an *elliptic* point, see Ex. 3, Sec. 5–8). Then we take two lines a_1, a_2 through C, find their poles A_1, A_2 as intersections of tangents and draw $A_1 A_2$. This line is the polar of C.

Each of two conjugate points such as A_1 and C lies on the polar of the other. Two lines such as a_1 and c such that the pole of one lies on the other are also called *conjugate.* Conjugate points on a line are in involution, and so are conjugate lines through a point.

The theory of poles and polars can also be developed by considering the conic as a class conic, and leads to the same results for nonsingular conics.

Let us now consider a singular point conic, consisting of two separate lines l_1, l_2 intersecting at P. To every point A belongs a polar line a given by Eq. (5–3). This line passes through P: *all polars of points in the plane pass through P.* The line a forms with PA a harmonic set with respect to l_1 and l_2. Hence a is the polar of *all* points on PA. When A lies on l_1 or l_2 its polar coincides with l_1 or l_2 respectively. If A lies in P all lines in the plane are its polars. Therefore, every line not passing through P has P as its polar, and when it passes through P it has a line of poles through P. This polarity is *singular.*

Dual to this polarity is the pole-polar relationship with respect to a singular class conic. See Ex. 5, Sec. 5–7.

5-6 Self-polar triangles. We select arbitrarily a point A_1 not lying on a nonsingular conic C, and take a point A_2 arbitrarily on the polar a_1 of A_1, but not on C. The polar a_2 of A_2 passes through A_1. Lines a_1 and a_2 intersect in A_3, the polar a_3 of A_3 passes through A_2, A_1 (Fig. 5-6). None of the three points A_1, A_2, A_3 lies on C; they form the vertices of a triangle of which the sides a_1, a_2, a_3 are the polars of the opposite vertices and the vertices the poles of the opposite sides.

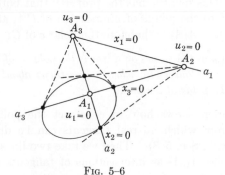

Fig. 5-6

Such a triangle is called a *self-polar triangle*. As A_1 can be taken in ∞^2 ways, and A_2 in ∞^1 ways, after which A_3 is determined, there belong to every nonsingular conic ∞^3 self-polar triangles.

When the conic is singular and consists of two separate lines l_1 and l_2 intersecting in P, then we still can find ∞^3 self-polar triangles, of which one vertex is $P = A_3$ and the two other vertices A_1, A_2 can be selected arbitrarily on two lines through P which are harmonic with respect to l_1 and l_2. In a dual way we can construct such triangles for a singular class conic consisting of two separate points (see Ex. 5, Sec. 5-7). When the conic of two coinciding lines l exists, any triangle with side l can be considered a self-polar triangle.

The main theorem of the theory of polars, that concerning the locus of the conjugate point of a fixed point with respect to a conic, is found in Apollonius' *Conics* (III, prop. 37). This theorem was further studied in the 17th century by Desargues and De la Hire. Philippe de la Hire (1640–1718), whose *Sectiones Conicae* (1685, Liber I, Prop. 27) contains the theorem that a line turns about a point if its polar rotates around the pole of the line, was a painter who became teacher of mathematics and astronomy at the Collège de France in Paris. The present theory dates back to Monge's period; Monge himself deals with it in his *Géométrie Descriptive*. The terms *pole* and *polar* are due to Servois and Gergonne [Gergonne's *Annales de Mathém.* **1** (1811), p. 337; **3** (1813), p. 293].

5-7 Polarity. A given nonsingular conic, as we have seen, associates with every point P in the plane one line p, and with every line p a point, which is exactly the point P. This relationship is called a *polarity*. Its equation follows from Eqs. (5-3) and (4-6b):

$$\rho u_i = a_{ij}x_j \qquad (7\text{-}1)$$

and the polarity is therefore, according to Sec. 4-4, a correlation. Since $a_{ij} = a_{ji}$, we can state that *a correlation is a polarity when its coefficients are symmetrical.* A polarity is an involutory relationship: when p corresponds to P, P corresponds to p and the points and lines in the plane are thus paired off together. We obtain the conic from a given polarity by asking which pairs of points and lines are incident. Then, according to Eq. (7-1), $u_i x_i = 0$, $u_i = a_{ij}x_j$, or

$$a_{ij}x_i x_j = 0, \qquad (7\text{-}2)$$

so that *in a polarity the locus of the points which lie on the corresponding lines is a conic, with respect to which the polarity represents the relation of pole and polar. The corresponding lines are the tangents at these points.*

Equation (7-2) may not represent a real conic, though the a_{ij} are real. We can therefore represent an imaginary conic by a particular polar relationship between real lines and points. To determine a polar relationship, we can start with an arbitrary self-polar triangle, but this is not enough. We need one more corresponding point and line, and this is necessary and sufficient for the purpose:

> *A polarity is determined when a self-polar triangle and one further corresponding pair of point and line are given.*

To prove it we can first show that every involutory correlation is a polarity, after which we show that any correlation which relates the three vertices of a triangle to the respective opposite sides is a polarity. The theorem then follows from the fact that four independent points and corresponding lines determine a correlation. We shall not go into the details of the proof, since the theorem follows immediately from the projective classification of conics discussed in the next section (see Ex. 6, Sec. 5–8).

1. Find the pole of the line $5x_1 - 7x_2 + 3x_3 = 0$ with respect to the conic $x_1^2 + x_2^2 - 3x_3^2 = 0$.

2. Given the conic $2x_1^2 + 3x_2^2 - 4x_3^2 = 0$. Find a self-polar triangle of which $(0:0:1)$ is a vertex.

3. Do the same for the conic $u_1^2 - u_2^2 = 0$, if $u_2 = 0$ is a vertex.

4. Find the equation of the tangents from the point $(4:3:1)$ to the conic $7x_1^2 - 8x_2^2 - 56x_3^2 = 0$.

5. Develop the polarity relationship for a singular class conic, and construct a self-polar triangle.

6. State and prove the dual of the theorem expressed by Eq. (5–2).

7. If two pairs of opposite vertices of a complete quadrilateral are pairs of conjugate points with respect to a conic, then the third pair is also conjugate. Prove and state the dual (von Staudt, *Geometrie der Lage*, p. 136).

8. To every triangle ABC not self-polar with respect to a given conic belongs a polar triangle $A_1B_1C_1$ such that A is the pole of B_1C_1, A_1 the pole of BC, etc. Show that both triangles are in perspective, that is, satisfy Desargues' theorem (von Staudt, *ibid.*, p. 135). We take the vertices to be different.

9. To every Desargues configuration $[10_3]$ belongs a (real or imaginary) conic with respect to which the ten points and ten lines are in relation of pole and polar (von Staudt, *ibid.*, p. 135). This conic is sometimes called the *order curve* (Ordnungskurve) of the configuration.

10. Show that conjugate points on a line form an involution. What are the double points? What happens when the line is a tangent line?

11. Two fixed lines l_1 and l_2 are drawn through a point P on a conic, and two variable chords PA, PB harmonic with respect to l_1 and l_2. Show that the chord AB passes through a fixed point.

5–8 Projective classification of conics. We consider a nonsingular conic and refer it to a coordinate system which has a self-polar triangle as its basic triangle. Let the equation of the conic be $a_{ij}x_ix_j = 0$; the a_{ij} are real. The point $(1:0:0)$ is the pole if the line $x_1 = 0$. Hence, according to Eq. (5–2),

$$0 = a_{12} \cdot 1 + a_{22} \cdot 0 + a_{23} \cdot 0, \quad 0 = a_{13} \cdot 1 + a_{23} \cdot 0 + a_{33} \cdot 0,$$

hence $\qquad\qquad a_{12} = a_{13} = 0, \quad a_{11} \neq 0.$

The point $(0:1:0)$ is the pole of the line $x_2 = 0$. This gives the additional condition $a_{23} = 0$, $a_{22} \neq 0$. When

$$a_{12} = a_{13} = a_{23} = 0, \quad a_{33} \neq 0, \tag{8–1}$$

then the point $(0:0:1)$ is the pole of $x_3 = 0$. The Eqs. (8–1) are thus the necessary and sufficient condition that the basic triangle be self-polar. The point equation of a nonsingular conic can then be reduced to the form

$$a_{11}x_1^2 + a_{22}x_2^2 + a_{33}x_3^2 = 0, \tag{8–2}$$

and its line equation to

$$b_{11}u_1^2 + b_{22}u_2^2 + b_{33}u_3^2 = 0, \tag{8–3}$$

where

$$a_{11}:a_{22}:a_{33} = b_{22}b_{33}:b_{33}b_{11}:b_{11}b_{22} = \frac{1}{b_{11}} : \frac{1}{b_{22}} : \frac{1}{b_{33}}. \tag{8–4}$$

None of the terms in Eq. (8–4) can be zero, which also follows from the fact that $D_3 = a_{11}a_{22}a_{33} \neq 0$.

The same reasoning can also be applied to a singular point conic provided it consists of two separate lines. In this case we can reduce its equation to the form (8–2), where one coefficient is zero, since one of the vertices of the basic triangle must be the point of intersection of the lines. In the case of a singular class conic consisting of two separate points, the equation can be reduced to the form (8–3) with one coefficient zero.

The Eqs. (8–2) and (8–3) can be further simplified by the choice of a unit point. This allows us to multiply each x_i by a convenient factor. We select the unit point in such a way that a_{11}, a_{22}, a_{33} are all ± 1, the corresponding b_{11}, b_{22}, b_{33} are then also ± 1. We have thus obtained the following result:

The equation of a nonsingular conic (with real coefficients in point and line coordinates) can, by suitable choice of the projective coordinates, be reduced either to the form

$\qquad$ (A) $x_1^2 + x_2^2 + x_3^2 = 0,$ $\qquad$ (A′) $u_1^2 + u_2^2 + u_3^2 = 0,$

or

$\qquad$ (B) $x_1^2 + x_2^2 - x_3^2 = 0,$ $\qquad$ (B′) $u_1^2 + u_2^2 - u_3^2 = 0.$

The forms (A), (A′) cannot represent a real conic. The equation of a real nonsingular conic can therefore always (by *real* coordinate transformations) be reduced to the form (B), (B′) (Fig. 5–6).

The singular point conic can similarly be reduced to the forms

or

$$(A_1) \ x_1^2 + x_2^2 = 0, \qquad (B_1) \ x_1^2 - x_2^2 = 0,$$

$$(A_2) \ x_1^2 = 0,$$

and the singular class conic to the forms

or

$$(A_1') \ u_1^2 + u_2^2 = 0, \qquad (B_1') \ u_1^2 - u_2^2 = 0,$$

$$(A_2') \ u_1^2 = 0.$$

The forms (A_1), (A_1') cannot be real. (B_1) represents two separate lines; (B_1') two separate points; (A_2) two coinciding lines; (A_2') two coinciding points.

This is the *projective classification* of conics, since it is obtained by projective transformations (change of basic triangle and unit point). Its main result can be summarized as follows:

From the projective point of view there is only one real nonsingular type of conic, and its equation can be reduced to $x_1^2 + x_2^2 - x_3^2 = 0$.

In other words, every nonsingular conic can by a projectivity be transformed into any other nonsingular conic. There is only one projective nonsingular conic.

The cases (A) can never be reduced by real transformations to (B), and conversely. This is expressed algebraically by the *law of inertia* of quadratic forms; see, for example, G. Birkhoff-S. McLane, *A Survey of Higher Algebra* (New York, 1947), p. 244.

In the case (A) and (B) the rank of the determinant D_3 and D_3' is 3; in the case (A_1), (B_1) the rank of D_3 is 2; in the case (A_1'), (B_1') the rank of D_3' is 2. In the case (A_2) the rank of D_3 is 1; in the case (A_2') the rank of D_3' is 1.

When we pass from one system of projective coordinates to another by means of $\rho x_i' = c_{ij}x_j, \sigma x_i = \gamma_{ji}x_j', C = \text{Det} \ (c_{ij}) \neq 0$, then the equation of the conic remains homogeneous and quadratic: $a_{ij}'x_i'x_j' = 0$, where

$$\rho_1 a_{ij}' = a_{kl}\gamma_{ki}\gamma_{lj} \quad (i,j,k,l = 1,2,3). \tag{8–5}$$

Then the new D_3' and the old D_3 are in the relationship

$$D_3 = D_3'C^2. \tag{8-6}$$

This shows that $D_3 = 0$ implies $D_3' = 0$, which simply expresses the obvious fact that a singular conic remains singular under a coordinate transformation. Equation (8-6) expresses that D_3 is a *relative projective invariant of weight* -2.

When a quantity is entirely unchanged under projective transformations, then we call it an *absolute projective invariant*. Such an invariant is the rank of D_3, which invariance is geometrically evident. Equation (8-6) shows it algebraically when the rank is 3.

The algebraic proof for ranks 2 and 1 can be given with the definition of rank in Sec. 3-8. See also A. C. Aitken, *Determinants and Matrices* (London, 1939), pp. 67-68.

EXERCISES

1. Prove Eq. (8-6).

2. Show that D_3' is a relative projective invariant of weight $+2$ and that its rank is an absolute projective invariant.

3. Show that through points for which $x_1^2 + x_2^2 - x_3^2 > 0$ two real tangents can be drawn to the conic $x_1^2 + x_2^2 - x_3^2 = 0$. Such points are *hyperbolic* points, and lie *outside* the conic.

4. Points which are not hyperbolic and do not lie on the conic (are not *parabolic* points) are called *elliptic* and lie *inside* the conic. Show that all lines through an elliptic point have two real points in common with a conic.

5. Let *elliptic* lines be lines which have no real point in common with the conic, and *hyperbolic* lines those which have two points in common with the conic (tangents are *parabolic* lines). Show that (a) the polar line of an elliptic point is elliptic, (b) that the pole of an elliptic line is elliptic.

6. Two elliptic points, as well as one elliptic and a hyperbolic point, are connected by a hyperbolic line. Prove this. What can you say about the line joining hyperbolic points?

7. Show that every self-polar triangle with respect to a real nonsingular conic has two hyperbolic vertices and one elliptic vertex.

8. Show that a polarity is determined by a self-polar triangle and one pair of conjugate elements. This is the theorem of Sec. 5-7, now to be demonstrated with the aid of Eq. (8-2).

9. Show that the equation of a real nonsingular conic can be reduced to $x_2^2 \pm x_1x_3 = 0$.

5–9 Pencils of conics. Let us consider two point conics C and C' with the equations $a_{ij}x_ix_j = 0$ and $a'_{ij}x_ix_j = 0$ respectively. Then the equation

$$a_{ij}x_ix_j - \lambda a'_{ij}x_ix_j = 0 \qquad (9\text{--}1)$$

represents for every value of λ a conic which passes through the points of intersection of C and C'. Since both conics are given by equations of degree 2, their equations have four roots in common, which may be real, imaginary, or coincident. We shall say that C and C' have always four points in common. Then Eq. (9–1) represents ∞^1 conics all passing through the four points of intersection of C and C'. These conics form a *pencil*, the points in common are called its *basic points*. These four points must be independent for pencils which contain non-singular conics. The λ is determined if one more point is given through which the conic must pass. Hence, we can state the theorem:

A nonsingular conic is uniquely determined by five independent points.

This is also made plausible by the fact that its equation depends on the ratio of its six coefficients.

To find the singular conics in the pencil we have to find the values of λ for which the determinant D_3 of the conic (9–1) vanishes:

$$\text{Det } (a_{ij} - \lambda a'_{ij}) = 0. \qquad (9\text{--}2)$$

This equation has three roots, real, imaginary or coincident, unless all conics of the pencil are singular. Let us consider only the case where the basic points are independent and real, so that they form the vertices 1,2,3,4 of a complete quadrangle. Then the opposite sides of this quadrangle form the three singular conics of the pencil, and Eq. (9–2) has three real and different roots. Conversely, if the three roots of Eq. (9–2) are real and different, we have four independent basic points.

This gives us a simple way to find the equation of a pencil through 4 independent points 1,2,3,4. Let $L_1 = 0$ be the equation of (12), $L_2 = 0$ of (34), $L_3 = 0$ of (14), $L_4 = 0$ of (23). Then $L_1L_2 = 0$ is one conic passing through the four points, and $L_3L_4 = 0$ another. The equation of the pencil is

$$L_1L_2 - \lambda L_3L_4 = 0. \qquad (9\text{--}3)$$

Suppose that points 3 and 4 come closer and closer together. Then line (34) will in the limit become the common tangent to all conics of the pencil. Hence we find that the pencil passing through points 1 and 2 and tangent to the line $L_2 = 0$ at the point 3 on this line is again given by Eq. (9-3),

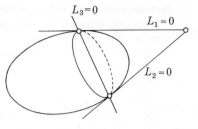

Fig. 5-7

$L_3 = 0$, $L_4 = 0$ now both passing through $3 = 4$. Similarly, we find that the pencil of all conics tangent to lines $L_1 = 0$, $L_2 = 0$ at their points of intersection with the line $L_3 = 0$ is given by (Fig. 5-7)

$$L_1 L_2 - \lambda L_3^2 = 0. \qquad (9\text{-}4)$$

For instance, all conics tangent to the sides $x_1 = 0$, $x_2 = 0$ at the points $(1:0:0)$ and $(0:1:0)$ are given by $x_1 x_2 - \lambda x_3^2 = 0$. If the conic passes through the unit point $\lambda = 1$, and the equation is $x_1 x_2 - x_3^2 = 0$ (cf. Ex. 9, Sec. 5-8).

That a nonsingular conic is uniquely determined by five points also follows from the generation of the conic by projective pencils, which are, as we know, determined when three corresponding pairs of lines are given.

Similarly, all class conics tangent to four lines are given by an equation of the form

$$b_{ij} u_i u_j - \lambda b'_{ij} u_i u_j = 0. \qquad (9\text{-}5)$$

There is one nonsingular conic tangent to five given independent lines. In every pencil (9-5), if not consisting of only singular conics, there are three singular class conics, which may be real, imaginary, or coincident. We can now proceed with the theory of these class pencils in a way dual to the previous theory of point pencils. For example,

$$P_1 P_2 - \lambda P_3^2 = 0$$

is the pencil of all conics having their points of contact at the points $P_1 = 0$, $P_2 = 0$ at their lines of connection with $P_3 = 0$.

The classification of conic pencils can be performed with the aid of the theory of elementary divisors, since this theory holds not only for λ-

matrices of the form indicated by Eq. (3–1), Sec. 4–3, but also for matrices of which the elements are polynomials in λ. Then no distinction has yet been made between real and imaginary intersections or contacts. It can be shown that the following cases exist:

[111]   Four distinct intersections.
[21]   Simple contact.
[(11)1]   Double contact.
[3]   Three-point contact (osculation).
[(21)]   Four-point contact.
[(111)]   Coincidence.

See J. A. Todd, *Projective and Analytic Geometry* (1946), p. 183; W. G. Welchman, *Introduction to Algebraic Geometry* (Cambridge, 1950), Chapter VIII.

5–10 Theorems of Pascal and Brianchon.   Since five independent points determine a conic, six points on a conic must be related. This relation between six points on a conic is expressed by the following theorem, called after Pascal:

The opposite sides of a hexagon inscribed in a conic intersect in three collinear points.

In other words, given six points 1,2,3,4,5,6 on a conic C (Fig. 5–8) — they need not be labeled successively — and such that the lines

$$(12),\ (45) \text{ intersect in } P,$$
$$(23),\ (56) \text{ intersect in } Q,$$
$$(34),\ (61) \text{ intersect in } R,$$

then P,Q,R lie on a straight line.

To prove it let us consider the conic C in two different ways as belonging to a pencil. For this purpose, let $l_{12} = 0$ be the equation of line (12), $l_{25} = 0$ of line (25), etc. Then

$$l_{12}l_{56} + \lambda l_{16}l_{25} = 0$$

represents the pencil of all conics passing through 1,2,5,6, and

$$l_{23}l_{45} + \mu l_{34}l_{25} = 0$$

the pencil of all conics passing through 2,3,4,5. The given conic C belongs to both pencils. Hence there exists by proper normalization

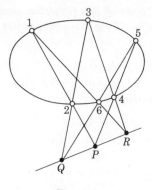

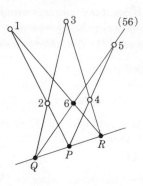

FIG. 5-8   FIG. 5-9

of these two equations a value of λ and of μ such that

$$l_{12}l_{56} + \lambda l_{16}l_{25} \equiv l_{23}l_{45} + \mu l_{34}l_{25},$$

or

$$l_{12}l_{56} - l_{23}l_{45} \equiv l_{25}(\mu l_{34} - \lambda l_{16}).$$

The conic with equation $l_{12}l_{56} - l_{23}l_{45} = 0$ is therefore singular and consists of lines $l_{25} = 0$ and $\mu l_{34} - \lambda l_{16} = 0$. This conic belongs to the pencil passing through the points 2,5, $[(12)(45)] = P$, and $[(23)(56)] = Q$. The line (25) passes through the basic points 2 and 5 of this pencil. Hence the line $\mu l_{34} - \lambda l_{16} = 0$, which passes through $[(15)(34)] = R$, passes through P and Q, which proves the theorem. The line PQR is called the *Pascal line* of the hexagon.

With the aid of this theorem we can construct, for any five given independent points, any number of points which lie on the conic determined by the five points, and this *with the straightedge alone*. Let the points be 1,2,3,4,5 and let us find the point 6 of the conic lying on an arbitrary line (56) through 5. Lines (12) and (45) intersect in P, (23) and (56) in Q. Then the Pascal line PQ and (34) intersect in R, after which we find point 6 as intersection of $(61) = (1R)$ with (56) (Fig. 5-9).

We can also consider this construction as that of a fourth corresponding pair of lines in the projective pencils obtained by connecting 1 and 5 with 2,3,4:

When three corresponding pairs of lines of two projective pencils· are given, then we can find any number of corresponding pairs by means of the straightedge alone.

When some of the points 1,2,3,4,5,6 come together, then we obtain from the theorem of Pascal variations dealing with inscribed pentagons, quadrangles, or triangles. We mention two of them.

If a pentagon 12345 is inscribed in a conic, and l is the tangent at 5, then the points of intersection of (12),(45); (23),l; (34),(51) lie on a line.

Here *l* has to be taken as (56), 5 = 6.

If a triangle is circumscribed to a conic, then the lines connecting two points of tangency intersect the third sid: three points on a line.

This line is sometimes called the *Hessian* line of the triangle.

There is a dual theory to that centering around Pascal's theorem. The dual of Pascal's theorem is called the *Brianchon theorem:*

The lines connecting opposite vertices of a hexagon circumscribed to a conic intersect in a point (Fig. 5–10). *This point is called the Brianchon point.*

This theorem allows us to construct any number of tangents to a conic if five tangents in a general position are given. Among the special cases, we mention the following theorem, called after Maclaurin:

If a triangle is circumscribed to a conic, then the lines connecting a vertex with the point of contact on the opposite side pass through a point.

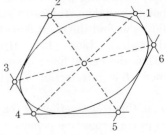

Fig. 5–10

Pascal's theorem appears first in the *Essay pour les Coniques*, which Blaise Pascal (1623–1662), then seventeen years of age, published in 1640 as a result of his study of Desargues. The essay was published on a single leaflet, of which most copies were lost. Leibniz saw a copy among Pascal's posthumous mathematical papers (which have disappeared). The copy reprinted in Pascal's *Oeuvres* I, p. 252, was later found by accident. Pascal's theorem was independently rediscovered by William Braikenridge (1726, 1733) and Colin Maclaurin (1727, 1735), both Edinburgh mathematicians. Many proofs have since been given. Charles Julien Brianchon (1783–1864) published his theorem in the *Journal de l'Ecole Polytechnique* **6** (1806), pp. 297–311; he found it by applying the principle of duality to Pascal's theorem. Pascal seems to have understood the importance of his theorem; we know at any rate from his contemporary, Father Mersenne, that Pascal "by means of a most universal theorem, supported by 400 corollaries, comprehended the whole of Apollonius." It was also Pascal who called his figure the "hexagramma mysticum," which name is still in use. English translations of Pascal's and Brianchon's texts are given in D. E. Smith, *Source Book of Mathematics*, pp. 326–336. The problem of determining a conic from five given points was already solved by Pappus, with the methods of ancient geometry. It was again taken up by Newton in his *Principia* I (1687), prop. 22, and *Arithmetica Universalis* (1673–1684), problem 55.

EXERCISES

1. Give a direct proof of Brianchon's theorem, without deriving it from Pascal's theorem.

2. Formulate an application of Pascal's and of Brianchon's theorem for a triangle inscribed in a conic.

3. Apply Pascal's theorem to a quadrangle inscribed in a conic. Formulate the dual theorem.

4. Our proof of Pascal's theorem does not use the condition that the conic is nonsingular. State the theorem for a singular conic. (Cf. Ex. 9, Sec. 3–7.)

5. A conic is given by five tangents. Construct the point of contact on one of these tangents.

6. The conics of a point pencil intersect a line in the points of an involution. The involution of six points (Sec. 1–7) offers a special case of this theorem. (See also Sec. 6–6 and Sec. 6–7.) What is the dual theorem?

7. Prove that there are two conics passing through four independent points and tangent to a line not passing through any of these points. State the dual theorem. Construct an arbitrary point of such a conic.

8. Prove that there are four conics passing through three noncollinear points and tangent to two lines not passing through any of these points. State the dual theorem.

9. Construct the polar of a given point with respect to a conic given by five points.

10. The sides of a triangle are intersected by a conic, each side in two points. Each point of intersection is joined to the opposite vertex by a line. Prove that the six lines thus obtained are tangent to another conic.

11. Show that six points on a conic determine sixty Pascal lines (J. B. Durrande, *Gergonne's Annales* **14**, pp. 29–60).

These Pascal lines together with their points of intersection have a number of remarkable properties, discovered by Steiner, Plücker, Hesse, Cayley, Salmon, and Kirkman. For instance, through each "Kirkman point" pass three Pascal lines, on every Pascal line there are three Kirkman points; they form a (60_3) consisting of six Desargues (10_3). The Pascal lines also form a $(20_3, 15_4)$ of "Steiner points" and "Plücker lines," these 20 Steiner points form 10 pairs of conjugate points with respect to the conic. See, e.g., Salmon, *Conic Sections, Notes* (p. 379 of the 6th ed.), and the exhaustive discussion in F. Levi, *Geometrische Konfigurationen* (Leipzig, 1929), Chapter V.

12. Two self-polar triangles with respect to a nonsingular conic, and with different vertices, have their vertices on one conic and their sides tangent to another. Prove.

13. Two triangles with different vertices inscribed in a nonsingular conic are circumscribed to another conic. Prove.

14. Show that there exists one point P' conjugate to a point P with respect to all conics of a pencil, and show that P is the conjugate of P'. This mating of the points in the plane is an example of a *plane involution* (Poncelet).

15. Any two triangles inscribed in a nonsingular conic can be considered as self-polar with respect to a (real or imaginary) conic.

16. Show that a conic passing through the vertices of the triangle formed by the lines $L_i = 0$, $i = 1,2,3$, has the point equation $a_1 L_2 L_3 + a_2 L_3 L_1 + a_3 L_1 L_2 = 0$, where the a_i are constants. What is the equation of the conic with respect to which the triangle is self-polar?

17. Construct the points of intersection of a given line with a conic determined by five points.

18. The conics $C_0 + \lambda_1 C_1 + \lambda_2 C_2 + \cdots + \lambda_r C_r = 0$, where $C_\alpha = 0$ $(\alpha = 0,1,\ldots,r)$ represent $r + 1$ fixed conics and the λ are variable parameters, represent a *linear system* of conics of r degrees of freedom (∞^r conics). For $r \geq 5$ all conics of the plane belong to the system. For $r = 1$ we have a

pencil, for $r = 2$ a *net*. Determine whether the following conics form a linear system, and if so, determine the degrees of freedom:

    (1) those which have a given pair of points as conjugate points,
    (2) those which are tangent to a given line,
    (3) those which admit a given triangle as self-polar triangle,
    (4) those which pass through two or three points,
    (5) those which pass through two points and are tangent to two lines.

Consider both the case that conics are point conics and the case that they are class conics.

19. Show that it is possible to find a coordinate system in which a given nonsingular conic can be represented by $x_1 : x_2 : x_3 = \lambda^2 : \lambda : 1$, λ a parameter.

20. *Eleven-point conic.* The locus of the poles of a given line l with respect to the point conics of a pencil (take its four basic points distinct and the line not passing through any of them) is a conic. Show this and also show that this conic passes through (a) the three diagonal points of the complete quadrangle formed by the basic points, (b) the two points where l is tangent to conics of the pencil, (c) the six points Q obtained in the following way: let l meet one of the sides AB of the quadrangle in P, then Q is the harmonic conjugate of P with respect to A and B [Steiner (1846), see *Werke II*, p. 335].

21. Show that the eleven-point conic of the line $(ux) = 0$ with respect to the pencil $a_1 x_1^2 + a_2 x_2^2 + a_3 x_3^2 - (x_1^2 + x_2^2 + x_3^2) = 0$ is $u_1(a_2 - a_3)x_2 x_3 + u_2(a_3 - a_1)x_3 x_1 + u_3(a_1 - a_2)x_1 x_2 = 0$.

22. Show that the equation of the two tangents through the point (p_i) to a conic (1–6) is

$$(a_{ij}x_i x_j)(a_{ij}p_i p_j) - (a_{ij}p_i x_j)^2 = 0.$$

23. Given a triangle ABC, sides a,b,c, and a point T not on one of the sides. The sides b,c can be considered as a pair of a line involution with vertex A of which AT is a double line; let l_1,l_2 be another corresponding pair of lines in this involution (b,c,AT). Similarly, let m_1,m_2 be a pair in the involution (c,a,BT) and n_1,n_2 be a pair in the involution (a,b,CT). Let P be $(m_1 n_2)$, equally $P'(m_2,n_1)$, $Q(n_1,l_2)$, $Q'(n_2,l_1)$, $R(l_1,m_2)$, $R'(l_2 m_1)$; the labeling depends on the particular way of assigning the symbols l_1,l_2 to the lines through A, etc. Prove that the six lines l_1,l_2,m_1,m_2,n_1,n_2 touch a conic. Moreover, show that (a) triangles PQR, $P'Q'R'$, (b) triangles ABC,PQR, (c) triangles ABC, $P'Q'R'$ are perspective, and (d) that the centers of perspectivity are collinear. [H. F. Baker, *Introduction to Plane Geometry* (Cambridge, 1943), p. 345.] See further Special Ex. 5.

CHAPTER 6

AFFINE AND EUCLIDEAN THEORY OF CONICS

6–1 Conjugate diameters. We pass from projective to affine theory by taking $x_3 = 0$ as the line at infinity and introducing the system of affine coordinates $x = x_1/x_3$, $y = x_2/x_3$. This system is oblique, and may be called Cartesian, but with the understanding that angle is not defined and the units of measure in the x- and y-directions are still arbitrary and independent of each other. The equation of the conic is

$$a_{11}x^2 + 2a_{12}xy + a_{22}y^2 + 2a_{13}x + 2a_{23}y + a_{33} = 0, \qquad (1\text{–}1)$$

and coordinate transformations are of the form

$$x' = c_{11}x + c_{12}y + c_{13}, \quad y' = c_{21}x + c_{22}y + c_{23} \quad (C = c_{11}c_{22} - c_{12}^2 \neq 0). \tag{1–2}$$

The pole M of the line at infinity has the property that all chords through M are bisected at M. We call this pole the *center* of the conic. Its coordinates satisfy the equation

$$0 = a_{1j}x_j, \quad 0 = a_{2j}x_j, \quad \rho = a_{3j}x_j \quad (j = 1,2,3),$$

or

$$
\begin{aligned}
a_{11}x + a_{12}y + a_{13} &= 0, \\
a_{12}x + a_{22}y + a_{23} &= 0.
\end{aligned}
\tag{1–3}
$$

These equations have a unique solution if

$$D_2 = a_{11}a_{22} - a_{12}^2 \tag{1–4}$$

is $\neq 0$. In this case there is one center, always real at finite distance from O. When $D_2 = 0$ there is no center at finite distance.

When x is changed into x' by means of Eq. (1–2), then the new D_2' and D_2 are related as follows:

$$D_2' = D_2(c_{11}c_{22} - c_{12}c_{21})^2. \tag{1–5}$$

Hence if $D_2 \gtrless 0$ in one coordinate system, it remains $\gtrless$ in any other system.

134

Transformations (1–2) of the special form $x' = x + c_{13}$, $y' = y + c_{23}$ are translations. By means of a translation, M can be made the origin of the coordinate system. Then Eqs. (1–3) have the solution $x = y = 0$, hence $a_{13} = a_{23} = 0$. The equation of the conic now takes the form

$$a_{11}x^2 + 2a_{12}xy + a_{22}y^2 + a_{33} = 0 \quad (a_{11}a_{22} - a_{12}^2 \neq 0). \quad (1\text{–}6)$$

Let us take a nonsingular conic, hence $D_3 \neq 0$ for Eq. (1–1) (see Sec. 5–2). Then $D_3 \neq 0$ also for Eq. (1–6), so that $a_{33} \neq 0$. We confine our study for the time being to this case of a *central conic*. It is characterized by $D_2 \neq 0$, $D_3 \neq 0$.

The pole of a diameter $y = mx$ is at infinity, since the diameter passes through M. To find it, let us return to projective coordinates, in which the pole of $x_2 - mx_1 = 0$ is determined by the equations [see Eq. (5–2), Chapter 5]

$$\rho m = a_{11}x_1 + a_{12}x_2, \quad -\rho = a_{12}x_1 + a_{22}x_2 \quad (0 = a_{33}x_3),$$

or

$$x_1 : x_2 : x_3 = -(ma_{22} + a_{12}) : (ma_{12} + a_{11}) : 0.$$

The pole of the diameter $y = mx$ is therefore the ideal point of the line

$$y = -\frac{a_{11} + ma_{12}}{a_{12} + ma_{22}} x. \quad (1\text{–}7)$$

The lines $y = mx$, line (1–7), and the line at infinity form a self-polar triangle, so that the pole of diameter (1–7) is the ideal point of $y = mx$. Such diameters, of which the ideal point of one is the pole of the other, are called *conjugate diameters*. From the properties of the polar triangle we can deduce the following theorem (Fig. 6–1):

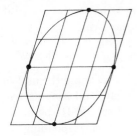

All chords in the direction of a diameter of a central conic are bisected by the conjugate diameter. The tangents at the points where a diameter intersects the conic are parallel to the conjugate diameter.

FIG. 6–1

The conic admits an infinity of pairs of conjugate diameters, and hence an infinity of circumscribed parallelograms. If two conjugate diameters are given by the equations

$$y = mx, \quad y = m_1x,$$

then, according to Eq. (1–7),

$$m_1 = -\frac{a_{11} + ma_{12}}{a_{12} + ma_{22}},$$

or

$$a_{22}mm_1 + a_{12}(m + m_1) + a_{11} = 0, \tag{1–8}$$

which is the equation of an involution:

> *The conjugate diameters of a central conic form a pencil in involution.*

The double lines of this pencil are the self-conjugate diameters. If the conic intersects $x_3 = 0$ in real points, these points are the ideal points of the self-conjugate diameters. These diameters can therefore be considered as lines through the center which are, at infinity, tangent to the conic. They are also called the *asymptotes*. The asymptotes are therefore obtained from Eq. (1–6) by omitting a_{33}:

$$a_{11}x^2 + 2a_{12}xy + a_{22}y^2 = 0. \tag{1–9}$$

They are real when $D_2 < 0$, imaginary when $D_2 > 0$.

6–2 Affine classification of conics. We now take as x- and y-axes two conjugate diameters. Then $m = 0$ must correspond to $m_1 = \infty$ in Eq. (1–8), which means that in the new coordinate system $a_{12} = 0$. The equation of a central conic can therefore be written, in ∞^1 ways, in the form:

$$a_{11}x^2 + a_{22}y^2 + a_{33} = 0, \quad a_{11}a_{22} \neq 0, \quad a_{33} \neq 0. \tag{2–1}$$

By selecting the unit of measure on the x- and on the y-axes appropriately, and keeping reality conditions in mind, we can obtain from this form (2–1) the *normal forms* for central conics. We add to our list the corresponding normal forms in line coordinates ($u = u_1/u_3$, $v = v_1/v_3$):

$$(A) \quad x^2 + y^2 + 1 = 0, \qquad (A') \quad u^2 + v^2 + 1 = 0,$$
$$(B) \quad x^2 + y^2 - 1 = 0, \qquad (B') \quad u^2 + v^2 - 1 = 0,$$
$$(C) \quad x^2 - y^2 - 1 = 0, \qquad (C') \quad u^2 - v^2 - 1 = 0.$$

Only the forms (B) and (C) represent real conics. The conic (B) has no real points in common with the line at infinity; it is an *ellipse*. The conic (C) has real points of intersection with the line at infinity; it is a *hyperbola*. The hyperbola has real asymptotes whose equations in projective coordinates, as tangents at the points $(1:\pm 1:0)$, are $x_1 \pm x_2 = 0$, hence in Cartesian coordinates: $y = \pm x$, or $x^2 - y^2 = 0$. The ellipse therefore, among real conics, is characterized by $D_3 \neq 0$, $D_2 > 0$; the hyperbola by $D_3 \neq 0$, $D_2 < 0$.

When $D_3 \neq 0$, but $D_2 = 0$, we have a nonsingular conic without a center. Solving $a_{ij}x_ix_j = 0$ for $x_3 = 0$, we see that since $a_{11}x_1^2 +$ 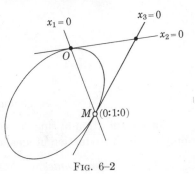 $2a_{12}x_1x_2 + a_{22}x_2^2$ is now a perfect square, the *conic is tangent to the line at infinity*. Let M be the point of contact, which we take as the point $(0:1:0)$. Let the axis $x_1 = 0$ intersect the conic again at a point O, where we take the axis $x_2 = 0$ as the tangent to the conic (Fig. 6–2). Then O $(0:0:1)$ and M $(0:1:0)$ lie on the curve, which means $a_{22} = a_{33} = 0$, and the lines $x_2 = 0$ and $x_3 = 0$ are the tangents

FIG. 6–2

at O and M respectively, which means $a_{12} = a_{13} = 0$. Taking $x_1 = 0$ and $x_2 = 0$ as y- and x-axes of a Cartesian system, we obtain for the equation of the conic

$$a_{11}x^2 + 2a_{23}y = 0 \quad (a_{11}a_{23} \neq 0),$$

which form can be obtained in ∞^1 ways (by choice of O). Selecting the units in an appropriate way, we obtain as the *normal form*

(D) $\quad x^2 + y = 0$ (with corresponding $u^2 + 4v = 0$).

The form $x^2 - y = 0$ can, by real change of axis direction, be changed into (D). There is only one normal form (D). The conic is a *parabola;* the lines through M are still called *diameters*, and they are all parallel.

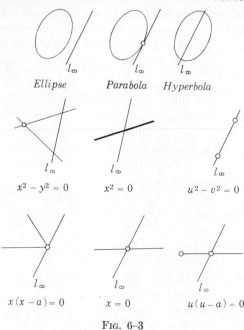

Fig. 6–3

The classification of singular conics differs from the projective one only by the introduction of ideal elements. First, we have the forms

Point conics	Line conics
$x^2 + y^2 = 0$ (not real),	$u^2 + v^2 = 0$ (not real),
$x^2 - y^2 = 0$,	$u^2 - v^2 = 0$,
$x^2 = 0$.	$u^2 = 0$.

Then we have to add to these forms those which involve ideal elements. The conic $x(x - a) = 0$ represents two parallel lines, $x = 0$ represents the y-axis and the line at infinity, $u(u - a) = 0$ a point on the special point of the x-axis, $u = 0$ the special point on the x-axis and the origin. The formula $1 = 0$ represents again, in its awkward way, the line at infinity in point coordinates, and the origin in line coordinates.

The relation $D_3 \neq 0$, $D_2 = 0$ characterizes the parabola, and $D_3 = 0$, $D_2 = 0$ two parallel or coinciding lines. Figure 6–3 shows the projective interpretation of affine forms.

6–3 Some affine constructions. Given five points 1,2,3,4,5 determining a conic, can we construct its center? To perform this construction, draw a line through 5 parallel to line (12) and find, by means of Pascal's theorem, the point 6, where this line intersects the conic. The line joining the centers of the chords (12) and (56) is a diameter. Repeating this construction with another selection of points on the conic, we obtain the center as the point of intersection of two diameters.

As another application of Pascal's theorem, let us construct a hyperbola (that is, as many points of a hyperbola as we like), if two asymptotes a_1, a_2 and a point A are given (Fig. 6–4). Giving a_1 means giving two coincident ideal points which we label 2,3. Similarly, giving a_2 means giving two ideal points 4,5. Draw through $1 = A$ an arbitrary line (16), on which a new point 6 of the hyperbola has to be determined. We find P by drawing a line through 1 parallel to a_1 and intersecting it with a_2. We find R as the ideal point on (16). The line of Pascal runs through P parallel to (16) and intersects a_1 in Q. The line through Q parallel to a_2 intersects (16) in the required point 6.

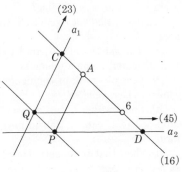

Fig. 6–4

This construction leads to the simple theorem:

When a line intersects a hyperbola in the points A and B, and the asymptotes in C and D, then the length of AC and of BD is the same (Fig. 6–4, here $B = 6$).

This theorem can now be used to find as many points of the hyperbola as we like.

EXERCISES

1. Show that there are in a pencil of conics two conics which are either parabolas, parallel lines, or coincident lines.

2. Consider the locus of the centers of the conics of a pencil as a special case of the eleven-point conic (Sec. 5–10, Ex. 19).

3. Given four independent points. Find the condition that two real parabolas can pass through them.

4. Construct a pair of conjugate diameters of (a) a conic defined by five points, (b) the hyperbola given by two asymptotes and a point.

5. A line parallel to an asymptote is said to have an *asymptotic direction*. Construct a hyperbola if three points and two asymptotic directions are given.

6. A conic is given by five points. Construct a circumscribed parallelogram. Is it always possible?

7. Show that all circumscribed parallelograms to an ellipse have equal area.

8. The centers of all parallel chords of a parabola, not in the direction of a diameter, lie on a diameter.

9. Can we speak of conjugate diameters in the case of a singular point conic or class conic?

10. Show why any two ellipses, or two hyperbolas, or two parabolas (all supposed real) can be transformed into each other by a (real) affine transformation.

11. Show that the equation of a hyperbola, when the asymptotes are taken as x- and y-axes, can be written in the form $xy = 1$.

12. A tangent at a point P of a hyperbola intersects the asymptotes in A and B. Show that $PA = PB$. Cast this theorem into a projective form.

13. A line is drawn parallel to each side of a triangle. Show that the intersections of these liens with the sides lie on a conic.

6–4 Euclidean classification of conics.

The Euclidean point of view is obtained from the affine by the introduction of a distance between points and an angle between lines. A vector $\mathbf{v}$ has a length $v = \sqrt{\mathbf{v} \cdot \mathbf{v}}$; two unit vectors $\mathbf{v}$ and $\mathbf{w}$ determine an angle ϕ such that $\cos \phi = \mathbf{v} \cdot \mathbf{w}$. If a conic is nonsingular, then by the introduction of conjugate diameters we can again reduce its equation to the form (2–1), but further reduction by selection of the unit of measure in different directions is now impossible. In the case of the ellipse we usually express a_{11}, a_{22}, a_{33} in terms of the intercepts a, b of the curve with the x- and y-axes, so that the equation of the ellipse becomes

$$\frac{x^2}{a^2} + \frac{y^2}{b^2} = 1, \tag{4–1}$$

where the coordinate axes are any pair of conjugate diameters. It is now possible to make a choice between the various pairs of conjugate diameters, using the property that they form an involution.   In such an involution there is one and only one set of corresponding lines (always real), which is perpendicular except for the case that all pairs of the involution are perpendicular (Sec. 2–10).   These perpendicular conjugate diameters are called the (*principal*) *axes* of the ellipse; the largest axis is the *major axis*, the other the *minor axis*.   Equation (4–1) is the *uniquely determined normal form of the equation of the ellipse, if the coordinates are referred to a system of principal axes*, and $a \neq b$ (Fig. 6–5).   Then we also call $2a, 2b$ the *axes*.   In the case of the ellipse the involution of the conjugate diameters is elliptic, since the self-conjugate diameters are imaginary.   In the case that the involution of conjugate diameters contains only perpendicular pairs, $a_{11} = a_{22}$ [according to Eq. (1–8) of this chapter and Eq. (10–3) of Chapter 2]. The ellipse now becomes a *circle:*

$$\frac{x^2}{a^2} + \frac{y^2}{a^2} = 1, \quad \text{or} \quad x^2 + y^2 = a^2. \tag{4-2}$$

Reasoning similarly in the case of the hyperbola, we find for its unique normal form

$$\frac{x^2}{a^2} - \frac{y^2}{b^2} = 1, \tag{4-3}$$

where the coordinate axes are again the principal axes, but only a is a real intercept.   The x-axis is here called the *transverse* axis, the y-axis is sometimes called the *conjugate* axis.   We also call $2a$ and $2b$ the *axes*.   The hyperbola

$$\frac{x^2}{a^2} - \frac{y^2}{b^2} = -1$$

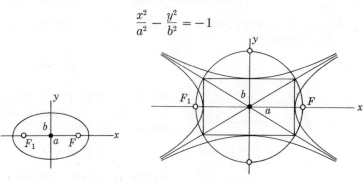

FIG. 6–5   FIG. 6–6

is called *conjugate* to the hyperbola (4–3) [Fig. 6–6]. Conjugate hyperbolas have the same asymptotes:

$$\frac{x^2}{a^2} - \frac{y^2}{b^2} = 0.$$

The case $a = b$ is called that of the *equilateral* or *rectangular* hyperbola; its asymptotes are perpendicular to each other.

For the parabola we obtain a normal form [from (D), Sec. 6–1],

$$y^2 = px, \quad p \text{ a constant}, \tag{4-4}$$

by selecting as x-axis a diameter, and as y-axis a tangent at the point O where this diameter intersects the parabola. Let M be the point where the parabola is tangent to the special line $x_3 = 0$. Then there is one point N harmonic to M on $x_3 = 0$ with respect to the isotropic points I and J (Sec. 4–8). We now select O such that the tangent to the parabola at O passes through N. Then ON is perpendicular to the diameter OM. The diameter through O is the *axis*, the point O the *vertex* (Fig. 6–7). Then Eq. (4–4) is the *uniquely determined normal form* of the parabola. The constant p is the *parameter*.

The corresponding normal equation for the real conics in line coordinates are:

$$\text{ellipse: } a^2u^2 + b^2v^2 = 1,$$
$$\text{hyperbola: } a^2u^2 - b^2v^2 = 1,$$
$$\text{parabola: } pv^2 = 4u.$$

Among the singular conics it is important to notice two intersecting lines through O,

$$\frac{x^2}{a^2} - \frac{y^2}{b^2} = 0;$$

and two distinct points at infinity, $a^2u^2 - b^2v^2 = 0$. The singular imaginary class conic

$$u^2 + v^2 = 0$$

represents the two isotropic points I and J.

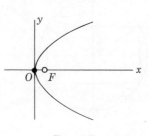

Fig. 6–7

The singular imaginary point conic

$$x^2 + y^2 = 0$$

represents the two isotropic lines through the origin.

We do not give here a systematic affine classification of conics by means of invariants. This, as well as the Euclidean classification, can be found in papers by C. C. Macduffee, L. J. Paradiso, P. Franklin, and R. S. Burington in *American Mathematical Monthly*, **33** (1926), pp. 243–252, 406–410; **34** (1927), pp. 453–467; and **39** (1932), pp. 527–532, where the classification is also carried out for n dimensions.

6–5 Reduction to the normal form. Let a conic

$$C \equiv f(x,y) \equiv a_{11}x^2 + 2a_{12}xy + a_{22}y^2 + 2a_{13} + 2a_{23}y + a_{33} = 0 \quad (5\text{–}1)$$

be given in the Euclidean plane, and referred to rectangular axes. We take the conic to be nonsingular and with a unique center (at finite distance), hence $D_3 \neq 0$, $D_2 \neq 0$. Then the center (x_0,y_0) is determined by the equations (1–3), hence:

$$D_2 x_0 = \begin{vmatrix} a_{12} & a_{13} \\ a_{22} & a_{23} \end{vmatrix}, \quad D_2 y_0 = \begin{vmatrix} a_{13} & a_{11} \\ a_{23} & a_{12} \end{vmatrix}. \quad (5\text{–}2)$$

We now bring the origin to the center by the translation $(x,y) \rightarrow (x',y')$:

$$x = x' + x_0, \quad y = y' + y_0. \quad (5\text{–}3)$$

Then Eq. (5–1), after the transformations (5–3) have been applied, assumes the form

$$a_{11}x'^2 + 2a_{12}x'y' + a_{22}y'^2 + f(x_0,y_0) = 0. \quad (5\text{–}4)$$

But because of Eqs. (5–2):

$$f(x_0,y_0) = (a_{11}x_0 + a_{12}y_0 + a_{13})x_0 + (a_{12}x_0 + a_{22}y_0 + a_{23})y_0$$
$$+ (a_{13}x_0 + a_{23}y_0 + a_{33}) = a_{13}x_0 + a_{23}y_0 + a_{33}$$

$$= \frac{a_{13}\begin{vmatrix} a_{12} & a_{13} \\ a_{22} & a_{23} \end{vmatrix} + a_{23}\begin{vmatrix} a_{13} & a_{11} \\ a_{23} & a_{12} \end{vmatrix} + a_{33}\begin{vmatrix} a_{11} & a_{12} \\ a_{12} & a_{22} \end{vmatrix}}{D_2} \quad (5\text{–}5)$$

$$= \frac{D_3}{D_2} \quad \text{(which is } \neq 0\text{)}.$$

Now we rotate the axes

$$\begin{aligned} x' &= x'' \cos \phi - y'' \sin \phi, \\ y' &= x'' \sin \phi + y'' \cos \phi, \end{aligned} \tag{5-6}$$

and select ϕ in such a way that the new a_{12}'' vanishes:

$$-a_{11} \cos \phi \sin \phi + a_{12}(\cos^2 \phi - \sin^2 \phi) + a_{22} \cos \phi \sin \phi = 0,$$

or

$$\tan 2\phi = \frac{2a_{12}}{a_{22} - a_{11}}. \tag{5-7}$$

This gives two values for ϕ between $0°$ and $180°$, differing by $90°$, hence corresponding to one new set of principal axes. When in Eq. (5–7) $a_{12} = 0$, $a_{11} = a_{22}$, all values of ϕ satisfy this equation. We obtain the *circle*.

With a value of ϕ satisfying Eq. (5–7), the normal form

$$a_{11}'(x'')^2 + a_{22}'(y'')^2 + f(x_0, y_0) = 0 \tag{5-8}$$

is obtained, where

$$\begin{aligned} a_{11}' &= a_{11} \cos^2 \phi + 2a_{12} \cos \phi \sin \phi + a_{22} \sin^2 \phi, \\ a_{22}' &= a_{11} \sin^2 \phi - 2a_{12} \cos \phi \sin \phi + a_{22} \cos^2 \phi. \end{aligned}$$

This shows that

$$D_1 = a_{11} + a_{22} = a_{11}' + a_{22}' = D_1', \tag{5-9}$$

hence *the sum $a_{11} + a_{22}$ is an invariant under rotations*, and even *under orthogonal transformations*.

Moreover, according to Eq. (1–5), D_2 is multiplied by a power of the determinant of the transformation, which in this case is [see Eq. (5–6)] $\cos^2 \phi + \sin^2 \phi = 1$. Hence $D_2' = D_2$, or ($a_{12}' = 0$),

$$a_{11}'a_{22}' = a_{11}a_{22} - a_{12}^2. \tag{5-10}$$

From Eqs. (5–9) and (5–10) follows that the coefficients a_{11}', a_{22}' of the normal form (5–8) are roots of the equation in S:

$$S^2 - D_1 S + D_2 = 0,$$

or

$$\begin{vmatrix} a_{11} - S & a_{12} \\ a_{12} & a_{22} - S \end{vmatrix} = 0, \tag{5-11}$$

the *characteristic equation* or *S-equation* of the conic (5–1). *Its roots are real*, since

$$(a_{11} + a_{22})^2 - 4(a_{11}a_{22} - a_{12}^2) = (a_{11} - a_{22})^2 + 4a_{12}^2 \geq 0. \quad (5\text{–}12)$$

When $a_{11} = a_{22}$, $a_{12} = 0$ the roots are equal; this is the case of a circle. From Eq. (5–10) follows again that for an ellipse (or imaginary conic) $D_2 > 0$, for a hyperbola $D_2 < 0$.

Let now the conic be a parabola, hence $D_3 \neq 0$, $D_2 = 0$. Transformation (5–3) is now not possible. We first perform the rotation expressed by Eq. (5–7), removing the term in xy. But since $D_2 = 0$, $a_{11}'a_{22}' = 0$, so that not only the coefficient of xy, but also that of either x^2 or y^2 vanishes. We choose $a_{11}' = 0$, and obtain for the equation of the conic, writing x,y and a_{22} for x'',y'' and a',

$$a_{22}y^2 + 2a_{13}x + 2a_{23}y + a_{33} = 0 \quad (a_{22} \neq 0), \quad (5\text{–}13)$$

which can be cast into the form

$$a_{22}(y - y_1)^2 = -2a_{13}(x - x_1). \quad (5\text{–}14)$$

Here $a_{13} \neq 0$, because $a_{13} = 0$ would turn Eq. (5–13) into a singular conic. Indeed, in this case $D_3 = a_{13}a_{22}a_{33} \neq 0$. From Eq. (5–14) we pass by a translation of axes to the form

$$y^2 = px,$$

which shows that the point (x_0,y_0) is the vertex of the parabola.

We can tabulate our results for nonsingular conics in the following table:

$$D_3 \neq 0, D_2 \neq 0 \quad \begin{cases} D_2 < 0\text{: hyperbola} \\ D_2 > 0\text{: } \begin{array}{l} a_{11}D_3 \text{ or } a_{22}D_3 < 0\text{: ellipse} \\ a_{11}D_3 \text{ or } a_{22}D_3 > 0\text{: imaginary conic} \end{array} \end{cases}$$

$D_3 \neq 0, D_2 = 0$: parabola

This can be complemented by the following table for singular conics:

$$D_3 = 0, D_2 \neq 0 \quad \begin{cases} D_2 < 0\text{: real pair of lines} \\ D_2 > 0\text{: imaginary pair} \end{cases}$$

$$D_3 = 0, D_2 = 0 \quad \begin{cases} \alpha_{11} \text{ or } \alpha_{22} < 0\text{: real pair of parallel lines} \\ \alpha_{11} \text{ or } \alpha_{22} > 0\text{: imaginary pair of parallel lines} \\ \alpha_{11} \text{ or } \alpha_{22} = 0\text{: doubly counted single line} \end{cases}$$

Here α_{11} is the cofactor of a_{11}, α_{22} that of a_{22} in D_3; in the same notation $D_2 = \alpha_{33}$.

As an example, we take a curve of which the equation can be written $\sqrt{x} + \sqrt{y} = \sqrt{a}$. If we take the square root with both signs, then this equation is equivalent to

$$x^2 - 2xy + y^2 - 2ax - 2ay + a^2 = 0.$$

Here $D_3 = -4a^2$, $D_2 = 0$, hence the conic is a parabola. We find

$$\tan 2\phi = \infty, \quad \phi = 45°, 135°,$$

and taking $\phi = 45°$,

$$x = \tfrac{1}{2}\sqrt{2}\,(x' - y'), \quad y = \tfrac{1}{2}\sqrt{2}\,(x' + y'),$$

hence

$$y'^2 - 2ax\sqrt{2} + a^2 = 0, \quad \text{or} \quad y'^2 = 2a\sqrt{2}\,(x' - \tfrac{1}{2}a\sqrt{2}).$$

When we take $x'' = x' - \tfrac{1}{2}a\sqrt{2}$, and drop the primes, we obtain the normal form $y^2 = 2ax\sqrt{2}$. The parabola has its vertex at distance $\tfrac{1}{2}a\sqrt{2}$ from O, hence the point $(\tfrac{1}{2}a, \tfrac{1}{2}a)$ is the vertex. The curve is tangent to OX and OY at points A and B at distance a from O. When in $\sqrt{x} + \sqrt{y} = \sqrt{a}$ only positive roots are considered, then this equation represents only the arc between A and B.

We find the first classification of conics by means of the general equation of the second degree in S. F. Lacroix, *Traité Élémentaire de Trigonométrie Rectiligne et Sphérique et d'Application de l'Algèbre à la Géométrie*, 1st ed. (Paris, 1789–99), followed by F. L. Lefrançais, *Essai sur la Ligne Droite et les Courbes du Second Degrée* (Paris, 1801). Silvestre François Lacroix (1765–1843), to whom we owe, to a considerable extent, our present methods of teaching elementary calculus and analytic geometry (even the term "analytic geometry" in our modern sense seems due to him), was for sixty years professor at the school for navigation in Rochefort, France. His textbooks also received wide circulation in England.

The first textbook on conics was written by Apollonius of Perga (late third century B.C.). Of the eight books, the four first have reached us in the original Greek, and Books V–VII in an Arabic translation. The eighth book is lost. See T. Heath, *Apollonius of Perga* (Cambridge, 1896). An English translation of the first three books has been published by St. John's College (Annapolis, 1939). A French translation has been published by P. Ver Eecke (Bruges, 1923).

EXERCISES

1. Bring to the normal form and find the vertices:

    (a) $xy + x + y + 6 = 0$,

    (b) $40x^2 + 36xy + 25y^2 + 8x - 64y - 101 = 0$,

    (c) $9x^2 + 24xy + 16y^2 - 10x + 70y - 75 = 0$.

2. A right angle turns about its vertex $P(a,a)$. One of the sides intersects the x-axis in a variable point A and the other side the line $y = 2x$ in a variable point B. Find the locus of the center of AB and sketch its construction.

3. Show that the coordinate axes are conjugate with respect to the conic (5–1), if $a_{12}a_{33} - a_{13}a_{23} = 0$.

4. *Construction of ellipse from given principal axes.* Every ellipse can be considered as the rectangular projection of a circle with diameter equal to the major axis of the ellipse. With the aid of this property, (1) explain the construction of an ellipse with axes $2a$ and $2b$ ($a > b$) by means of two concentric circles of radius a and b (Fig. 6–8); (2) prove that two conjugate diameters of the ellipse are the projection of two perpendicular diameters of the circle; (3) construct the tangent from a point to an ellipse, if its major and minor axes are given in position and in length; (4) construct in this case the points of intersection of a given line with the ellipse; (5) prove the theorem of Archimedes that the area of an ellipse is πab.

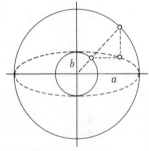

5. Prove that the area of an ellipse is

$$\pi \frac{D_3}{(D_2)^{3/2}}.$$

Fig. 6–8

6. For a conic (5–1) to be a circle, two conditions are necessary, namely, $a_{11} = a_{22}$, $a_{12} = 0$. How can this be reconciled with the fact that for a conic to be a circle it is sufficient that the two principal axes are equal, which is only one condition, namely $a = b$?

7. From a point P the tangents PA and PB are drawn to a parabola. Let PS be the diameter through P, and C and D the points in which the tangent at S intersects PA and PB. Prove (a) that this tangent is parallel to AB, and (b) that the area of $\triangle ASB$ is twice that of area $\triangle PCD$.

8. Prove that the *area of a parabolic segment* is two-thirds the area of the triangle formed by its chord and the tangents at its chord and the tangents at its extremities (Archimedes).

9. Show that the asymptotes through O of the conic (5-1) with finite center $(x_0 y_0)$ are given by the equation

$$a_{11}(x - x_0)^2 + 2a_{12}(x - x_0)(y - y_0) + a_{22}(y - y_0)^2 = 0.$$

10. Let $a_{33} = 0$. Show that the tangent to the conic (5-1) at the origin is given by the linear terms $= 0$, or $a_{13}x + a_{23}y = 0$.

11. If a class conic is given by $b_{11}u^2 + 2b_{12}uv + \cdots + b_{33} = 0$, explain the geometrical meaning of (a) $b_{11}u^2 + 2b_{12}uv + b_{22}v^2 = 0$, and (b) $b_{33} = 0$. $b_{13}u + b_{23}v = 0$.

12. *Circle of Monge* (or *director circle*). The locus of the points under which an ellipse or hyperbola can be seen at right angles (that is, through which two perpendicular tangents can be drawn) is a circle. Prove. In the case of a parabola it is a line, the *directrix*.

13. *The normal forms of Apollonius*. Show that the equations of the non-singular conics can be written in the form

$$y^2 = (b^2/a^2)x(2a + \epsilon x) = px + \epsilon(p/2a)x^2,$$

where $\epsilon = -1$ for an ellipse, $\epsilon = +1$ for a hyperbola, and $\epsilon = 0$ for a parabola. We call p the *parameter* (comp. Sec. 6-4). This is the form from which the names ellipse → deficit, hyperbola → excess, and parabola → application are derived. Apollonius derived these properties in the form of theorems on the so-called "application" of areas of rectangles, a geometrical device to solve quadratic equations.

14. A circle with a three-point contact with an ellipse at a point P is its *circle of curvature* at P. This circle intersects the ellipse in one more point Q. Prove that PQ and the tangent at P make equal angles with a principal axis.

15. *A problem of Pappus and Descartes*. Find the locus of the points whose distances d_1, d_2, d_3, d_4 at an arbitrary given angle to two pairs of given lines satisfy the condition $d_1 d_2 = d_3 d_4$. This problem of Pappus was used by Descartes in his *Géométrie* (1637) to test his method of the application of algebra to geometry, which eventually led to analytic geometry.

16. Show that equilateral hyperbolas are characterized by $D_1 = 0$.

17. Given a pencil of point conics $C_1 - \lambda C_2 = 0$, where C_1 and C_2 are defined as in Eq. (1-1), the axes now being rectangular. Show (a) that there is, in general, no circle in this pencil, but when there are two circles, all conics are circles, (b) that there is either one equilateral hyperbola in this pencil or all conics are equilateral hyperbolas.

18. Using Ex. 17, show (a) that the altitudes of a triangle pass through one point H, (b) that all equilateral hyperbolas passing through the vertices of the triangle pass through H.

19. All conics passing through three given independent points form a net (Ex. 18, Sec. 5–10).   (a) Show that the equilateral hyperbolas in a net form a pencil.   (b) Find the equation of this pencil when the three given points are (0,0), (0,1), (1,0).

6–6 The circle.   The circle is characterized by an equation of the form (5–1) in which $a_{11} = a_{22}$, $a_{12} = 0$.   Such an equation can therefore be reduced to the form

$$x^2 + y^2 + 2ax + 2by + c = 0. \qquad (6\text{–}1)$$

All perpendicular diameters can be taken as principal axes, as well as conjugate diameters.   *The circle is* therefore *the conic for which the involution of the conjugate diameters is the involution of perpendicular lines* (Sec. 6–4).   The property can be used to characterize the circle in the real domain.   When we introduce imaginaries, we can express it by stating that *the circle is the nonsingular conic passing through the isotropic points.*   This is also evident from the equation

$$(x_1^2 + x_2^2) + x_3(2ax_1 + 2bx_2 + cx_3) = 0, \qquad (6\text{–}2)$$

which is Eq. (6–1) written in projective coordinates, and which shows that the circle passes through the points where the ideal line $x_3 = 0$ intersects the singular conic $x_1^2 + x_2^2 = 0$.

This property was first announced by Poncelet (*Traité*, Nos. 94,95), who showed that two circles have always four points in common.   Michel Chasles, F. Klein, and S. Lie have shown the great importance of this theorem for the study of curves in the real domain.   But a friendly warning may be occasionally in order: "Every student of plane geometry is thrilled to learn that a circle passes through two imaginary points at infinity.   It is an indecent and disloyal thrill of which he should be ashamed.   The geometry of the plane with points having complex coordinates is not the geometry of two dimensions but of four, and it is only the bullying algebraist who holds the contrary" [J. L. Synge, *Mathematical Gazette* **33** (1949), p. 263].   We may add that these isotropic points only appear when circle geometry is considered in the framework of complex projective geometry, and may not appear when we study circles in other coordinates, such as the so-called tetracyclic coordinates (see F. S. Woods, *Higher Geometry*, Ch. IX, especially p. 143).

Equation (6-1) can be written $(x_0 = -a, y_0 = -b)$:

$$(x - x_0)^2 + (y - y_0)^2 - r^2 = 0, \qquad (6\text{-}3)$$
$$r^2 = a^2 + b^2 - c,$$

which introduces the center (x_0, y_0) and the radius r, and expresses Euclid's definition of a circle as the locus of the points at equal distances from a point. However, r^2 is only positive if

$$a^2 + b^2 - c > 0, \quad \text{or} \quad a_{13}^2 + a_{23}^2 - a_{11}a_{33} > 0. \qquad (6\text{-}4)$$

When this condition is not fulfilled the circle is imaginary. When $c = a^2 + b^2$ the radius is zero, and the circle can by choice of center be represented by $x^2 + y^2 = 0$. This is a *null circle*, with only one real point, the center. In the imaginary domain it consists of two isotropic lines.

The left-hand side of Eq. (6-3) is the square of the length of the tangent $PT_1 = PT_2$ drawn from a point $P(x, y)$ to the circle. This square,

$$C(x, y) \equiv (x - x_0)^2 + (y - y_0)^2 - r^2, \qquad (6\text{-}5)$$

is the *power* of P with respect to the circle. When P is outside the circle $C > 0$; when P is inside it, then $C < 0$ (see Sec. 5-8; this property can be used to define the inside and outside of the circle algebraically). When $C < 0$ it cannot be defined as the square of a line PT_1. In this case, as well as in the case $C > 0$, it can be defined as the product of the segments PA and PB on a chord through P, with the appropriate sign.

Two circles $C_1 = 0$, $C_2 = 0$:

$$C_1 \equiv x^2 + y^2 + 2a_1x + 2b_1y + c_1, \qquad (6\text{-}6)$$
$$C_2 \equiv x^2 + y^2 + 2a_2x + 2b_2y + c_2,$$

define a *pencil* of *coaxial* circles $C_1 - \lambda C_2 = 0$, consisting of circles passing through the two real or imaginary points in common to $C_1 = 0$, $C_2 = 0$, the *basic points* (together with the isotropic points). There is one line in the pencil,

$$R = C_1 - C_2 = 0, \qquad (6\text{-}7)$$

the *radical axis* of the two circles, which is the locus of the points of equal power with respect to the circles. When the circles intersect,

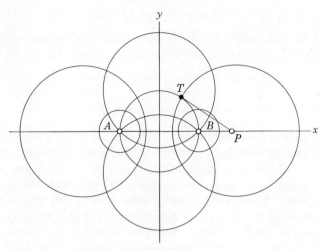

FIG. 6–9

this line passes through the points of intersection A,B; when they are
tangent it is the common tangent.   The radical axis is perpendicular
to the line joining the centers of the circles (Ex. 1, this section).
The circle with center P and radius PT (Fig. 6–9, PT tangent) intersects the circle through T,A,B orthogonally, that is, the angle of the
tangents to the circle at the points of intersection is a right-angle.

The equation of the pencil can be written

$$C - \lambda R = 0, \tag{6–8}$$

where $C = 0$ represents any circle of the pencil. When the line
$R = 0$ intersects the circles in two real points, the pencil is *hyperbolic*,
when it is tangent the pencil is *parabolic* (Fig. 6–10). When $R = 0$
lies outside the circles the pencil is *elliptic*.

In the projective theory the circle pencil with basic points A,B has
three singular conics, the isotropic lines IA,JB and IB,JA, together with
the radical axis AB and the line at infinity IJ. The radical axis does not
appear here as a circle with infinite radius, as happens in the theory of
inversion (see Sec. 6–7).

To find the equation of a hyperbolic pencil, let us take $A(l,0)$ and
$B(-l,0)$ as the basic points.   Then the pencil is

$$x^2 + y^2 - l^2 - \lambda y = 0. \qquad (6\text{--}9)$$

The circle with center $P(\mu,0)$ on the radical axis intersecting a circle of the pencil orthogonally has the equation [comp. Eq. (6–5)]

$$(x - \mu)^2 + (y - 0)^2 = \mu^2 + 0 - l^2 - \lambda 0$$

or

$$x^2 + y^2 + l^2 - 2\mu x = 0, \qquad (6\text{--}10)$$

in which the λ has disappeared. Hence a circle with center on the radical axis intersecting one circle of the pencil (6–9) orthogonally intersects all circles orthogonally. Equation (6–10) represents an elliptic pencil with basic points $(0,il)$, $(0,-il)$, with the y-axis as radical axis. There are two null circles A,B in this elliptic pencil, with centers on the x-axis at distance l from O (Fig. 6–9). We obtain them for $\mu = l$ in Eq. (6–10). Every circle with center on the radical axis of this pencil (6–10) intersecting one circle of this pencil orthogonally, intersects them all. They form the hyperbolic pencil (6–9). Hence we have found the theorem (Fig. 6–9):

All circles of a hyperbolic pencil are orthogonal to all circles of a corresponding elliptic pencil and conversely, and the radical axes of the two pencils are orthogonal.

When $l = 0$ we obtain two perpendicular parabolic pencils (Fig. 6–10).

We now see in its proper setting the construction of the points in involution on a line presented in Sec. 1–7. It shows that a line is *intersected by the circles of a pencil in points in involution.* In this form it is a special case of the theorem of Ex. 6, Sec. 5–10.

The geometry of the circle can further be studied by introducing circles intersecting at arbitrary angles, and taking three, four, etc., circles into account. We mention only one theorem dealing with such circles:

The three radical axes of three circles taken in pairs are concurrent or parallel.

Indeed, if the circles are $C_1 = 0$, $C_2 = 0$, $C_3 = 0$ [in the form (6–2)], then the three radical axes are $C_1 - C_2 = 0$, $C_2 - C_3 = 0$,

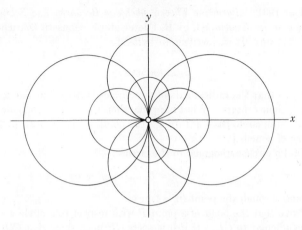

Fɪɢ. 6–10

$C_3 - C_1 = 0$, and the three left-hand members of these linear equations add up to zero.   The point of intersection (ordinary or ideal) of the three radical axes is called the *radical center* of the three circles. It is the center of a circle orthogonal to the three circles, real when this center lies outside the circle.   When the radical center is at infinity, this circle becomes a straight line.   The theorem can be readily proved by means of Euclid's theorems, but we must then distinguish various cases.

The theory of coaxial circles can be found, without algebra but with imaginaries, in Poncelet, *Traité* I (Section I, Chapter II).   The term *radical axis* is due to Gaultier, *Journal Ecole Polytechnique* cah. **16** (1812), pp. 124–214.   The present algebraic treatment is due to Plücker.   It was indeed the proof of the theorem on the radical center given in this section which led Plücker to his method of abbreviated notation.   In his own words: "In that period I once drew without any special purpose some circles on a scrap of paper.   Looking at the figure I conjectured that the three common chords of each pair of three given circles intersect in one point.   While verifying this theorem analytically I expected to meet eliminations, and did not find any.   I arrived at the proof of this theorem by the simplest combination of three symbols" (*Analytisch-geometrische Entwicklungen* II, p. 111).   Jacob Steiner also studied the theory of circles and spheres extensively, but his main work on this subject was only published in 1931: *Allgemeine Theorie über das Berühren und Schneiden der Kreise und der Kugeln*, ed. by R. Fueter and F. Gonseth (Zürich-Leipzig, 1931), 344 pp. It was written in 1825–26.

EXERCISES

1. Prove that the radical axis of two circles is perpendicular to the line connecting their centers. What happens when the centers coincide?

2. Find the circle passing through the points $(2,4)$, $(4,-2)$, $(3,3)$. [Use the theory of pencils.]

3. Find a circle orthogonal to the circles

$$x^2 + y^2 - 4x - 6y + 9 = 0, \quad x^2 + y^2 + 6x - 4y + 4 = 0$$

and passing through the point $(6,-4)$.

4. Prove that the polar of a point P with respect to a circle with center C is perpendicular to CP. If it intersects CP in Q, show that $CQ \cdot CP = r^2$ (r is radius of circle C).

5. Show that the locus of a point P, whose distances from two points A,B have a given ratio $\neq 1$, is a circle. This is the *circle of Apollonius* of $\triangle PAB$ with respect to side AB.

6. A triangle has three circles of Apollonius, one with respect to each side. Show that these three circles belong to a pencil. The common points of intersection are called *isodynamic points*.

7. A complete quadrangle is inscribed in a circle. Through the centers of the six sides perpendiculars are drawn to the opposite sides. Show that these six lines are concurrent.

8. The bisectors of the angles of opposite sides of a cyclic quadrangle (a quadrangle inscribed in a circle) are perpendicular.

9. Two circles, one outside the other, have two external and two internal common tangents. The external tangents intersect in a point S_1, the internal ones in a point S_2. Points S_1 and S_2 are the *centers of similitude* of the circles. Show that S_1 and S_2 are harmonic with respect to the centers of the circles.

10. Find the centers of similitude of the circles

$$x^2 + y^2 - 4x - 2y + 4 = 0, \quad x^2 + y^2 + 4x + 2y - 4 = 0.$$

11. Find the circle through the points of intersection of the circles $x^2 + y^2 - 6x - 10y - 15 = 0$, $x^2 + y^2 + 2x + 4y - 17 = 0$ with its center on $5x - 3y + 1 = 0$.

12. Show that the circle circumscribed to the $\triangle A_1 A_2 A_3$ formed by the lines $N_1 = 0$, $N_2 = 0$, $N_3 = 0$ has the equation

$$N_2 N_3 \sin A_1 + N_3 N_1 \sin A_2 + N_1 N_2 \sin A_3 = 0.$$

Here A_i is the angle of the triangle at vertex A_i, N_i represents the normal form $x \cos \alpha_i + y \sin \alpha_i - p_i$. (Comp. Eq. 22, Sec. 3–7.)

13. *Nine-point circle.* The mid-points of the sides, the feet of the altitudes, and the mid-points of the lines joining the orthocenter to the vertices of a triangle lie on a circle. Show this by using the theorem on the eleven-point conic (Ex. 19, Sec. 5–10). This circle is also called the *circle of Feuerbach.* It was found by C. J. Brianchon and J. V. Poncelet, *Ann. de Mathém.* 11 (1820–1821), pp. 205–220, and by K. W. Feuerbach, *Eigenschaften einiger merkwürdigen Punkte* (Nürnberg, 1822; new ed. Haarlem-Berlin, 1908).

14. *Line of Simson.* From a point P on the circumscribed circle of triangle $A_1A_2A_3$ the perpendiculars PP_1, PP_2, PP_3 are drawn to the sides; P_1 is on A_2A_3, P_2 on A_3A_1, P_3 on A_1A_2. Show that P_1, P_2, P_3 lie on a line, the line of Simson. (See Ex. 22, Sec. 3–7.)

15. Find the locus of the poles of the line $x = p$ with respect to the pencil $x^2 + y^2 - 2\lambda x + a^2 = 0$. How does the answer check with Ex. 17, Sec. 5–10?

16. *Theorem of Bodenmiller.* The circles whose diameters are the diagonals of a complete quadrilateral belong to a pencil. (See Ex. 10, Sec. 2–9; also Möbius, *Werke II*, p. 237.) Prove by considering the pencil of class conics tangent to the lines of the quadrilateral and applying the Dual Theorem in Ex. 6, Sec. 5–10.

17. Show that the locus of the points for which the polars with respect to three given circles pass through one point Q is a circle orthogonal to the given circles and passing through P and Q (Steiner, loc. cit., Sec. 6–6, p. 55).

PROBLEMS ON INVERSION

1. Given a circle C with center O and radius a. Associate with a point $P(x,y)$ a point $P'(x',y')$ on OP such that $OP \cdot OP' = a^2$ (P,P' on same side of O). The transformation $P \leftrightarrow P'$ is involutory, that is, when P leads to P', the P' leads back to P. Show that if $\overrightarrow{OP} = \mathbf{r}$, $\overrightarrow{OP'} = \mathbf{r}'$:

$$\mathbf{r}' = \frac{a^2\mathbf{r}}{\mathbf{r} \cdot \mathbf{r}}, \quad \mathbf{r} = \frac{a^2\mathbf{r}'}{\mathbf{r}' \cdot \mathbf{r}'}.$$

The transformation is called *inversion*, O is the *pole*, C the *circle* of inversion.

2. Inversion is not a linear transformation. Show that straight lines pass into circles through O, and circles into circles, with the exception of circles through O which pass into straight lines.

3. There exist transformations $\rho x_i' = f_i(x_1, x_2, x_3)$ between projective coordinates in which the f_i are homogeneous polynomials of the same degree n, and of which the converse is of the form $\sigma x_i = \phi_i(x_1', x_2', x_3')$, where the ϕ_i are again homogeneous polynomials of degree n. Such transformations are

called *birational* or *Cremona transformations*. When $n = 1$ we obtain the collineations. Show that inversion is a quadratic Cremona transformation.

4. Show that inversion is *conformal*, that is, preserves the angle at which two curves intersect.

5. When P,P' and Q,Q' correspond under an inversion, then show that the distances $PQ, P'Q'$ satisfy the relations

$$P'Q' = a^2 \frac{PQ}{OP \cdot OQ}, \quad PQ = a^2 \frac{P'Q'}{OP' \cdot OQ'}.$$

6. *Theorem of Ptolemy.* Sides and diagonals of a cyclic triangle $ABCD$ satisfy the relation

$$AB \cdot CD + AD \cdot BC = AC \cdot BD.$$

The sides are all taken positive. Prove this theorem. See Ptolemy's astronomical classic, the *Almagest*, Book I, Chapter 10. When AB is a diameter, the theorem is essentially equivalent to the addition theorem of trigonometrical functions, hence Ptolemy's interest.

7. Prove that the relation $AD \cdot BC + BD \cdot CA + CD \cdot AB = 0$ (established for four points on a directed line in Sec. 1–1) applied, with appropriate signs, to four points in the plane means that the four points $ABCD$ lie on a circle. This is the *converse of Ptolemy's theorem*.

8. Construct a circle through two given points P,Q intersecting a given circle at a given angle. [*Hint:* Invert the figure with either P or Q as poles.]

9. Show that by introducing the concept of the *point at infinity* P of the plane, which is the point corresponding in inversion to the pole, we can state that without exception under inversion (a) points pass into points, (b) circles pass into circles. Here a straight line appears as a circle through P.

10. *Inversor of Peaucellier.* This is a linkage consisting of six rods, two of which, OA and OB, are of length a; the other four, all of length b, form a rhombus $ACBD$. The point O is fixed; there are hinges at all other points. Show that when C moves on a circle, D moves on a line (Peaucellier, 1864).

Where the projective theory leads to the concept of the *line at infinity*, the theory of inversions thus leads to the concept of the *point at infinity* of the plane. This suggests the relation of inversion to transformations in complex function theory since here only a point at infinity of the plane is recognized ($w = 1/z, z \to 0$).

The equations of Ex. 1 already appear in Pappus. In modern times, especially, Steiner and Plücker showed the usefulness of inversion. A systematic study was undertaken by Möbius, *Theorie der Kreisverwant-schaften*, Ges. Werke II (1855), pp. 205, 219, 243. See further J. L. Coolidge, *A Theory of the Circle and the Sphere* (Oxford, 1916); H. Schmidt,

Die Inversion und ihre Anwendungen (Munchen, 1950), 93 pp. Books on so-called "college geometry" also discuss inversion, e.g., D. R. Davis, *Modern College Geometry* (Cambridge, 1949), Chapter 9.

6–7 Foci. An ancient definition of the ellipse characterizes it as the locus of the points P for which the sum of the distances to two points F, F_1 is constant. Taking rectangular axes in such a way that F and F_1 have the coordinates $(c,0)$ and $(-c,0)$, and that

$$PF + PF_1 = 2a \quad (a > c), \tag{7-1}$$

then we find for the locus of P the equation of the ellipse in normal form:

$$\frac{x^2}{a^2} + \frac{y^2}{b^2} = 1,$$

where $b^2 = a^2 - c^2$. We call F, F_1 the *foci*, a name which goes back to Kepler (Fig. 6–5).

We find the hyperbola as the locus of the points P for which

$$PF - PF_1 = \pm 2a \quad (a < c). \tag{7-2}$$

Here we obtain (Fig. 6–6)

$$\frac{x^2}{a^2} - \frac{y^2}{b^2} = 1, \quad b^2 = c^2 - a^2.$$

From this follows that the system of ∞^1 conics

$$\frac{x^2}{a^2 - \lambda} + \frac{y^2}{b^2 - \lambda} = 1 \quad (a > b) \tag{7-3}$$

consists of ellipses for $\lambda < b^2$, and of hyperbolas for $b^2 < \lambda < a^2$, all with the same foci $F, F_1(\pm c, 0)$, $c^2 = a^2 - b^2$. They are called *confocal conics* (Fig. 6–11). They depend on a parameter λ which enters quadratically into the equation, and therefore do not form a pencil of point conics. However, if we write Eq. (7–3) in line coordinates, then we obtain

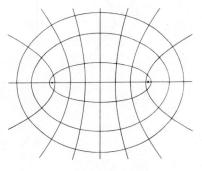

Fig. 6–11

$$u^2(a^2 - \lambda) + v^2(b^2 - \lambda) = 1,$$

or

$$(a^2u^2 + b^2v^2 - 1) - \lambda(u^2 + v^2) = 0,$$

which is the equation of a pencil of class conics. The four common tangents to these conics are imaginary and consist of the tangents to the ellipse $a^2u^2 + b^2v^2 = 1$ which pass through the isotropic points $u - iv = 0$, $u + iv = 0$. These tangents are therefore isotropic lines:

A system of confocal conics (7–3) can be considered as a pencil of class conics tangent to the four isotropic tangents of a given ellipse or hyperbola.

The equations of the four isotropic tangents are ($\lambda = b^2$, $\lambda = a^2$):

$$u^2 = (a^2 - b^2)^{-1} = c^{-2}, \quad v^2 = -c^{-2},$$

and their points of intersection are therefore $(\pm c, 0)$, $(0, \pm ic)$. This means that there are two real points of intersection on the x-axis (the foci) and two imaginary ones on the y-axis. We also call these points the *foci* (F_2 and F_3 in the schematic Fig. 6–12), and thus obtain the following theorems:

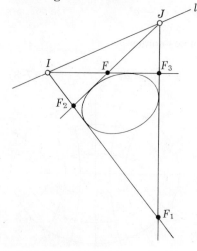

FIG. 6–12

The conics of a confocal system are tangent to the four isotropic tangents through the foci. An ellipse and a hyperbola have four foci, two real ones on one of the principal axes, two imaginary ones on the other axis.

Since the tangents through a real point are the double lines of the involution of conjugate lines (Sec. 5–5) through this point, and the tangents through a focus are isotropic, we find that *the involution of conjugated lines through a real focus consists of perpendicular lines.* This theorem can also be taken as the definition of a real focus.

A line l intersects the conics of a point pencil in the points of an involution. This theorem can be derived from the corresponding theorem concerning coaxial circles (Sec. 6–6) by a projectivity in the complex plane which transforms two arbitrary points and the isotropic points into four arbitrary points; under such a projectivity involutions are invariant. (See also Ex. 6, Sec. 5–10.) The double points of this involution are the points where the line l is tangent to the conics of the pencil. These points are therefore harmonic conjugates of the points in which the singular conics of the pencil intersect the lines (these points form a six-involution of Desargues; see Sec. 1–7). Applying the dual theorem to the class pencil formed by confocal conics, which has the isotropic points as one of its singular conics, we obtain the theorem:

> *When two conics of a confocal system intersect, they intersect at right angles.*

Other simple proofs of this theorem can be given by elementary analytic geometry (comp. Sec. 10–8) or by means of the mapping of the complex function $w = \sin z$. See, e.g., Struik, *Classical Differential Geometry* (Cambridge, 1950), p. 104.

By the same token, *the lines connecting a point of intersection P of two such conics with two real foci are harmonic with respect to the tangents to the conic at P.* The theorem also holds for the two imaginary foci, since harmonic relationships of points and lines can be carried over into the complex domain. *The tangent at P therefore bisects $\angle FPF_1$ or its supplementary* angle.

A special case of our class pencil occurs when it contains the line at infinity, l_∞, as common tangent line, necessarily counted twice (Fig. 6–13). The pencil consists of parabolas, all tangent at one point A of l_∞. There is only one focus F at finite distance. If we

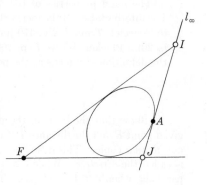

Fig. 6–13

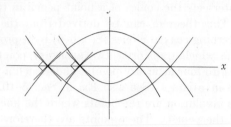

Fig. 6–14

take F $(u_3 = 0)$, A $(u_2 = 0)$, then the class pencil has the equation $u_2 u_3 - \lambda(u_1^2 + u_2^2) = 0$, or

$$v - \lambda(u^2 + v^2) = 0;$$

in point coordinates:

$$x^2 - 4\lambda y - 4\lambda^2 = 0. \tag{7-4}$$

This is the system of *confocal parabolas* (Fig. 6–14). They all have the origin as their focus. When a parabola intersects the x-axis in A and B, and the y-axis in C, then O is the focus and $OA = OB = 2OC$. This property of the focus of the parabola helps us in locating the positions of the focus on the axis, when the parabola is given. When $y^2 = px$, then the focus has the coordinates $(p,0)$ (Fig. 6–7). This also gives a geometrical meaning to the parameter p of a parabola.

The main properties of the foci are discussed in Apollonius' *Conics*. The interpretation of the foci as the intersection of isotropic tangents is due to Poncelet, *Traité* I, No. 470 [published in *Annales de Mathém.* **8** (1818), p. 20]. Plücker, *Werke I*, p. 290, generalized to curves of higher order the definition of a focus as the point of intersection of isotropic tangents.

EXERCISES

1. Show that the locus of the points P for which the distance PF to a given point F and the distance PH to a given line d are in constant ratio is a nonsingular conic. This ratio e is called the *eccentricity*, F is the focus, and d is called the *directrix*. When $e > 1$ the conic is a hyperbola, when $e = 1$ a parabola, when $e < 1$ an ellipse. This property, found in Pappus, gives a unique definition of all nonsingular conics.

2. Show that for an ellipse and a hyperbola $e = c/a$ when $2a$ is the major axis of the ellipse and the real axis of the hyperbola, and $2c$ is the focal distance.

3. Ellipses and hyperbolas have two foci and to each focus corresponds a directrix; a parabola has one focus and one directrix. Prove that the directrix is the polar of the corresponding focus.

4. Show that in polar coordinates, taking a focus as origin, the conics have the equation $r = p/(1 + e \cos \theta)$, where e is the eccentricity and p a constant. This equation is useful in the theory of planetary motion, where we prove that a mass point under the influence of a central force inversely proportional to the square of the distance has as its orbit a conic with the center of force as its focus (Newton).

5. The tangent at a point P of a nonsingular conic meets the directrix corresponding to the focus F at A. Prove that FP is perpendicular to FA.

6. If we connect a point P on an ellipse with the foci F and F_1, then PF and PF_1 form equal angles with the tangent at P. What is the corresponding theorem for a hyperbola? In the case of a parabola the tangent at P makes equal angles with PF and a diameter. These theorems are basic for the construction of elliptic, hyperbolic, and parabolic mirrors. Prove these properties without the use of imaginaries.

7. Starting with the equation of a conic in rectangular Cartesian coordinates, show that a focus is the vertex of an involution of conjugate and perpendicular lines.

8. Show that confocal parabolas intersect at right angles (Fig. 6–14).

9. Show by geometrical considerations that the real focus and the imaginary focus each lie on a principal axis.

10. If two conjugate lines to a nonsingular conic C are drawn, one through I and one through J (the isotropic points), then their point of intersection P is the intersection of two perpendicular tangents. Show this and then prove that the locus of P is a circle in the case that C is an ellipse or a hyperbola, and the directrix in the case that C is a parabola. The circle is the *circle of Monge* or *director circle* of C (Ex. 12, Sec. 6–6).

11. When in Ex. 10 the isotropic points are replaced by arbitrary points A,B, the locus of P is a conic, the *director conic* C_1 of C with respect to A and B. When is C_1 singular? Prove that AB has the same pole with respect to C and to C_1.

12. On an axis of a nonsingular conic we establish a point involution $P \leftrightarrow P'$ such that conjugate lines through P and P' are perpendicular. Show that the foci are the double points of this involution (Steiner).

13. Show that the orthocenter of a triangle circumscribed to a parabola lies on the directrix (Steiner).

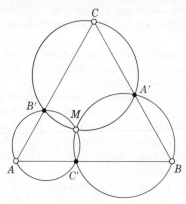

FIG. 6–15

14. The circumscribed circle of the triangle of Ex. 13 passes through the focus. Prove.

15. *Miquel point.* (a) When a point C' is taken on the side AB, B' on the side CA, and A' on the side BC of a $\triangle ABC$, then the circumscribed circles of triangles $AB'C'$, $BC'A'$, $CA'B'$ pass through one point, the Miquel point M (Fig. 6–15) [this can be proved by elementary geometry].   (b) Show that the circumscribed circles of the four triangles formed by the sides of a complete quadrilateral pass through one point, the Miquel point of the quadrilateral. (c) Show that the focus of a parabola is the Miquel point of all quadrilaterals circumscribed to the parabola.

16. Through a point P on a conic two perpendicular chords PA, PB are drawn. Show that the chord AB passes through a fixed point F on the normal at P. This point is the *Frégier point* (Gergonne's *Ann. de Mathém.* **6** (1816), pp. 229–234).

CHAPTER 7

PROJECTIVE METRIC

7-1 Metric with respect to a singular conic. It was Laguerre who, by a remark made in 1853, first showed the connection between the metrical concept of angle and the projective one of cross ratio. We reported on his result in Sec. 4–8. The angle ϕ between two lines l_1, l_2 through a point M is here defined by

$$\phi = \frac{i}{2} \ln (l_1, l_2; i_1, i_2) \quad (\text{mod. } \pi), \tag{1-1}$$

where i_1, i_2 are the isotropic lines through P, taken in a definite order.

A generalization of the notion of angle is implicit in this formulation; we have only to replace the isotropic lines by two lines m_1, m_2 connecting M with any two given real or imaginary points A, B. Then

$$\phi = k \ln (l_1, l_2; m_1, m_2) = \phi(l_1, l_2) = \angle (l_1, l_2) \tag{1-2}$$

satisfies the summation properties of an angle for any constant k:

$$\angle (l_1, l_2) = -\angle (l_2, l_1), \quad \angle (l_1, l_2) + \angle (l_2, l_3) + \angle (l_3, l_1) = 0. \tag{1-3}$$

This "angle" ϕ is, however, in general a complex number, determined except for multiples of $2\pi i k$, so that the equalities in Eq. (1–3) are also congruences mod $2\pi i k$.

To the form (1–2) for an angle belongs a dual formula, defining a distance. Given any two real or imaginary lines a, b and two points L_1, L_2 on a line m intersecting a in M_1 and b in M_2, then

$$d = K \ln (L_1 L_2, M_1 M_2) = d(L_1, L_2) \tag{1-4}$$

satisfies the summation properties of a distance for any given K:

$$d(L_1, L_2) = -d(L_2, L_1), \quad d(L_1, L_2) + d(L_2, L_3) + d(L_3, L_1) = 0.$$

We can call $d(L_1, L_2)$ the *distance* of points L_1 and L_2. This constant K can be arbitrarily chosen. This "distance," however, is in general a complex number and determined except for multiples of $2\pi i K$.

7–2 Angle with respect to a nonsingular conic. A further generalization, which maintains the dual aspect, is obtained by replacing the singular class conic consisting of A and B and the singular point conic consisting of a and b by a nonsingular conic. This was done by Cayley in 1859. If C is the conic, in point and line coordinates

$$a_{ij}x_ix_j = 0, \quad A_{ij}u_iu_j = 0, \tag{2-1}$$

then there are two tangents a_1, a_2 through every point M (we consider both real and imaginary points and lines) not on the conic, and every line m not tangent to the conic intersects C in two points A_1, A_2. Then, in accordance with Eqs. (1–2) and (1–3), the angle ϕ of two lines l_1, l_2 through P will be defined as

$$\phi = k \ln (l_1l_2, a_1a_2) = \phi(l_1, l_2), \tag{2-2}$$

and the distance d of two points L_1, L_2 on m as

$$d = K \ln (L_1L_2, A_1A_2) = d(L_1, L_2), \tag{2-3}$$

where k and K are constants of which we still can dispose. In order to find an analytical expression for ϕ, we remark that the pencil of lines formed by $l_1(u_i)$ and $l_2(v_i)$ and given by $u_i + \lambda v_i$ contains a_1 and a_2. The values of λ belonging to a_1 and a_2 are the roots of the equation

$$A_{ij}(u_i + \lambda v_i)(u_j + \lambda v_j) = 0,$$

or

$$P\lambda^2 + 2Q\lambda + R = 0, \quad P = A_{ij}v_iv_j, \quad Q = A_{ij}u_iv_j, \quad R = A_{ij}u_iu_j.$$

Then

$$(l_1l_2, a_1a_2) = (0, \; \infty \,; \lambda_1, \lambda_2) = \frac{\lambda_1}{\lambda_2} = \pm \frac{Q - \sqrt{Q^2 - PR}}{Q + \sqrt{Q^2 - PR}}.$$

We take the $+$ sign and one specific value of the square root, which may be real or imaginary, depending on the sign of $Q^2 - PR$. First, let $Q^2 - PR < 0$. This happens for real lines l_1, l_2 and a real conic when the (real) point M is inside the conic (see Exs. 3, 4, Sec. 5–8), and for all (real) points M when the conic is imaginary. Then taking $\sqrt{Q^2 - PR} = iS, S^2 = PR - Q^2, S = +\sqrt{PR - Q^2}$,

$$\phi = k \ln \frac{Q - iS}{Q + iS} = ki \text{ angle} \frac{Q - iS}{Q + iS} = -2ki\alpha,$$

where, since $Q^2 + S^2 = PR > 0$ (P,R have the same sign):

$$\sin \alpha = \frac{S}{\sqrt{PR}}, \quad \cos \alpha = \frac{Q}{\sqrt{PR}} \quad (\sqrt{} \text{ positive}). \quad (2\text{--}4)*$$

In Eq. (2–2), we take $k = i/2$, $\phi = \alpha$, and we have defined in

$$\phi = \frac{i}{2} \ln (l_1 l_2, a_1 a_2), \quad \cos \phi = \frac{Q}{\sqrt{PR}}, \quad \sin \phi = \frac{\sqrt{PR - Q^2}}{\sqrt{PR}} \quad (2\text{--}5)$$

a real angle between two real lines, determined except for multiples of π. The sign of ϕ in Eq. (2–5) depends on the choice of a_1, a_2, and this can be established by adopting such a sense on C that $\sin \phi$ in Eq. (2–5) has the desired sign.

When $Q^2 - PR > 0$, which happens for (real) points M outside the real conic C, then the angle ϕ is determined by

$$\frac{\phi}{k} = \ln \frac{Q - T}{Q + T}, \quad T = +\sqrt{Q^2 - PR}.$$

Now we can conveniently introduce hyperbolic functions:

$$\cosh \frac{\phi}{2k} = \frac{1}{2} \sqrt{\frac{Q - T}{Q + T}} + \frac{1}{2} \sqrt{\frac{Q + T}{Q - T}} = \frac{Q}{\sqrt{PR}},$$

$$\sinh \frac{\phi}{2k} = \frac{\sqrt{Q^2 - PR}}{\sqrt{PR}} \quad (\sqrt{} \text{ positive}). \quad (2\text{--}6)$$

The so-called hyperbolic functions are defined as follows:

$$\cosh x = \frac{e^x + e^{-x}}{2}, \quad \sinh x = \frac{e^x - e^{-x}}{2}.$$

These hyperbolic cosines and hyperbolic sines behave in many ways as ordinary cosines and sines, because $\cosh ix = \cos x$, $\sinh ix = i \sin ix$. However, they are not periodic in the real domain. [See G. B. Thomas, *Calculus and Analytic Geometry* (Cambridge, 1953), Ch. 9.]

Hence, changing k into $2k$, we find that

$$\phi = 2k \ln (l_1 l_2, t_1 t_2), \quad \cosh \frac{\phi}{k} = \frac{Q}{\sqrt{PR}}, \quad \sinh \frac{\phi}{k} = \frac{\sqrt{Q^2 - PR}}{\sqrt{PR}}$$

---

* Formula (2–4) can be verified by a figure in the complex plane.

is an angle uniquely defined in the real domain, since Eq. (2–6) only defines one real ϕ.

We obtain the Laguerre formula for an angle if we take for C the singular conic $u_1^2 + u_2^2 = 0$. Then $Q^2 - PR = -(u_1v_2 - u_2v_1)^2 < 0$, so that according to Eq. (2–5)

$$\cos \phi = \frac{u_1v_1 + u_2v_2}{\sqrt{u_1^2 + u_2^2}\,\sqrt{v_1^2 + v_2^2}},$$

in accordance with the expression for the angle in line coordinates in the Euclidean case (Sec. 3–3).

7–3 Distance with respect to a nonsingular conic.

In order to compute the distance of two points L_1, L_2 with respect to the conic (2–1), we proceed in the same way as in the case of the angle. We find that the points A_1, A_2 are given by the roots of the equation

$$p\lambda^2 + q\lambda + r = 0, \quad p = a_{ij}y_iy_j, \quad q = a_{ij}x_iy_j, \quad r = a_{ij}x_ix_j,$$

where λ determines the points of the point range $x_i + \lambda y_i$ on the line through $L_1(x_i)$ and $L_2(y_i)$. There are again two cases.

When $q^2 - pr < 0$, which happens for a real conic when the (real) line L_1L_2 does not intersect the conic, and for all real points L_1, L_2 when the conic is imaginary, then $[K = iM$ in Eq. (2–3)] the formulas

$$d = iM \ln (L_1,L_2; A_1,A_2), \quad \cos \frac{d}{M} = \frac{q}{\sqrt{pr}}, \quad \sin \frac{d}{M} = \frac{\sqrt{pr - q^2}}{\sqrt{pr}}$$
$$(\sqrt{}\ \text{positive}) \quad (3\text{–}1)$$

determine a distance $d(L_1,L_2)$ which is real and determined except for multiples of $2M\pi$.

When $q^2 - pr > 0$, which happens for (real) points L_1, L_2 inside a real conic and for all points such that L_1L_2 intersects the conic, then the formulas $[K = 2M$ in Eq. (2–3)]

$$d = 2M \ln (L_1,L_2; A_1,A_2), \quad \cosh \frac{d}{M} = \frac{q}{\sqrt{pr}}, \quad \sinh \frac{d}{M} = \frac{\sqrt{q^2 - pr}}{\sqrt{pr}} \quad (3\text{–}2)$$

determine a distance which is real and uniquely determined in the real domain. When L_1 approaches either A_1 or A_2, either p or r tends to zero and $d \to \infty$. In this system of measurement the points on the conic are at infinite distances from the points inside the conic. We call the conic the *absolute*.

The Euclidean distance is not obtained by taking a singular point conic as the absolute. In Euclidean geometry, as we have already remarked, distance and angle are not dual concepts.

These ideas on a projective metric were published by Cayley in his *Sixth Memoir upon Quantics*, Philosoph. Transactions 149 (1859), Coll. Papers, II, pp. 583–592. This was the sixth paper of a series on "quantics," that is, on homogeneous rational forms in several variables. Arthur Cayley (1821–1895), who started as a lawyer and became a professor at Cambridge, England, was one of the leading algebraists of England.

7–4 Non-Euclidean geometry. In 1871, Felix Klein discovered that Cayley's projective metric was of fundamental importance for the understanding of the so-called non-Euclidean geometry.

Non-Euclidean geometry, at that time, was chiefly known through the works of J. Bolyai and N. Lobačevskiǐ. Both authors had constructed, about 1830, a form of geometry which satisfies all axioms of Euclid's *Elements*, with the exception of the so-called parallel axiom. This axiom, in the slightly varied form into which Ptolemy had already cast it in Antiquity, states that in the plane one and only one line can be drawn through a point outside a line and parallel to it.   It leads to the theorem that the sum of the angles of a triangle is equal to two right angles.   In non-Euclidean geometry this axiom was replaced by the following one:

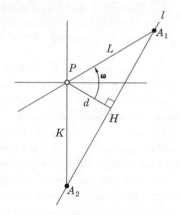

> *All lines passing through a point P in a plane can be divided in their behavior with respect to a line l in this plane, not passing through P, into two classes: lines which intersect l, and lines which do not intersect l.*

These two classes of lines (Fig. 7–1) are separated by two lines, the

Fig. 7–1

two *parallels* PK and PL through P to line l. In this geometry there is only one perpendicular PH to l, since this fact is independent of the parallel axiom. The $\angle HPL = \angle HPK$ is a function of the distance $PH = d$ and is called the *parallel angle* $\Pi = \Pi(d)$. When $\Pi(d) = \pi/2$ (radians can be defined independently of the parallel axiom) for one combination of point and line, this holds for all combinations of points and lines. These were the main features of the non-Euclidean geometry of Bolyai and Lobačevskiǐ. All triangles in this geometry have the sum of their angles $< \pi$.

For several decades this non-Euclidean geometry did not enjoy the full confidence of the mathematicians. It was felt that its logical consistency was not quite established, so that eventually contradictions might very well be discovered. A certain conservatism towards geometries which deviated in their principles from the familiar geometry underlying the mechanics of solid bodies added to the distrust.

The fundamental papers are N. L. Lobačevskiǐ (1793–1845), *Geometrical Researches on the Theory of Parallels* (1840, translated by G. B. Halsted, new ed. Chicago-London, Open Court, 1914); *New Principles of Geometry with Complete Theory of Parallels* (translated by H. P. Manning, in D. E. Smith *Source Book*, pp. 360–374), and J. Bolyai (1802–1860), *The Science Absolute of Space* (1832, translated by G. B. Halsted, new ed., Chicago-London, 1914). The name "non-Euclidean geometry" dates from Gauss, who anticipated the main results of Bolyai and Lobačevskiǐ.

There is reason to believe that Bolyai himself was never quite convinced of the logical consistency of his theory. In his posthumous papers there exists a renewed attempt at a proof of the Euclidean parallel axiom.

In 1868, however, E. Beltrami showed that every theorem of plane non-Euclidean geometry can be interpreted as a theorem holding for a class of surfaces (the so-called pseudospherical surfaces) in three-dimensional Euclidean space. A logical flaw in non-Euclidean geometry could now be interpreted as a logical flaw in classical Euclidean surface geometry. This proved the logical consistency of non-Euclidean geometry to the satisfaction of all mathematicians of that period, since they felt no logical scruples against ordinary Euclidean geometry. Beltrami's paper was written under the influence of Riemann's investigations into the general nature of our space concept (1854) [see Sec. 7–6]. Beltrami's and Riemann's work showed, moreover, that there are forms of non-Euclidean geometry different from those of Bolyai-Lobačevskiĭ.

7–5 Klein's interpretation of hyperbolic geometry.

Klein's paper constituted an alternate approach to the understanding of the logical consistency of non-Euclidean geometry. If, he said, we consider the definition of angle and distance according to Cayley, and consider only points inside a real conic C, then the angle, as defined by Eqs. (2–5), and the distance, uniquely defined by Eqs. (3–2), behave exactly as the angle and distance required by the non-Euclidean geometry of Bolyai-Lobačevskiĭ. We shall not follow the proof in all axiomatic details, but shall stress the fundamental elements. Points on the absolute C are at infinite distances from points inside the conic. If we therefore call lines intersecting on C *parallel* lines, then we can draw two lines PA_1, PA_2 through a point P outside a line l parallel to l (Fig. 7–2), if l intersects C in A_1 and A_2. The lines PA_1 and PA_2 separate the lines through P which intersect (inside C), and we only consider the part of the plane inside C. The non-Euclidean parallel axiom is thus realized.

Perpendicular lines $(u_i)(v_i)$ are lines for which in Eq. (2–4) $Q = 0$, or $A_{ij}u_iv_j = 0$. They are therefore conjugate lines; in other words: *when two lines are such that each passes through the pole of the other*, then they are perpendicular lines (l, l_1 in Fig. 7–2). Through a point outside of a line (not on C) one and only one perpendicular can be drawn to that line.

Let us see if the relation $\Pi = \Pi(d)$, mentioned in Sec. 7–4, holds in this geometry. We take the arbitrary line l as the side $x_3 = 0$ of a

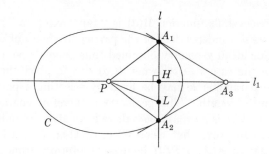

Fig. 7–2

basic triangle $A_1A_2A_3$ of which the sides A_3A_1 and A_3A_2 are tangents to the conic (Fig. 7–2). By choice of the unit point we can cast the equations of the conic into the form

$$x_1x_2 - x_3^2 = 0, \qquad -4u_1u_2 + u_3^2 = 0. \qquad (5\text{–}1)$$

Let $P(a_i)$ be a point inside the conic, hence $a_1a_2 - a_3^2 > 0$ [this because A_3 $(0{:}0{:}1)$ is outside the conic]. The line PA_3 is perpendicular to l and has the equation $x_2a_1 - x_1a_2 = 0$, or $u_1{:}u_2{:}u_3 = a_2{:}-a_1{:}0$. It intersects $x_3 = 0$ in H $(a_1{:}a_2{:}0)$. The line PA_2 is parallel to l and has the equation $x_3a_1 - x_1a_3 = 0$, or $v_1{:}v_2{:}v_3 = a_3{:}0{:}-a_1$. The angle Π between PA_2 and PA_3 is, according to Eq. (2–5) [with $P = a_1^2$, $Q = 2a_1a_3$, $R = 4a_1a_2$], given by

$$\cos \Pi = \frac{a_3}{\sqrt{a_1a_2}}.$$

The distance d of P and H is, according to Eq. (3–2) [with $p = a_1a_2$, $q = a_1a_2$, $r = a_1a_2 - a_3^2$, $q^2 - pr = a_3^2$ and $k = M$], given by

$$\tanh \frac{d}{k} = \frac{a_3}{\sqrt{a_1a_2}} \qquad (\tanh x = \sinh x / \cosh x),$$

hence

$$\tanh \frac{d}{k} = \cos \Pi$$

or, with the appropriate sign:

$$\tan \frac{\Pi}{2} = \exp (-d/k).$$

Hence Lobačevskiĭ's function $\Pi(d)$ is $2 \tan^{-1} \exp (-d/k)$. This result is, as we see, independent of the particular choice of coordinates. The non-Euclidean geometry obtained thus depends on a parameter k, which in the case $k \to \infty$, when $\Pi(d) \to \pi/2$, gives the Euclidean case. The parameter k may be fixed by selecting a particular distance as unit of length. This geometry is therefore characterized by the fact that *there is no similitude*: there is an absolute unit of length.

We next can prove that when we draw (Fig. 7–2) a line PL not perpendicular to A_1A_2, $\angle PLH$ increases uniformly from zero to $\pi/2$ when L moves from A_2 to H (see Ex. 3, Sec. 7–6). From this follows that the sum of the angles of $\triangle PLH$ is $< \pi$, and from this that the sum of the angles of any triangle $< \pi$ (Ex. 4, Sec. 7–6).

These examples will sufficiently illustrate how the geometry of the interior of a real conic satisfies the conditions of a non-Euclidean geometry of Bolyai-Lobačevskiĭ. This geometry is called *hyperbolic*.

7–6 Elliptic geometry. It now seems natural to explore also a geometry with a projective metric defined with respect to an imaginary conic. Such a conic can always be defined in the real domain by a polarity without (real) self-conjugate elements. In this case we shall again assume Eq. (2–5) for the angle, and Eq. (2–1) for the distance, and write k for M. Now no (real) parallel can be drawn through a (real) point to a (real) line not passing through it. *This geometry has no parallels;* every line intersects every other line. Two (real) points are always at finite distance from each other, but this distance is no longer uniquely determined.

A real point L_1 in this geometry has a real polar line l. If we connect a point L_2 of l with L_1, the number q in Eq. (3–1) is zero, hence $d/k = n(\pi/2)$, and $n = 1$, because otherwise there would be a point conjugate to L_1 between L_1 and L_2. Hence $d = k(\pi/2)$, and this holds for all points on l. Hence l is the locus of all points at equal distance $k(\pi/2)$ from L_1. If we continue on L_1L_2 beyond l, we come to a point L_3 at distance $k\pi$ from L_1 which is the pole of a line m through L_2. But this line can only be l, since if it were another line through L_2 this point L_2, being the intersection of l and m, would be the pole of L_1L_3, which is impossible in a geometry with an imaginary conic as the absolute. Hence L_3 coincides with L_1: *all lines are closed and have length* $k\pi$. This geometry is called *elliptic*. The sum of the angles of a self-polar triangle is $3\pi/2$.

This geometry shows remarkable similarity to the geometry of a sphere, if great circles are interpreted as "lines." Every "line" intersects every other "line"; there are triangles with three right angles; the locus of the points at distance $(\pi/2)r$ (r = radius of sphere) is a "line." There is an important difference: two great circles meet in two opposite points of the sphere; a great circle has two poles. The geometry of the sphere therefore cannot, in this interpretation, be derived completely from a projective geometry. If, however, following the ideas expressed in Sec. 3–9, we identify opposite points, and thus substitute for the geometry of the sphere that of a family of ∞^2 lines through a point, then we do obtain, by proper identification, an elliptic geometry. The geometry of the sphere is sometimes called a *doubly elliptic* or *spherical geometry*.

When B. Riemann's (1826–1866) address "On the hypotheses which lie at the bases of geometry" (1854) was posthumously published in 1867 (translated by W. K. Clifford, *Mathem. Papers*, pp. 55–71) and was followed by the paper of the physiologist H. Helmholtz "On the facts underlying geometry" (Gottinger Nachr., 1868), it became clear to mathematicians that space may be unbounded yet not infinite, and that consequently straight lines need not have ideal elements. The fundamental ideas here were elaborated by F. Klein, *Ges. Math. Abh.* I (1871–73), pp. 254–305, 310–343; see also his book *Vorlesungen über Nicht-eaklidische Geometrie* (1892–93, published Berlin, 1928). Klein later confessed (*Ges. Math. Abh.* I, p. 242) that Cayley and R. Ball always suspected that there was somewhere a circular reasoning in his work: first cross ratios were introduced metrically and then projective metric was based on them. This suspicion was removed after Klein, in accordance with von Staudt, introduced cross ratios independently of any previous metrical consideration; this led to an axiomatic construction of projective geometry independent of Euclidean geometry, see Sec. 3–9.

Textbooks on non-Euclidean geometry have been written by J. L. Coolidge (Oxford, 1909), and H. S. M. Coxeter (Toronto, 2nd ed., 1947); good German expositions by F. Klein (see above) and H. Liebmann (3rd ed., Berlin-Leipzig, 1923). See also H. DeVries, *Die vierte Dimension* (1925, German transl. from the Dutch by Ruth Struik, Leipzig, 1926). Most texts on projective geometry deal with projective metrics, see, e.g., Veblen-Young II, Ch. 8, or F. S. Woods, Ch. 7.

EXERCISES

The first eight problems deal with hyperbolic geometry (we always consider the angle as lying between 0 and 2π).

1. Show that the angle of two parallel lines is zero (or π).

2. Indicate a triangle of which the sum of the interior angles is zero.

3. Prove that $\angle PLH$ increases uniformly when L moves from A_2 to H in Fig. 7–2.

4. Show that the sum of the interior angles of a triangle is less than two right angles.

5. The locus of the points at equal distance from a point P inside the absolute C is a nonsingular conic. This curve can be called a *circle* (sometimes called *pseudocircle*).

6. Show that when, in Ex. 5, we take P on the conic, we obtain conics tangent to the conic C at P. These curves are called *horicycles*.

7. Show that the points equally distant from a line inside C lie on a conic, which can be considered as a pseudocircle with center outside of C and imaginary radius. These curves are called *hypercycles*.

8. Show that when line l is parallel to line l_1, line l_1 is parallel to line l.

9. Prove that the sum of the interior angles of a triangle in elliptic and doubly elliptic geometry is greater than two right angles.

10. Consider parabolic geometry as the geometry with respect to a real conic $u_1^2 + u_2^2 - \epsilon u_3^2 = 0$, with $\epsilon \to 0$. Show how in this case we can obtain the Euclidean formula for distance from the hyperbolic one.

11. Establish angle and distance for a geometry with an absolute consisting of two distinct points on the ideal line of the affine plane. This geometry has received attention in special relativity.

12. Establish some properties of the geometry outside of the conic inside which a hyperbolic geometry is established.

CHAPTER 8

POINTS, LINES, AND PLANES

8–1 Projective coordinates. In *real projective space* P_3 a point A is determined by the ratio of four real numbers x_λ, $\lambda = 1,2,3,4$, which are not all zero. We write A $(x_1:x_2:x_3:x_4)$ or $A(x_\lambda)$. The x_λ are the projective point coordinates of A. A linear relation between the x_λ:

$$(ux) \equiv u_\lambda x_\lambda \equiv u_1 x_1 + u_2 x_2 + u_3 x_3 + u_4 x_4 = 0 \qquad (1\text{–}1)$$

determines for fixed u_λ a *plane* π, provided the u_λ are not all zero. This plane has the *projective plane coordinates* u_λ, of which only the ratio is essential and which cannot all be zero. We write $(u_1:u_2:u_3:u_4)$ or (u_λ). For variable u_λ and fixed x_λ, Eq. (1–1) represents the equation of point $A(x_\lambda)$ in plane coordinates. For point $A(x_\lambda)$ and plane $\pi(u_\lambda)$, Eq. (1–1) is the expression of the *incidence* of point and plane.

A line in space can be conceived as the connection of two points $P(x_\lambda)$, $Q(y_\lambda)$, or as the intersection of two planes $\pi(u_\lambda)$, $\sigma(v_\lambda)$. The coordinates z_λ of a point on the line PQ can therefore be expressed by the equation

$$\rho z = x_\lambda + t y_\lambda \quad (t \text{ a variable parameter}), \qquad (1\text{–}2)$$

and the coordinates w_λ of a plane through the line of intersection $(\pi\sigma)$ of π and σ can be expressed by

$$\sigma w_\lambda = u_\lambda + t v_\lambda \quad (\text{comp. Sec. 8–3, Ex. 5}). \qquad (1\text{–}3)$$

Elimination of t from Eq. (1–2) gives us the point equations of a line as the points common to two planes:

$$(ax) = 0, \quad (bx) = 0 \quad (a_\lambda, b_\lambda \text{ constants, not proportional}). \qquad (1\text{–}4)$$

Elimination of t from Eq. (1–3) gives the plane equations of a line as the connection of two points:

$$(cu) = 0, \quad (du) = 0 \quad (c_\lambda, d_\lambda \text{ constants, not proportional}). \qquad (1\text{–}5)$$

Equations (1–4) and (1–5) therefore express a line by means of two equations between their point or their line coordinates.

The planes $x_\lambda = 0$ form the *basic tetrahedron* of the coordinate system. Its vertices A_λ are the points $u_\lambda = 0$ (Fig. 8–1). The six

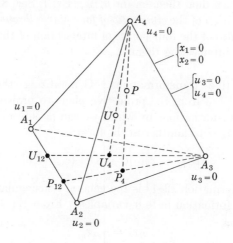

$$A_4$$
$$u_4 = 0$$
$$\begin{cases} x_1 = 0 \\ x_2 = 0 \end{cases}$$
$$\begin{cases} u_3 = 0 \\ u_4 = 0 \end{cases}$$
$$P$$
$$u_1 = 0$$
$$A_1$$
$$U$$
$$U_{12}$$
$$U_4$$
$$A_3$$
$$u_3 = 0$$
$$P_{12}$$
$$P_4$$
$$A_2$$
$$u_2 = 0$$

Fig. 8–1

edges of the tetrahedron are given by such equations as those for
$A_3A_4 : x_1 = 0$, $x_2 = 0$, or $u_3 = 0$, $u_4 = 0$. There exists a unit point
$U\ (1:1:1:1)$ and a unit plane $(1:1:1:1)$, not incident; and which are
called *harmonic* with respect to the tetrahedron. The five points
A, U are such that no four of them lie in a plane. Such points are
called (linearly) *independent*. The coordinate planes and the unit
plane are similarly called independent, since no four of them pass
through a point.

The coordinates x_λ and u_λ can be defined as cross ratios, in a way
which is analogous to that followed in the case of the plane. For instance, let us connect A_4 with U and with an arbitrary point $P(x_\lambda)$,
and call the intersections of A_4U and A_4P with plane $x_4 = 0$, U_4 and
P_4 respectively. Then the coordinates of U are $(1:1:1:1)$ and those
of P_4 are $(x_1 : x_2 : x_3 : 0)$. The interpretation of the coordinates x_1, x_2, x_3
can now proceed in plane $x_4 = 0$ in the way indicated in Chapter 3.
We then arrive at the theorem:

*If $U_{\lambda\mu}, P_{\lambda\mu}$ are the points of intersection with the edge $A_\lambda A_\mu$ of the
planes through the edge opposite to $A_\lambda A_\mu$ and U, P respectively, then*

$$x_\lambda : x_\mu = (A_\lambda A_\mu;\ U_{\lambda\mu}, P_{\lambda\mu}) \quad (\lambda, \mu = 1, 2, 3, 4). \tag{1–6}$$

There exists a dual theorem for $u_\lambda : u_\mu$ (Ex. 1, Sec. 8–3). Here we need the definition of the *cross ratio of four planes through a line*, which is the cross ratio of the four points of intersection of these four planes with any line intersecting them.

8–2 Projective transformations.

Generalizing the results obtained in Sec. 4–3 from the projective plane to projective space, we obtain the transformations by which we can pass from one set of five basic points A_λ, U to another in the form:

$$\rho x'_\lambda = c_{\lambda\mu} x_\mu \quad [C = \mathrm{Det}\ (c_{\lambda\mu}) \neq 0]. \qquad (2\text{–}1)$$

The transformation (2–1) is the general nonsingular linear homogeneous transformation in four variables. From Eq. (2–1) follows:

$$\rho_1 x_\lambda = \gamma_{\mu\lambda} x'_\mu, \qquad (2\text{–}2)$$

where

$$\gamma_{\lambda\mu} = \text{cofactor of } c_{\lambda\mu} \text{ in } C. \qquad (2\text{–}3)$$

In order to obtain the corresponding transformation of the plane coordinates, we use the relation $u'_\lambda x'_\lambda = \sigma u_\lambda x_\lambda$, which expresses that $(ux) = 0$, the equation of the plane, passes into $(u'x') = 0$. We obtain the equations

$$\rho_2 u'_\lambda = \gamma_{\lambda\mu} u_\mu, \quad \rho_3 u_\lambda = c_{\mu\lambda} u'_\mu. \qquad (2\text{–}4)$$

The transformations (2–1) constitute the *projective group* G_{15} in four variables. Under it the cross ratio of four points on a line is an invariant, as well as the cross ratio of four planes through a line.

There is an interesting difference between the G_{15} of P_3 and the G_8 of P_2 (Sec. 3–9). In the plane no positive or negative sign can be attached to Det (c_{ij}), since $x_i \rightarrow -x_i$ changes the sign. In P_3 the sign of Det $(c_{\lambda\mu})$ is preserved under such a transformation. This also happens on the line, where there are two variables x_a. It means that no orientation is possible in the projective plane, but on the projective line and in projective space an orientation is possible. In P_3 we can, for instance, take four independent points A_μ with coordinates $(_\mu x_\lambda)$, and assign to them a sense $A_1 \rightarrow A_2 \rightarrow A_3 \rightarrow A_4$. This sense can be indicated by the determinant

$$\begin{vmatrix} {}_1x_1 & {}_1x_2 & {}_1x_3 & {}_1x_4 \\ {}_2x_1 & {}_2x_2 & {}_2x_3 & {}_2x_4 \\ {}_3x_1 & {}_3x_2 & {}_3x_3 & {}_3x_4 \\ {}_4x_1 & {}_4x_2 & {}_4x_3 & {}_4x_4 \end{vmatrix}.$$

If this determinant is transformed by means of Eq. (2-2), it is multiplied by the fourth power of Det $(\gamma_{\lambda\mu})$. Its sign is therefore preserved. Hence,

Projective space is orientable, the projective plane is nonorientable.

A sense $A_1 \to A_2 \to A_3 \to A_4$ is called a *spatial* sense, or *screw* sense.

8-3 Line coordinates. A line can be represented either by Eqs. (1-2), (1-3), or Eqs. (1-4), (1-5). Another method of representation has been discovered by Plücker. Since the line PQ is determined by $P(x_\lambda), Q(y_\lambda)$, it is also expressed by the matrix

$$\begin{Vmatrix} x_1 & x_2 & x_3 & x_4 \\ y_1 & y_2 & y_3 & y_4 \end{Vmatrix},$$

in which each row can be replaced by a linear combination of the two rows, provided they are not proportional. From this matrix we can obtain twelve determinants:

$$p_{\lambda\mu} = x_\lambda y_\mu - x_\mu y_\lambda \quad (\lambda,\mu = 1,2,3,4). \tag{3-1}$$

Similarly, starting with the planes $\pi(u_\lambda), \sigma(v_\lambda)$, we can express their line of intersection $(\pi\sigma)$ by the twelve determinants

$$q_{\lambda\mu} = u_\lambda v_\mu - u_\mu v_\lambda. \tag{3-2}$$

The $p_{\lambda\mu}, q_{\lambda\mu}$ are not independent. By virtue of the relation

$$p_{\mu\lambda} = -p_{\lambda\mu}, \quad q_{\mu\lambda} = -q_{\lambda\mu}, \tag{3-3}$$

we can reduce the $p_{\lambda\mu}, q_{\lambda\mu}$ to six each. Moreover, we can verify by direct substitution of the values (3-1), (3-2), that

$$p_{12}p_{34} + p_{13}p_{42} + p_{14}p_{23} = 0, \tag{3-4}$$

$$q_{12}q_{34} + q_{13}q_{42} + q_{14}q_{23} = 0. \tag{3-5}$$

The line is determined by the ratios $p_{12}:p_{13}:p_{14}:p_{23}:p_{34}:p_{42}$, or $q_{12}:q_{13}:q_{14}:q_{23}:q_{34}:q_{42}$. Either set is called the *set of coordinates* of the line (in space). The ratio of the six $p_{\lambda\mu}$, between which the quadratic relation (3-4) exists, leaves four degrees of freedom, corresponding to the ∞^4 lines in P_3.

When instead of the points P,Q on the line we take another set of points on the line, then, according to Eq. (1-2), the ratio of the $p_{\lambda\mu}$ does not change. Similarly, the ratio of the $q_{\lambda\mu}$ does not change when we substitute for π,σ two other planes through the line.

The $p_{\lambda\mu},q_{\lambda\mu}$ cannot be independent of each other. We find the relation between them by passing a plane through PQ and A_1 $(1:0:0:0)$, and a plane through PQ and A_2 $(0:1:0:0)$; if PQ passes through A_1 or A_2 we select other vertices. These planes have the equations

$$u_1:u_2:u_3:u_4 = 0:(x_3y_4 - x_4y_3):(x_4y_2 - x_2y_4):(x_2y_3 - x_3y_2),$$
$$v_1:v_2:v_3:v_4 = (x_3y_4 - x_4y_3):0:(x_4y_1 - x_1y_4):(x_1y_3 - x_3y_1).$$

From this we derive relations like the following:

$$q_{12} = u_1v_2 - u_2v_1 = -(x_3y_4 - x_4y_3)(x_3y_4 - x_4y_3) = -(x_3y_4 - x_4y_3)p_{34},$$
$$q_{13} = u_1v_3 - u_3v_1 = -(x_3y_4 - x_4y_3)(x_4y_2 - x_2y_4) = -(x_3y_4 - x_4y_3)p_{42},$$

etc., so that we obtain the result (we can always make $x_3y_4 - x_4y_3 \neq 0$):

$$q_{12}:q_{13}:q_{14}:q_{23}:q_{34}:q_{42} = p_{34}:p_{42}:p_{23}:p_{14}:p_{12}:p_{13}.$$

General projective coordinates were first systematically used by Plücker, Crelle 5 (1829), *Ges. Math. Abh.*, pp. 124–150. It was also Plücker who introduced the line coordinates. He states their possibility in his *System der Geometrie des Raumes* (1846), p. 322, but only developed the full theory in his later mathematical work: *Neue Geometrie des Raumes*, 2 volumes (1868, 1869). A detailed account of projective coordinates in space is found in the translation, by W. Fiedler, of G. Salmon, *Analytic Geometry of Three Dimensions* (German, 2 volumes, 3rd ed., 1879–80).

EXERCISES

1. Express the ratio $u_\lambda:u_\mu$ in terms of a cross ratio [comp. Eq. (1-6)].

2. Find the point coordinates of the point of intersection of the three planes $(ux) = 0$, $(vx) = 0$, $(wx) = 0$. Express the dual proposition.

3. All planes through the line of intersection of the planes $(ax) = 0$, $(bx) = 0$ form a *pencil of planes*. Its equation can be written $(a_\lambda + tb_\lambda)x_\lambda = 0$.

Show that four planes of this pencil given by t_1, t_2, t_3, t_4 have a cross ratio

$$(t_1 t_2, t_3 t_4) = \frac{t_1 - t_3}{t_1 - t_4} : \frac{t_2 - t_3}{t_2 - t_4}.$$

4. Given four planes of a pencil. Show how the value of the cross ratio enables us to determine whether two of the planes do or do not *separate* the other two (comp. Sec. 1–4).

5. Prove Eqs. (1–2) and (1–3).

6. The line through $P(x_\lambda)$ and $Q(y_\lambda)$ intersects the plane (u_λ) in R. Find the coordinates of R. Discuss the dual case.

7. What is the condition that 4 points lie in a plane, and that 4 planes pass through a point?

8. Take n independent points in space with their connecting lines and planes. Intersect this figure with a plane not incident with any of these lines. Show that we obtain in the plane a configuration $\Pi_n = \left[\binom{n}{2}_{n-2}, \binom{n}{3}_3\right]$. What do we obtain for $n = 3,4,5$?

9. State the dual to Ex. 8, leading to a $\Pi'_n = \left[\binom{n}{3}_3, \binom{n}{2}_{n-2}\right]$.

10. Given two skew lines l and m; on l the points A_1, A_2, A_3; on m the points B_1, B_2, B_3. Through an arbitrary point P a line a_1 is drawn meeting $A_2 B_3$, $A_3 B_2$; a line a_2 meeting $A_3 B_1, A_1 B_3$; and a line a_3 meeting $A_1 B_2, A_2 B_1$. Show that a_1, a_2, a_3 lie in a plane.

11. Given two skew lines l, m, and a point P. A line is drawn through P meeting l and m in A and B respectively. The harmonic conjugate Q of P with respect to A and B is called *the harmonic conjugate of P with respect to l and m*. (a) Show that when P describes a plane π, Q describes a plane σ; (b) that when P describes a line a, Q describes a line b. We call π, σ and a, b *(harmonic) conjugates with respect to l and m*. (c) Show that when a, b are conjugate with respect to l, m, then l and m are conjugate with respect to a, b.

12. When a line l intersects two opposite edges of a tetrahedron, its two conjugates with respect to the other pairs of opposite edges coincide into one line m. We call l and m *conjugate with respect to the tetrahedron*.

13. The three conjugates of a point P with respect to the three pairs of opposite edges of a tetrahedron (Ex. 11) lie in the *harmonic or polar plane* of P with respect to the tetrahedron. (a) Show by a duality consideration that a plane π has a (harmonic) *pole* with respect to the tetrahedron. (b) Show that when π is the polar plane of P, P is the pole of π, and (c) that the unit point and unit plane of Sec. 8–1 have this harmonic relationship.

14. *Self-polar tetrahedra.* If the vertices of a tetrahedron I are the poles of their opposite faces with respect to a tetrahedron II (Ex. 13), then the ver-

tices of tetrahedron II are the poles of their opposite faces with respect to tetrahedron I. Each tetrahedron is called *self-polar* with respect to the other.

15. *Theorem of Desargues for tetrahedra.* If corresponding faces of two tetrahedra intersect in coplanar lines, then the lines joining corresponding vertices pass through one point, and conversely. These tetrahedra are said to be *in perspective*.

See, on problems related to Exs. 12–15, N. Altschiller-Court, *Modern Pure Solid Geometry*, (New York, 1935).

8–4 Affine space. Projective space passes into affine space by singling out one plane. We take it as $x_4 = 0$, and call it the *ideal plane*, or *plane at infinity*. Then, if we introduce new coordinates x,y,z by means of the equation

$$x:y:z:1 = x_1:x_2:x_3:x_4, \qquad (4\text{–}1)$$

we can interpret x,y,z as oblique affine coordinates in a space of which $x_4 = 0$ is the plane at infinity (since $x_4 \to 0$ results in $x,y,z \to \infty$). The unit of measure on the coordinate axes remains undefined. With the aid of this plane we can define *parallel lines* and *parallel planes*. A point in $x_4 = 0$ represents a family of ∞^2 parallel lines, a line in $x_4 = 0$ a family of ∞^1 parallel planes, incidence of point and line at infinity means parallel lines parallel to or lying in parallel planes. In affine geometry, the equation of a plane not through the origin is

$$ux + vy + wz + 1 = 0, \qquad (4\text{–}2)$$

where u,v,w:

$$u:v:w:1 = u_1:u_2:u_3:u_4, \qquad (4\text{–}3)$$

are the *plane coordinates* of plane (4–2). The origin corresponds to $u_4 = 0$.

Two parallel planes are given by equations of the form

$$a_1x + a_2y + a_3z + a_4 = 0, \quad b_1x + b_2y + b_3z + b_4 = 0;$$
$$a_1:b_1 = a_2:b_2 = a_3:b_3 \neq a_4:b_4.$$

Two nonparallel planes determine a line whose points P, expressed in terms of two points on it, $A(a_i), B(b_i)$, $i = 1,2,3$, are given by

$$x = \frac{a_1 - \lambda b_1}{1 - \lambda}, \quad y = \frac{a_2 - \lambda b_2}{1 - \lambda}, \quad z = \frac{a_3 - \lambda b_3}{1 - \lambda}, \qquad (4\text{–}4)$$

where $\lambda = PA : PB$ is the *division ratio* of P with respect to A and B (see Sec. 1–2). The value of λ determines which of the A,B,P lies *between* the others.

Transformation from one system of oblique coordinates to another is given by

$$x' = c_{11}x + c_{12}y + c_{13}z + c_{14},$$
$$y' = c_{21}x + c_{22}y + c_{23}z + c_{24} \quad [C = \text{Det } (c_{ij}) \neq 0, \quad i,j = 1,2,3], \quad (4\text{–}5)$$
$$z' = c_{31}x + c_{32}y + c_{33}z + c_{34}.$$

These equations express the fact that any four independent points O,A,B,C can be used to define a system of coordinate axes OA,OB,OC, with OA,OB,OC as units of measure in their respective directions (the latter possibility corresponds to the free choice of the unit point in projective coordinates). When $c_{14} = c_{24} = c_{34} = 0$, we obtain all affine transformations which leave the origin unchanged. This underlies the *centro-affine* theory, which, from a projective point of view, is self-dual. In this case, writing x_1,x_2,x_3 for x,y,z, Eq. (4–5) can be cast into the form

$$x_i' = c_{ij}x_j \quad [C = \text{Det } (c_{ij}) \neq 0, \quad i,j,k = 1,2,3] \quad (4\text{–}6)$$

with the corresponding transformation

$$x_i = C_{ji}x_j',$$

with

$$C_{ij} = \frac{\text{cofactor of } c_{ij} \text{ in } C}{C}. \quad (4\text{–}7)$$

For the plane coordinates u_1,u_2,u_3 of a plane $u_1x_1 + u_2x_2 + u_3x_3 + 1 = 0$ the transformations are

$$u_i' = C_{ij}u_j, \quad u_i = c_{ji}u_j'.$$

8–5 Vectors and bivectors. Following the pattern of Sec. 4–6, we can define in centro-affine space contravariant vectors v_i, of which the coordinates transform according to Eq. (4–6), $v_i' = c_{ij}v_j$, and covariant vectors w_i transforming according to Eq. (4–7), $w_i' = C_{ij}w_j$. We often write contravariant vectors with superscript indices v^i and covariant vectors with subscript indices w_i. When we refer to vectors and bivectors, we always mean quantities with real coordinates. The geometrical representation of a contravariant vector as an arrow remains the same in space and plane, *but the covariant vector w_i of space can be represented by a combination of O and a plane $\pi(w_i)$ with a sense from O to π.* We cannot assign a numerical value (like "distance" or "length") to w_i, but we can represent the vector λw_i by a combination of O and a plane parallel to π and λ times closer to O. When λ changes sign, the sense of the vector changes. Instead of the combination (O, π) we can also take the combination of π with a plane through O parallel to π.

Two other elementary figures appear in affine space geometry. We obtain them by defining as the *outer product* of two contravariant vectors v^i, w^i a set of three numbers:

$$p^{23} = v^2 w^3 - v^3 w^2, \quad p^{31} = v^3 w^1 - v^1 w^3, \quad p^{12} = v^1 w^2 - v^2 w^1. \quad (5\text{--}1)$$

Writing for p^{23}, p^{31}, p^{12} the symbols p_1, p_2, p_3 respectively, we obtain that they transform according to the formulas

$$p_i' = CC_{ij}p_j = \Gamma_{ij}p_j, \quad \Gamma_{ij} = \text{cofactor of } C_{ij} \text{ in Det } (C_{ij}).$$

We say that the p_i form a *contravariant bivector*. When we build the combinations (5–1) for two covariant vectors, we obtain three numbers q_1, q_2, q_3 which transform according to the formulas

$$q_i' = Cc_{ij}q = \gamma_{ij}q_j, \quad (5\text{--}3)$$

and we say that the q_i form a *covariant bivector*. Using metrical language for a moment, we can prove [see Sec. 4–5, Eq. (5–3) and Ex. 9, Sec. 4–9] that the area of the parallelogram formed by the vectors v^a and w^a, $a = 1,2$, in the XOY-plane is proportional to $v^1 w^2 - v^2 w^1$ [comp. Eq. (9–4), Chapter 4]. The ratio of areas in a plane is an affine concept. In this ratio we can replace the area of a parallelogram by that of any closed figure of equal area with it. We can thus represent a contravariant bivector p_i by the oriented area of a closed figure in a plane through O (determined by the plane of v^i, w^i, in the case that the bivector is formed as the outer product of two vectors v^i and w^i), the term "area" only meaning that the ratio of areas in the same plane is an affine invariant [Fig. 8–2(c)]. The bivector λp_i has the same plane, but the area is λ times that of p_i. When λ changes sign the orientation of the area changes. Reasoning

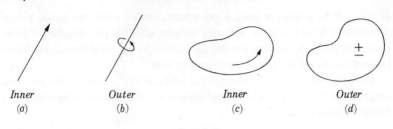

| Inner | Outer | Inner | Outer |
| (a) | (b) | (c) | (d) |

Fig. 8–2

dually, we see that a covariant bivector q_i can be represented by a cylinder and a sense of rotation around it. We cannot assign a numerical value to it, but we can represent λq_i by a cylinder of the same direction and a cross section λ times smaller than the corresponding parallel cross section of q_i.

In the case of a contravariant vector and bivector, we have an *inner* orientation of their line and plane respectively [Fig. 8–2(a,c)]. In that of a covariant vector and bivector we have an *outer* orientation [Fig. 8–2(b,d)]. Let us now take three independent contravariant vectors v^i, w^i, u^i. Then after the transformation (2–6) their determinant

$$\begin{vmatrix} v^1 & v^2 & v^3 \\ u^1 & u^2 & u^3 \\ w^1 & w^2 & w^3 \end{vmatrix}$$

is multiplied by C. This can be interpreted by stating that *the ratio of two volumes is an affine invariant.* Moreover, it shows that for all transformations with $C > 0$ the sign of the determinant remains the same. The sign changes when two of the three vectors are interchanged. This can be interpreted as defining a *spatial sense, a right-handed or left-handed screw sense.* If, for instance, $v^i \rightarrow w^i \rightarrow u^i$ is right-handed, $w^i \rightarrow v^i \rightarrow u^i$ is left-handed.

The transformations with $C = \pm 1$ preserve volume; they form the *equivoluminous* group. Those with $C = +1$ form the *special affine group.* For the special affine group, Eq. (3–2) is identical with Eq. (2–7), and Eq. (3–3) with Eq. (2–6). We can interpret this by saying that *under the special affine group a contravariant bivector is identical with a covariant vector, and a covariant bivector with a contravariant vector.* Indeed, we can associate with a contravariant bivector of area A in a unique way a covariant vector with the same plane direction whose distance d to the origin satisfies the relation $dA =$ unit volume. A similar correspondence can be established between the cylinder and the arrow in the other case.

In other words, *under the special affine group we only have co- and contravariant vectors.* These vectors admit more than one geometrical interpretation.

EXERCISES

1. Show that the medians of a tetrahedron pass through one point. Such a median is the line connecting the vertex with the centroid of the triangle in the opposite face.

2. Find the center of gravity of masses m_1, m_2, m_3, m_4 at the four vertices of a tetrahedron (see Sec. 3–5).

3. Let v^i be a contravariant and w_i a covariant vector. What is the geometrical meaning of $v^i w_i$? What of $v^i w_i = 0$?

4. Consider the bivector p^{ij} of Eq. (5–1) and a contravariant vector q^i. Study the behavior under special affine transformations of $q^1 p^{23} + q^2 p^{31} + q^3 p^{12}$, and interpret this quantity geometrically.

5. Show that the equation of the line through the point $(x_1 y_1 z_1)$ and $(x_2 y_2 z_2)$ is

$$\frac{x - x_1}{x_2 - x_1} = \frac{y - y_1}{y_2 - y_1} = \frac{z - z_1}{z_2 - z_1}.$$

6. The equations of a line l in an oblique coordinate system can be given in the form $y = mx + a$, $z = nx + b$. Find the condition (a) that l intersects another line m: $y = m_1 x + a_1$, $z = n_1 x + b_1$; (b) that the plane through a point $P(x_0, y_0, z_0)$ and l passes through the origin.

7. Find the equation of the line through P intersecting l (Ex. 6).

8. Given the planes $A_i x + B_i y + C_i z + D_i = 0$, $i = 1, 2, 3$. What is the condition (a) that they are parallel, (b) that their lines of intersection are parallel, (c) that they pass through one line?

9. A line can be given by the equation $x = az + p$, $y = bz + q$. Find the point of intersection with the plane $Ax + By + Cz + D = 0$.

10. A point A moves on a line l and a point B on a line m such that AB is parallel to a given plane (not parallel to l and m). Show that the mid-point of AB describes a line.

8–6 Euclidean geometry.

We consider an affine space obtained by taking a projective space with the plane $x_4 = 0$ singled out as the plane at infinity. We now proceed by singling out, in this plane

$x_4 = 0$, an imaginary nonsingular conic. This conic may be replaced by an elliptic polarity if we prefer to stay in the real domain. By choice of coordinates, we assign to this *absolute conic* the equation

$$x_1^2 + x_2^2 + x_3^2 = 0, \quad x_4 = 0. \tag{6–1}$$

Every plane intersects the special plane $x_4 = 0$ in a line, its ideal line. This line intersects the conic (6–1) in the two isotropic points I and J of the plane. In every plane we can therefore define angle and distance in accord with Sec. 4–8; the distance of two points P,Q of space is then defined by [comp. Eq. (8–6), Sec. 4–8]:

$$d = \frac{(x_1 y_4 - x_4 y_1)^2 + (x_2 y_4 - x_4 y_2)^2 + (x_3 y_4 - x_4 y_3)^2}{x_4 y_4}. \tag{6–2}$$

Introducing the coordinates x,y,z; $x:y:z:1 = x_1:x_2:x_3:x_4$, and assigning to P the coordinates (ξ, η_1, ζ_1) and to $Q(\xi_2, \eta_2, \zeta_2)$, then Eq. (6–2) can be written

$$d = \sqrt{(\xi_1 - \xi_2)^2 + (\eta_1 - \eta_2)^2 + (\zeta_1 - \zeta_2)^2}. \tag{6–3}$$

This geometry is *Euclidean geometry*. A pair of points on a line in the special plane $x_4 = 0$ harmonic with the isotropic points on the line give the ideal points of a pair of perpendicular lines. Such a pair therefore represents a pair of perpendicular directions. From this follows that a point in the ideal plane $x_4 = 0$ and its polar with respect to the absolute conic represent a family of ∞^2 parallel lines with the pencil of ∞^1 planes perpendicular to these lines. A self-polar triangle in $x_4 = 0$ represents three mutually perpendicular pencils of parallel planes and their lines of intersection. Through each point passes one plane of each pencil, which can be taken as a coordinate plane of a rectangular coordinate system.

The form of Eq. (6–1) shows that our original selection of a coordinate system x_i has been such that the special points of the coordinate axes form a self-polar triangle with respect to the absolute. We write x_i, $i = 1,2,3$, for (x,y,z). If we now change to a new system x_i' which is also rectangular, then the absolute again takes the form (6–1): $(x_1')^2 + (x_2')^2 + (x_3')^2 = 0$. Hence all transformations

$$x_i' = c_{ij} x_j \tag{6–4}$$

by which one rectangular system passes into another are characterized by the condition that they change $x_1^2 + x_2^2 + x_3^2$ only by a multi-
plicative factor. This imposes the following conditions upon the
$c_{\lambda\mu}$:

$$c_{41} = c_{42} = c_{43} = 0, \qquad (6\text{--}5)$$

$$c_{11}^2 + c_{21}^2 + c_{31}^2 = c_{12}^2 + c_{22}^2 + c_{32}^2 = c_{13}^2 + c_{23}^2 + c_{33}^2, \qquad (6\text{--}6)$$

$$c_{11}c_{12} + c_{21}c_{22} + c_{31}c_{32} = c_{11}c_{13} + c_{21}c_{23} + c_{31}c_{33}$$
$$= c_{12}c_{13} + c_{22}c_{23} + c_{32}c_{33} = 0. \qquad (6\text{--}7)$$

From Eq. (6–7) follow the relations

$$c_{11}:c_{21}:c_{31}: \ldots :c_{33} = \gamma_{11}:\gamma_{21}:\gamma_{31}: \ldots :\gamma_{33}, \qquad (6\text{--}8)$$

where the γ_{ij} are the cofactors of the c_{ij} in the determinant $C =$
Det (c_{ij}). The transformations (6–4) are nonsingular, hence $C \neq 0$.

We now introduce the additional assumption that the distance d
between two points is an invariant under the transformations (6–4).
This means that Eqs. (6–6) pass into

$$c_{11}^2 + c_{21}^2 + c_{31}^2 = c_{12}^2 + c_{22}^2 + c_{32}^2 = c_{13}^2 + c_{23}^2 + c_{33}^2 = 1. \quad (6\text{--}9)$$

The Eqs. (6–7) and (6–9) can be united in the formula

$$c_{ij}c_{ik} = \delta_{jk},$$

where δ_{jk}, the *Kronecker symbol*, is a matrix of three rows and three col-
umns such that $\delta_{11} = \delta_{22} = \delta_{33} = 1$, and $\delta_{jk}(j \neq k) = 0$ (hence $\delta_{jk} = \delta_{kj}$).

The Eqs. (6–7) and (6–9) are known as the *orthogonality relations*.
They establish six relations between the nine c_{ij}, so that the c_{ij} have
three degrees of freedom. We can, for instance, express all c_{ij} in
terms of three angles (the *Euler angles*, Ex. 14, Sec. 8–8). The transformations (6–4) with conditions (6–7) and (6–9) form a group G_3, the
orthogonal group.

From Eq. (6–8) and such equations as $c_{11}\gamma_{11} + c_{21}\gamma_{21} + c_{31}\gamma_{31} = C$
follows that

$$\gamma_{ij} = Cc_{ij} \qquad (6\text{--}10)$$

and

$$C_{ij} = c_{ij}, \quad C_{ij} = \gamma_{ij}/C. \qquad (6\text{--}11)$$

This identity of C_{ij} and c_{ij} has important results for covariant and
contravariant vectors. Comparing Eq. (4–6) with Eq. (4–8), we see
that *the transformation of the x_i is the same as that of the u_i. The differ-*

ence between covariant and contravariant vectors disappears under orthogonal transformations of rectangular coordinate systems. We simply speak of *vectors* v_i, with transformation

$$v_i' = c_{ij}v_i. \qquad (6\text{--}12)$$

The difference between covariant and contravariant bivectors also disappears; we speak simply of *bivectors*. Under this orthogonal group we call vectors *polar*, bivectors *axial* quantities. The simplest representation of a vector is an arrow; of a bivector, an area with a sense of rotation.

We are accustomed to write for a vector v_i the symbol **v**. Two vectors **v,w** have an invariant, the *scalar product* $\mathbf{v} \cdot \mathbf{w} = v_i w_i$. With the aid of this product we can define the *length* of vector v_i (we consider only real v_i) as

$$v = \sqrt{\mathbf{v} \cdot \mathbf{v}} \quad (\sqrt{\ } \text{ positive}) \qquad (6\text{--}13)$$

and the angle ϕ of two vectors v_i, w_i by means of

$$\cos \phi = \mathbf{v} \cdot \mathbf{w}/vw. \qquad (6\text{--}14)$$

We can show that when the definition of this angle, defined for half-rays, is applied to lines, we obtain the Laguerre definition (Sec. 7–1).

We can now define a unit length: all vectors of unit length starting at the origin have their end points on a sphere. It is now possible to define a unit area as the area of a *square* of unit side, and a unit volume as the volume of a *cube* of unit side.

We have here constructed a geometry which is isomorphic with the ordinary Euclidean geometry of space. We say that our geometry *is* the Euclidean geometry of space. It contains the ordinary solid geometry of our textbooks and of Euclid, with the addition of vectors, that is, of oriented line and plane segments.

8–7 Oriented Euclidean space. We find by the application of the rule of multiplication of determinants and the orthogonality relations (6–7) and (6–9) to $C = \mathrm{Det}\,(c_{ij})$, that

$$C^2 = 1, \qquad (7\text{--}1)$$

which expresses the invariance of volume.

Let us now select those transformations (6–4) for which $C = +1$. They also form a group, the *rotational group* G_3. This group leaves a sense of orientation in space invariant. Space under the rotational G_3 is therefore oriented. We can indicate this by calling the sense $OX \to OY \to OZ$ the *positive* sense. It is now possible to assign to every inner sense on a line a unique inner sense (sense of rotation) in a plane intersecting this line, namely, the sense which completes the sense in the line to the positive sense of space.

This can be expressed as follows in terms of transformations. The contravariant bivector p_i of Eqs. (5–1) and (5–2) transforms under orthogonal transformations as follows:

$$p_i' = Cc_{ij}p_j, \tag{7–2}$$

which is also the transformation of the covariant bivector q_i of Eq. (5–3). When $C = +1$ the bivectors transform like vectors. We express it by saying that *under rotations vectors and bivectors are identical.*

The vector p_i, according to its definition (5–1) represents the *vector product* of the vectors $\mathbf{v}$ and $\mathbf{w}$:

$$\mathbf{p} = \mathbf{v} \times \mathbf{w}. \tag{7–3}$$

Its usual representation is by a vector perpendicular to the plane of $\mathbf{v}$ and $\mathbf{w}$ such that the sense $\mathbf{v} \to \mathbf{w} \to \mathbf{p}$ is positive, and of length equal to the area of the parallelogram formed with $\mathbf{v}$ and $\mathbf{w}$ as sides. This last equation of length and area units is possible as soon as a unit length has been established.

There are many geometrical representations of a vector $\mathbf{v}$ in oriented Euclidean space. The most commonly used are the following:

(a) The arrow of given length v, given line direction, and inner orientation (the *polar* vector). [Fig. 8–3 (a)]

(b) The arrow of given length v, given line direction, and outer orientation (the *axial* vector). [Fig. 8–3 (d)]

(c) The plane segment of area v, given plane direction, and inner orientation. [Fig. 8–3 (c)]

With the aid of representations under the more comprehensive groups we can find other equivalent figures. For instance, we can

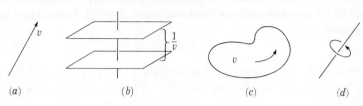

FIG. 8-3

take a set of two parallel planes at distance $1/v$, of given plane direction and an outer orientation (from one plane to another). [Fig. 8-3 (b)]

When we also admit reflections of the coordinate system, so that $C = \pm 1$, then space is no longer oriented. In this case we can discriminate between polar vectors and axial vectors. A vector product is an axial vector. A polar vector changes its sense under reflections; an axial vector retains its sense.

These quantities have all been defined under the orthogonal or rotational group, keeping the origin invariant. If we widen these groups to include translations, $x_i' = c_{ij}x_j + a_i$ (the c_{ij} satisfying the orthogonality relations either with $D = \pm 1$ or with $D = +1$), then we obtain the group G_6 of motions in space, with or without reflections. Under motions vectors are no longer invariant, but are moved parallel to each other so as to form a *vector field*. In this case we also speak of a *free* vector, saying that in space a vector may be moved parallel to itself. We write $\overrightarrow{OP} = \mathbf{v}$ to indicate a vector pointing from O to P of length $|OP|$.

The calculus of vectors under rotations of rectangular coordinate systems is the ordinary vector calculus, deduced in our form from the works of Hamilton and Grassman by Josiah Willard Gibbs (1839–1903), professor at Yale (1881–1884, Coll. Works 2, pp. 17–90, see E. B. Wilson, *Vector Analysis*, New Haven, 1901, 2nd ed., 1913). Gibbs developed his calculus in an attempt to simplify the work with Maxwell's equations. The difference between vectors and bivectors appears in Grassman's *Ausdehnungslehre*, in which the difference between polar and axial quantities is also implicit. The names *polar* and *axial* appear in W. Voigt. For a more detailed classification of directed quantities see J. A. Schouten, *Tensor Analysis for Physicists* (Oxford, 1951).

8–8 Points, lines, planes in Euclidean geometry. A point x_i can be given by a radius vector **x** from the origin, a point P on a line l by the equation

$$\mathbf{x} = \mathbf{a} + s\mathbf{i} \tag{8–1}$$

where **a** is the radius vector of an arbitrary point A on l and **i** is a unit vector in the direction of the line. The parameter s is the distance AP.

A plane can be given by the equation

$$\mathbf{n} \cdot (\mathbf{x} - \mathbf{a}) = 0, \tag{8–2}$$

where **n** is a vector normal to the plane, and **a** is the radius vector of an arbitrary fixed point A in the plane. When **n** makes angles $\alpha_1, \alpha_2, \alpha_3$ with the positive x-, y-, and z-axis, then

$$\cos^2 \alpha_1 + \cos^2 \alpha_2 + \cos^2 \alpha_3 = 1, \tag{8–3}$$

which expresses that $\mathbf{n} \cdot \mathbf{n} = 1$ when **n** is a unit vector, since in this case **n** has the coordinates ($\cos \alpha_1$, $\cos \alpha_2$, $\cos \alpha_3$). Then Eq. (8–2) gives us the equation of the plane as

$$N \equiv x \cos \alpha_1 + y \cos \alpha_2 + z \cos \alpha_3 - p = 0, \tag{8–4}$$

where p is the perpendicular from O on the plane. This is the *Hessian* or *normal form* of the equation of the plane. The questions concerning the sign of p in Eq. (8–4), as well as the corresponding questions occurring in the theory of pencils of planes $N_1 + \lambda N_2 = 0$, can be answered by elementary generalization of the results obtained in Chapter 2 on lines and line pencils.

A plane through the three points given by **a**,**b**,**c** has the equation

$$(\mathbf{x} - \mathbf{a}, \mathbf{b} - \mathbf{a}, \mathbf{c} - \mathbf{a}) = (\mathbf{x} - \mathbf{a}) \cdot \{(\mathbf{b} - \mathbf{a}) \times (\mathbf{c} - \mathbf{a})\}, \tag{8–5}$$

or

$$\begin{vmatrix} x - a_1 & y - a_2 & z - a_3 \\ a_1 - b_1 & a_2 - b_2 & a_3 - b_3 \\ a_1 - c_1 & a_2 - c_2 & a_3 - c_3 \end{vmatrix} = \begin{vmatrix} x & y & z & 1 \\ a_1 & a_2 & a_3 & 1 \\ b_1 & b_2 & b_3 & 1 \\ c_1 & c_2 & c_3 & 1 \end{vmatrix} = 0. \tag{8–6}$$

The combination (**abc**) is called the *parallelepiped product* or *triple scalar product;* it can be written in several ways:

$$(\mathbf{abc}) = \mathbf{a} \cdot (\mathbf{b} \times \mathbf{c}) = \mathbf{b} \cdot (\mathbf{c} \times \mathbf{a}) = \mathbf{c} \cdot (\mathbf{a} \times \mathbf{b}) = -\mathbf{a} \cdot (\mathbf{c} \times \mathbf{b}) = \ldots ;$$

it is an invariant under rotations and changes its sign under reflections. Its absolute value represents the volume of the parallelepiped of which the vectors $\mathbf{a}, \mathbf{b}, \mathbf{c}$, pointing from the origin, are adjacent sides (Ex. 1 below). Comparing Eqs. (8–5) and (8–6), we see that the $\mathbf{n}$ of Eq. (8–2) is proportional to $(\mathbf{b} - \mathbf{c}) \times (\mathbf{c} - \mathbf{a})$.

As an example in the analytic geometry of lines and planes we solve the following problem.

Given two skew lines l_1: $\mathbf{x} = \mathbf{a} + t_1\mathbf{u}$, l_2: $\mathbf{x} = \mathbf{b} + t_2\mathbf{v}$. Find the line m intersecting both lines at right angles and the perpendicular distance of these lines.

We first remark that the plane through l_1 and a line of direction $\mathbf{i} \neq \mathbf{u}$ has the equation $(\mathbf{x} - \mathbf{a}) \cdot (\mathbf{u} \times \mathbf{i}) = 0$. For the common perpendicular $\mathbf{i} = \mathbf{u} \times \mathbf{v}$. This line is therefore the intersection of the planes through l_1 and m: $(\mathbf{x} - \mathbf{a}) \cdot (\mathbf{u} \times \mathbf{i}) = 0$; and through l_2 and m: $(\mathbf{x} - \mathbf{b}) \cdot (\mathbf{v} \times \mathbf{i}) = 0$.

When we take $\mathbf{a}(a_1, a_2, 0)$, $\mathbf{b}(b_1, b_2, 0)$, $\mathbf{u}(u_1, u_2, 1)$, $\mathbf{v}(v_1, v_2, 1)$, we obtain the equation of the lines in the form ($t_1 = z$, $t_2 = z$).

$$
\begin{aligned}
(l_1)&: \quad x = u_1 z + a_1, \quad y = u_2 z + a_2, \\
(l_2)&: \quad x = v_1 z + b_1, \quad y = v_2 z + b_2,
\end{aligned}
\tag{8-7}
$$

and the two equations for the common perpendicular take the form

$$
\begin{aligned}
(u_1 - v_1)(x - u_1 z - a_1) + (u_2 - v_2)(y - u_2 z - a_2) + (u_1 v_2 - u_2 v_1) \\
[u_2(x - a_1) - u_1(y - a_2)] = 0, \\
(u_1 - v_1)(x - v_1 z - b_1) + (u_2 - v_2)(y - v_2 z - b_2) + (u_1 v_2 - u_2 v_1) \\
[v_2(x - b_1) - v_1(y - b_2)] = 0.
\end{aligned}
$$

As to the length L of the common perpendicular, it is the projection of the vector $\mathbf{a} - \mathbf{b}$ on a line of direction $\mathbf{u} \times \mathbf{v}$. The projection has therefore the length $(\mathbf{a} - \mathbf{b}) \cdot \mathbf{w}$, when $\mathbf{w}$ is a unit vector in direction $\mathbf{u} \times \mathbf{v}$. Hence

$$
L = \left| \frac{(\mathbf{a} - \mathbf{b}) \cdot (\mathbf{u} \times \mathbf{v})}{\sqrt{(\mathbf{u} \times \mathbf{v}) \cdot (\mathbf{u} \times \mathbf{v})}} \right|.
\tag{8-8}
$$

This equation can be modified by the use of the identity

$$
(\mathbf{u} \times \mathbf{v}) \cdot (\mathbf{u} \times \mathbf{v}) = (\mathbf{u} \cdot \mathbf{u})(\mathbf{v} \cdot \mathbf{v}) - (\mathbf{u} \cdot \mathbf{v})^2.
\tag{8-9}
$$

In the case of the coordinate equations (8–7), Eq. (8–8) takes the form

$$L = \left| \frac{(a_1 - b_1)(u_2 - v_2) - (a_2 - b_2)(u_1 - v_1)}{\sqrt{(u_1 - v_1)^2 + (u_2 - v_2)^2 + (u_1v_2 - u_2v_1)^2}} \right|.$$

The application of algebra to geometry of space began to take form during the eighteenth century in the work of Clairaut and Euler, but a treatment similar to that of our modern elementary analytic geometry of space had to wait until Monge and Hachette: G. Monge, *Application de l'Algèbre à la Géométrie* (Paris, 1807). G. Salmon, *Analytic Geometry of Three Dimensions* (1862, several editions, German edition by W. Fiedler) is still a good textbook. See also Briot-Bouquet, *Leçons de Géométrie Analytique* (1847, 14th ed., 1893, English translation by J. H. Boyd, 1896); D. M. Y. Sommerville, *Analytical Geometry of Three Dimensions* (Cambridge, 1934).

EXERCISES

1. Show that $\mathbf{a} \cdot \mathbf{b} = ab \cos \phi$, if ϕ is the angle of $\mathbf{a}$ and $\mathbf{b}$, that the length of $\mathbf{a} \times \mathbf{b}$ is $ab \sin \phi$, and that $(\mathbf{abc}) = 6$ times the volume of the tetrahedron $OABC$, if A,B,C are the end points of the vectors $\mathbf{a},\mathbf{b},\mathbf{c}$ placed at O.

2. Show that the projection of the vector $\mathbf{v}$ on the line $\mathbf{x} = \mathbf{a} + s\mathbf{u}$ is $(\mathbf{v} \cdot \mathbf{u})\mathbf{u}$, if $\mathbf{u}$ is a unit vector.

3. Show that the distance of the point $\mathbf{x}_0$ to the plane $\mathbf{n} \cdot (\mathbf{x} - \mathbf{a}) = 0$ is $\mathbf{n} \cdot (\mathbf{x}_0 - \mathbf{a})$, if $\mathbf{n}$ is a unit vector. What is the meaning of the sign of $\mathbf{n} \cdot (\mathbf{x}_0 - \mathbf{a})$?

4. Show that the distance of the point $\mathbf{x}_0$ to the line $\mathbf{x} = \mathbf{a} + s\mathbf{u}$ is $\sqrt{\{(\mathbf{x}_0 - \mathbf{a}) \times \mathbf{u}\} \cdot \{(\mathbf{x}_0 - \mathbf{a}) \times \mathbf{u}\}}$, if $\mathbf{u}$ is a unit vector. Write it out in coordinates if the line is given as $x = az + p$, $y = bz + q$.

5. Find the equation of the line through point $\mathbf{x}_0$ perpendicular to the line $x = az + p$, $y = bz + q$.

6. Find the vector equation of the line passing through the points $\mathbf{a}$ and $\mathbf{b}$.

7. Representing vectors by oriented plane segments, express $\mathbf{v} + \mathbf{w}$, $\mathbf{v} - \mathbf{w}$, $\mathbf{v} \cdot \mathbf{w}$.

8. Show the invariance of $(\mathbf{abc}) = \mathbf{a} \cdot (\mathbf{b} \times \mathbf{c})$ under rotations of the (rectangular) coordinate system. How about reflections?

9. Prove $(\mathbf{a} \times \mathbf{b}) \cdot (\mathbf{c} \times \mathbf{d}) = (\mathbf{a} \cdot \mathbf{c})(\mathbf{b} \cdot \mathbf{d}) - (\mathbf{a} \cdot \mathbf{d})(\mathbf{b} \cdot \mathbf{c})$. [Comp. Eq. (8–9).]

10. Complete the rotation of the (rectangular) coordinate system:

$$x_1' = (\tfrac{2}{7})x_1 + (\tfrac{3}{7})x_2 + (\tfrac{6}{7})x_3,$$
$$x_2' = (\tfrac{3}{7})x_1 - (\tfrac{6}{7})x_2 + (\tfrac{2}{7})x_3,$$
$$x_3' = ?$$

11. Prove that the six planes which bisect the angles between the faces of a tetrahedron pass through one point.

12. Show that the orthogonality relations can also be written in the form $c_{ji}c_{ki} = \delta_{jk}$.

13. Take the transformation matrix c_{ij}:

$$\begin{Vmatrix} -\dfrac{3}{5} & \dfrac{16}{25} & -\dfrac{12}{25} \\[2mm] \dfrac{4}{5} & \dfrac{12}{25} & -\dfrac{9}{25} \\[2mm] 0 & -\dfrac{3}{5} & -\dfrac{4}{5} \end{Vmatrix}$$

If $x_i' = c_{ij}x_i$, express x_i in terms of x_i'. Verify that the orthogonality relations exist. Compute C.

14. *Euler angles.* Show that the orthogonality relations are satisfied for the matrix c_{ij} if

$$c_{11} = \cos\psi\cos\phi - \sin\psi\sin\phi\cos\theta,$$
$$c_{12} = \sin\psi\cos\phi + \cos\psi\sin\phi\cos\theta,$$
$$c_{13} = \sin\phi\sin\theta,$$
$$c_{21} = -\cos\psi\sin\phi - \sin\psi\cos\phi\cos\theta,$$
$$c_{22} = -\sin\psi\sin\phi + \cos\psi\cos\phi\cos\theta,$$
$$c_{23} = \cos\phi\sin\theta,$$
$$c_{31} = \sin\psi\sin\theta,$$
$$c_{32} = -\cos\psi\sin\theta,$$
$$c_{33} = \cos\theta.$$

The angles $\theta = \angle Z_1OZ_2$, $\phi = \angle NOX_2$, $\psi = \angle X_1ON$, where ON is the line of intersection of the planes X_1OY_1 and X_2OY_2, are the Euler angles.

15. Show that transformation of the axes of a rectangular coordinate system with fixed origin may be produced by a rotation about an axis passing through the origin. This theorem explains why we call such a transformation rotational.

CHAPTER 9

PROJECTIVE THEORY OF QUADRICS

9–1 Intersections and tangents. A quadric surface, surface of the second order, or *quadric*, is given by a homogeneous equation of the second degree in projective point coordinates:

$$a_{11}x_1^2 + 2a_{12}x_1x_2 + \cdots + 2a_{34}x_3x_4 + a_{44}x_4^2 = 0, \qquad (1\text{--}1)$$

or

$$F(x) = a_{\lambda\mu}x_\lambda x_\mu = 0, \quad a_{\lambda\mu} = a_{\mu\lambda} \quad (\lambda,u = 1,2,3,4), \qquad (1\text{--}1a)$$

where we take the $a_{\lambda\mu}$ to be real numbers. A change of coordinate system $x_\kappa' = c_{\kappa\lambda}x_\lambda$ changes Eq. (1–1) into another homogeneous equation of the second degree. We find that the *discriminant*,

$$D_4 = \text{Det } (a_{\lambda\mu}), \qquad (1\text{--}2)$$

is a relative invariant under this transformation.

We take a point $P(p_\lambda)$ on the surface S of Eq. (1–1), and connect it with another point $Q(q_\lambda)$ of space by means of a line l. The points on l are given by $\rho x_\lambda = p_\lambda + tq_\lambda$ (t variable parameter); the points of intersection of l with S are given by the value of t satisfying the equation

$$F(p) + tF(p,q) + t^2F(q) = 0, \quad F(p,q) = a_{\lambda\mu}p_\lambda q_\mu, \qquad (1\text{--}3)$$

where $F(p) = 0$, since we took P on S. There will be, in general, two roots of Eq. (1–3), of which one is $t = 0$:

A straight line has in general two points in common with the surface, which may be real, coincident real, or imaginary. There is one exception:

$$F(p,q) = 0, \quad F(q) = 0, \qquad (1\text{--}4)$$

where *the line lies entirely on the surface.* Such a line is called a *generating* line, or *generator.* That this actually can occur is clear from the case of cones and cylinders. If $F(p,q) = 0$, $F(q) \neq 0$, then the line has two coincident points in common with the surface. All lines through P for which this condition holds have the property that their points $Q(x_\lambda)$ satisfy the equation

$$a_{\lambda\mu}p_\lambda x_\mu = 0, \qquad (1\text{--}5)$$

194

which represents a plane unless P is such that the four equations

$$a_{\lambda\mu}p_\lambda = 0 \tag{1-6}$$

hold.　These equations only have a solution when

$$D_4 = 0. \tag{1-7}$$

We thus find that when $D_4 \neq 0$ all lines having two points in common with the surface at a point P lie in a plane π.　The lines in π through P are called *tangent lines*, the plane π the *tangent plane* at P. *The tangent plane intersects the surface in two lines.*　To prove it, take this plane as $x_4 = 0$ and P (1:0:0:0), then Eqs. (1–1) and (1–5) give $a_{11} = a_{12} = a_{13} = 0$, so that the intersection is given by

$$a_{22}x_2^2 + 2a_{23}x_2x_3 + a_{33}x_3^2 = 0, \quad a_{22}a_{33} - a_{23}^2 \neq 0,$$

which indicates two distinct lines, which may be real or imaginary.

When $D_4 = 0$ and the rank of matrix $\|a_{\lambda\mu}\|$ is 3, then Eq. (1–6) has only one solution, the coordinates of the *vertex*. If we connect the vertex with an arbitrary point Q on the surface, Eq. (1–3) remains satisfied for all t, which means that the line lies entirely on the surface.　The surface consists of lines through the vertex; it is a *cone*, called a *quadratic cone*.　The lines are generating lines of the cone. Every line through the vertex not on the cone has two coincident points in common with the cone.　A tangent plane at a point P of the cone, not the vertex, contains the line connecting P with V: *all points on a generating line of a cone have the same tangent plane.*

When the rank of matrix $\|a_{\lambda\mu}\|$ is two, then the solutions of Eq. (1–6) give points on a line: *there is a line l of vertices.*　Any point on the surface not on l, connected with any point on this line l, lies on the surface: *the surface consists of two planes.*　These planes are different: if we take these planes as $x_3 = 0$, $x_4 = 0$, then we see that D_4 is of rank 2; when D_4 is of rank 1 *the surface consists of two coincident planes.*　In this case the form $F(x)$ is the square of a linear form. When the rank is 1 or 2 we call the quadric ˙singular.　When we use the term quadric, we mean a nonsingular quadric.

Let us now intersect a quadric with a plane, for which we take $x_4 = 0$.　The intersection is given by

$$a_{ij}x_ix_j = 0 \quad (i,j = 1,2,3),$$

which represents a conic. This conic can be imaginary, real nonsingular, or singular. When the plane is a tangent plane the conic is singular. Another case is a plane through the vertex of a cone. Hence:

A plane intersects the quadric in a conic, which in general is nonsingular real or imaginary.

9-2 Class quadric. A class quadric, or *plane quadric*, is defined by an equation of the second degree in plane coordinates:

$$b_{\lambda\mu}u_\lambda u_\mu = 0, \quad b_{\lambda\mu} = b_{\mu\lambda}.$$

We take $b_{\lambda\mu}$ real. This equation defines ∞^2 planes which *envelop* the surface. If we now reproduce the argument of Sec. 9-1 in the dual version, then we obtain the following results.

Through every line pass in general two tangent planes to the surface, which may be real, coincident real, or imaginary. There is one exception, when all the planes through the line are tangent planes to the surface. All lines in a tangent plane $\pi(p_\lambda)$, for which the tangent planes coincide, pass through a point P with equation $b_{\lambda\mu}p_\lambda u_\mu = 0$, unless the discriminant

$$D_4' = \text{Det } (b_{\lambda\mu})$$

vanishes. When $D_4 \neq 0$ the point P is called the *point of contact* of π; the lines through P in π are *tangent lines*. Through the point of contact pass two distinct lines on the surface, which may be real or imaginary.

When $D_4' = 0$ and the rank of the matrix $\|b_{\lambda\mu}\|$ is 3, then there exists a plane such that the surface consists of lines in this plane. These lines envelop a plane curve, hence a *class conic*. The tangent planes to the quadric are pencils of planes through the tangent lines of this class conic. We sometimes express this by saying that the class quadric in this case is a (class) conic.

When the rank of matrix $\|b_{\lambda\mu}\|$ is two, then the surface consists of two distinct points and the planes through them. Rank one gives a single point counted twice. In these two cases we have *singular* class quadrics.

The tangent planes through a point to a nonsingular class quadric envelop a cone which can be imaginary, real, or decomposed into two planes. When the point is a point of contact the cone is singular and intersects the tangent plane in two lines. Another case where the cone is singular is when the point lies in the plane of a class conic (D_4' rank 3).

The analogy between the properties of nonsingular point quadrics and class quadrics is explained by the theorem:

> *A nonsingular class quadric with discriminant of rank 4 is also a nonsingular point quadric with discriminant of rank 4, and conversely.*

The proof does not differ essentially from that of the corresponding theorem on conics. The class equation of $a_{\lambda\mu}x_\lambda x_\mu = 0$ is $A_{\lambda\mu}u_\lambda u_\mu = 0$, where

$$A_{\lambda\mu} = \text{cofactor of } a_{\lambda\mu} \text{ in } D_4.$$

9–3 Polar relationship. By a reasoning similar to that followed in the case of conics, we find the theorem:

> *If on every line through a point the harmonic conjugate point is taken with respect to the points of intersection with the quadric, then the locus of these points is a plane.*

The plane is called the *polar plane*, the point its *pole*. To every point $P(p_\lambda)$ belongs one *polar plane* π with respect to a nonsingular quadric $a_{\lambda\mu}x_\lambda x_\mu = 0$:

$$a_{\lambda\mu}p_\lambda x_\mu = 0, \tag{3–1}$$

provided P is not the vertex of a cone. To every plane π belongs one pole. The polar plane of a point on the quadric is its tangent plane, the pole of the tangent plane is the point of contact.

When a point $Q(q_\lambda)$ lies in the polar plane of a point $P(p_\lambda)$, the relation

$$a_{\lambda\mu}p_\lambda q_\mu = 0 \tag{3–2}$$

exists, which is symmetrical in P and Q. Hence: *when π is the polar plane of P, then the polar plane of a point Q of π passes through P.*

Since Eq. (3–2) is linear in p_λ as well as q_λ, we can prove the following theorem for any quadric which is not a cone:

When a point moves on a line, its polar plane turns about another line.

Indeed, the equation in plane coordinates of the polar plane π of $P(p_\lambda)$ is $\rho u_\lambda = a_{\lambda\mu}p_\mu$; of the polar plane π' of $P'(p'_\lambda)$ is $\sigma u'_\lambda = a_{\lambda\mu}p'_\mu$; hence the polar plane of a point $p_\lambda + tp'_\lambda$ is $a_{\lambda\mu}(p_\mu + tp'_\mu) = \rho u_\lambda + \sigma t' u'_\lambda$, which are the coordinates of the pencil of planes passing through the line of intersection of π and π'. Conversely, when a plane turns about a line l, its pole moves on a line l'. These lines are called *polar lines;* they are in general skew. When they intersect, their plane is the polar plane of the point of intersection. This is the case of a point P on the quadric and its tangent plane π. Then the two polar conjugates at P in l are harmonic with respect to the lines in which l intersects the surface. A *self-polar* line is a generator, and conversely. When the quadric is a cone it may happen that u_λ and u'_λ represent the same plane, in which case the polar plane is stationary. This happens along a line through the vertex of the cone.

The polar plane π of a point P intersects the quadric in a conic, which is nonsingular when P is not on the quadric. Suppose this conic to be real. Then the lines connecting P with the points of the quadric are tangent lines, and form the *tangent cone* to the quadric at P (Fig. 9–1). This tangent cone is a cone of the second degree. It is a self-dual figure. In the case that the quadric is a cone the tangent cone splits into the two tangent planes through the line connecting P with the vertex. When the polar plane intersects the quadric in an imaginary conic, the tangent cone is also imaginary.

Where a conic possesses ∞^3 self-polar triangles, a quadric possesses ∞^6 self-polar tetrahedra. We obtain them by selecting a point P_1 arbitrarily, but not on the quadric (∞^3 ways); selecting a point P_2 arbitrarily in the polar plane π_1 of P_1, but not on the quadric (∞^2 ways); selecting a point P_3 arbitrarily on the intersection $(\pi_1\pi_2)$ of x_1 and the polar plane π_2 of P_1, but not on the quadric (∞^1 ways); after which the point P_4 is determined as the intersection $(\pi_1\pi_2\pi_3)$ of $(\pi_1\pi_2)$ with the polar plane π_3 of P_3. The points $P_1P_2P_3P_4$ form the vertices of a *self-polar tetrahedron,* since every vertex is the pole of its opposite face (Fig. 9–2). The three pairs of opposite edges are polar lines. When we take some of the vertices on the quadric we obtain other kinds of self-polar tetrahedra with different properties.

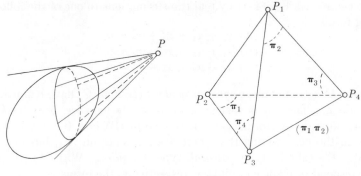

Fig. 9–1   Fig. 9–2

In the case of a cone, we find that every plane through the vertex V has a line of poles through V; and every point except V has one polar plane passing through V. To V as pole all planes belong as polar planes; every plane not through V has V as its pole. There are again ∞^6 self-polar tetrahedra; they have one vertex A_4 at V, and the other three vertices are vertices of any self-polar triangle $A_1A_2A_3$ with respect to any plane intersection of the cone not through V.

We can also verify that it is possible to construct self-polar tetrahedra in the case that the quadric is singular (comp. Sec. 5–7 on conics).

The theory of poles and polars of quadrics begins with Monge, *Géométrie Descriptive* (1797–98) and was further elaborated by Gergonne, Brianchon, Poncelet. Brianchon found the theorem called after him (Sec. 5–10) by a study of the polar relations of quadrics:

9–4 Projective classification of quadrics. Take as the basic tetrahedron of a coordinate system a self-polar tetrahedron. Then $a_{\lambda\mu} \neq 0$, $\lambda \neq \mu$ (comp. Sec. 5–8), and the equation of the quadric becomes

$$a_{11}x_1^2 + a_{22}x_2^2 + a_{33}x_3^2 + a_{44}x_4^2 = 0. \tag{4–1}$$

Since the rank is a projective invariant, the matrix of the coefficient of Eq. (4–1) has the same rank as the original equation. When this rank is 4, all $a_{11}, \ldots, a_{44}$ are $\neq 0$; they may be positive or negative. Then, by selecting the unit point by a transformation

$$\rho x_1' = \sqrt{|a_{11}|}x_1, \quad \rho x_2' = \sqrt{|a_{22}|}x_2, \quad \rho x_3' = \sqrt{|a_{33}|}x_3, \quad \rho x_4' = \sqrt{|a_{44}|}x_4,$$

we can reduce Eq. (4–1) by real transformations to one of the following forms

$$\text{(A)} \quad x_1^2 + x_2^2 + x_3^2 + x_4^2 = 0,$$
$$\text{(B)} \quad x_1^2 + x_2^2 + x_3^2 - x_4^2 = 0,$$
$$\text{(C)} \quad x_1^2 + x_2^2 - x_3^2 - x_4^2 = 0.$$

Case (A) is that of an *imaginary quadric;* (B) and (C) have real points on them. The law of inertia of quadratic forms (Sec. 5–8) teaches that no real transformation can transform (B) into (C). We shall see in the next section that there are real lines on (C), but not on (B). We call the type (B) *oval,* type (C) *ruled.* With (A),(B),(C) correspond in plane coordinates, respectively, the forms

$$\text{(A')} \quad u_1^2 + u_2^2 + u_3^2 + u_4^2 = 0,$$
$$\text{(B')} \quad u_1^2 + u_2^2 + u_3^2 - u_4^2 = 0,$$
$$\text{(C')} \quad u_1^2 + u_2^2 - u_3^2 - u_4^2 = 0.$$

When the matrix $\|a_{\lambda\mu}\|$ has the rank 3, one of the $a_{\lambda\mu}$ in Eq. (4–1) is zero. The equation of the quadratic cone can therefore be cast into one of the two forms,

$$\text{(A}_1\text{)} \quad x_1^2 + x_2^2 + x_3^2 = 0, \qquad \text{(B}_1\text{)} \quad x_1^2 + x_2^2 - x_3^2 = 0,$$

of which only (B₁) is real. The vertex is $(0:0:0:1)$. Two distinct planes (rank 2) can be given the equations

$$\text{(A}_2\text{)} \quad x_1^2 + x_2^2 = 0, \qquad \text{(B}_2\text{)} \quad x_1^2 - x_2^2 = 0,$$

of which only (B₂) is real, while two coincident planes (rank 1) can be represented by

$$\text{(C)} \quad x_1^2 = 0.$$

For class quadrics, we find that

$$\text{(A}_1'\text{)} \quad u_1^2 + u_2^2 + u_3^2 = 0, \qquad \text{(B}_1'\text{)} \quad u_1^2 + u_2^2 - u_3^2 = 0$$

represent class quadrics in the plane $x_4 = 0$;

$$\text{(A}_2'\text{)} \quad u_1^2 + u_2^2 = 0, \qquad \text{(B}_2'\text{)} \quad u_1^2 - u_2^2 = 0$$

represent two distinct points; and

$$\text{(C')} \quad u_1^2 = 0$$

a point counted twice.

We summarize:

There exist three projectively different types of nonsingular real point quadrics, whose equations can be reduced to

$$x_1^2 + x_2^2 + x_3^2 - x_4^2 = 0, \quad x_1^2 + x_2^2 - x_3^2 - x_4^2 = 0, \quad x_1^2 + x_2^2 - x_3^2 = 0.$$

The third type is a cone.

9–5 The regulus. The ruled quadric (type C)

$$x_1^2 + x_2^2 - x_3^2 - x_4^2 = 0 \tag{5-1}$$

contains two families of ∞^1 (real) lines. We obtain their equation by writing Eq. (5–1) in the form

$$x_1^2 - x_3^2 = x_4^2 - x_2^2, \tag{5-2}$$

or

$$(x_1 + x_3)(x_1 - x_3) = (x_4 - x_2)(x_4 + x_2),$$

from which follows immediately that the two families of lines with equations

$$\text{(I) } x_1 - x_3 = \lambda(x_4 - x_2), \qquad \text{(II) } x_1 - x_3 = \mu(x_4 + x_2),$$
$$x_1 + x_3 = \frac{1}{\lambda}(x_4 + x_2), \qquad\qquad x_1 + x_3 = \frac{1}{\mu}(x_4 - x_2), \tag{5-3}$$

where λ and μ are parameters, lie on the surface (5–2). Each family is called a *regulus*.

The lines of each regulus are skew. We show this for regulus (I) by taking two lines $\lambda = \lambda_1$, $\lambda = \lambda_2$, $\lambda_1 \neq \lambda_2$. Then, since

$$\begin{vmatrix} 1 & \lambda_1 & -1 & -\lambda_1 \\ 1 & -\dfrac{1}{\lambda_1} & 1 & -\dfrac{1}{\lambda_1} \\ 1 & \lambda_2 & -1 & -\lambda_2 \\ 1 & -\dfrac{1}{\lambda_2} & 1 & -\dfrac{1}{\lambda_2} \end{vmatrix} = -4\,\frac{(\lambda_1 - \lambda_2)^2}{\lambda_1 \lambda_2},$$

there exist no values of x_4 which satisfy the equations for two lines of set (I). Hence their lines cannot intersect. A similar reasoning holds for set (II).

Every line of one regulus has a point in common with every line of the other regulus. Indeed,

$$\begin{vmatrix} 1 & \lambda & -1 & -\lambda \\ 1 & -\dfrac{1}{\lambda} & 1 & -\dfrac{1}{\lambda} \\ 1 & -\mu & -1 & -\mu \\ 1 & \dfrac{1}{\mu} & 1 & -\dfrac{1}{\mu} \end{vmatrix} = 0 \quad \text{(the rank is 3)}.$$

We can therefore solve the x_λ from (I) and (II) and obtain one and only one answer:

$$x_1:x_2:x_3:x_4 = (1 + \lambda\mu):(\lambda - \mu):(1 - \lambda\mu):(\lambda + \mu), \quad (5\text{-}4)$$

which gives us a parametric representation of the quadric in terms of λ and μ. The value $\lambda = $ constant gives us the equation of one of the lines of regulus (I), the value $\mu = $ constant that of one of the lines of regulus (II). The two reguli I and II are called *associated*.

Through each point P of the quadric (1–5) *passes one line of each regulus,* since we can find for each P the corresponding value of λ and μ from Eq. (5–3). The plane through these lines is the tangent plane at P, which follows from the considerations of Sec. 9–1 and also by direct evaluation from Eq. (5–4) [see Ex. 1, below]. When P moves along a line l of a regulus, the tangent plane changes. No two points on l have the same tangent plane, since this would involve that two lines of the other regulus intersect. Moreover, every plane through l is at one point a tangent plane, since there passes a line of the other regulus through every point of l. Hence: *when a point P passes along l, then the tangent plane at P passes through all positions on l and that only once.*

A regulus is determined by three arbitrary skew lines. To prove it, take one of the lines, l_1, along the side A_3A_4, another of the lines, l_2, along the side A_1A_2 of a coordinate tetrahedron, while the third line, l_3, connects a point P of A_2A_4 with a point Q of A_1A_3. This can always be achieved, since through every point of one of the lines (such as A_1 on l_2) a line can be laid (such as A_3QA_1) intersecting both other lines. If $P\,(0:a:0:1)$, $Q\,(b:0:1:0)$, then an arbitrary point R on l_3 is given by $(\lambda b : a : 1)$. The plane through R and l_1, and the plane through R and l_2 are given by

$$ax_1 - \lambda b x_2 = 0, \quad x_3 - \lambda x_4 = 0,$$

respectively. These equations determine a line m through R intersecting both l_1 and l_2. When R moves along the line l_3, then the line m describes a surface with the equation

$$ax_1 x_4 - b x_2 x_3 = 0,$$

which by a real transformation of coordinates can be transformed into the Eq. (5–1) of a ruled quadric.

Hence both l_1, l_2, l_3 and the variable m lie on a quadric of the type (5–1). The l_i form part of one regulus, the m form the other. *Three arbitrary lines therefore determine not only the single regulus to which they belong, but also another regulus, the associated one.*

Four mutually skew lines do not, in general, determine a regulus. When they do, they form a *coregular* or *hyperboloid group*, and we speak of *four hyperboloid lines*. Such a group of four lines admits a regulus of lines which intersects all four. For four lines l_1, l_2, l_3, l_4 to constitute a hyperboloid group it is, however, only necessary that three lines m_1, m_2, m_3 exist which intersect all four. These three lines m must be skew, since otherwise the l would be coplanar, and hence the m form a regulus intersecting all l. Two lines m are not sufficient to determine the hyperboloid group, since the following theorem holds (for real lines):

> *Four mutually skew lines are, in general, met by at most two lines; if they are met by three, they are met by the lines of a regulus.*

The last part of the theorem has already been proved. As to the first part, the regulus formed by three of the four lines, e.g., l_1, l_2, l_3 forms a quadric Q which has two points P_1, P_2 in common with the

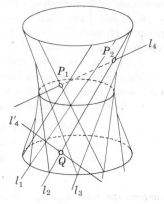

Fig. 9–3

fourth line l_4, unless l_4 lies on Q (Fig. 9–3).   The line through P_1 on Q which intersects l_1, l_2, l_3, and the similar line through P_2 are the two lines intersecting l_1, l_2, l_3.   They may be real or imaginary; when l_4 touches Q (l'_4 in Fig. 9–3) the two lines coincide.

Systems of four hyperboloid lines are of frequent occurrence in space geometry.   They form, in many cases, the space analogue of three concurrent lines in the plane (see, e.g., Ex. 4, Sec. 10–6).

We use the term *hyperboloid*, although this concept is affine.   The term *coregular* is more correct in projective theory.

1. Using the equations (5–4) show that the plane through the two lines passing through a point of the quadric is the tangent plane.

2. Show that except for the two reguli there are no more lines on a hyperbolic quadric.

3. Find the equation of the imaginary lines on the quadric

$$x_1^2 + x_2^2 + x_3^2 - x_4^2 = 0$$

and show that there are no real lines on this surface.

4. Four lines of one regulus intersect the lines of the conjugate regulus in points of constant cross ratio.

5. *Projective pencils of planes.*   When $P_\lambda = 0$, $\lambda = 1,2,3,4$ are four independent planes, then the pencils $P_1 - tP_2 = 0$ and $P_3 - uP_4 = 0$ intersect in the lines of a regulus, if between t and u a bilinear relation exists.   These pencils are called *projective*.   Prove this and the dual theorem (Steiner).

6. If four lines, each in one face of a tetrahedron, form a hyperboloid group, then each face is met by the lines in the three other faces in three collinear points.   Prove and dualize.

7. *Conical sets.*   Five noncoplanar lines through a point determine a quadratic cone, therefore six lines through a point lying on such a cone satisfy a relation.   Formulate such a relation.

8. Show that the transformation

$$
\begin{aligned}
x_1 &= x'_1 - a_{12}x'_2 + \beta_{13}x'_3 + \alpha_{14}x'_4, \\
x_2 &= a_{11}x'_2 + \beta_{23}x'_3 + \alpha_{24}x'_4, \\
x_3 &= \phantom{x'_1 - a_{12}x'_2 +} \beta_{33}x'_3 + \alpha_{34}x'_4, \\
x_4 &= \phantom{x'_1 - a_{12}x'_2 + \beta_{13}x'_3 +} \alpha_{44}x'_4,
\end{aligned}
\qquad (a_{11}\beta_{33}\alpha_{44} \neq 0),
$$

changes the form $a_{\lambda\mu}x_\lambda x_\mu = 0$ into $a_{11}x_1'^2 + a_{11}\beta_{33}x_2'^2 + \beta_{33}\alpha_{44}x_3'^2 + \alpha_{44}Ax_4'^2$, which has the form (4–1).   Here $\alpha_{\lambda\mu}$ is the cofactor of $a_{\lambda\mu}$ in $A = \text{Det}\ (a_{\lambda\mu})$;

$\beta_{13} = a_{21}a_{32} - a_{22}a_{31}$, $\beta_{23} = a_{31}a_{12} - a_{11}a_{32}$, $\beta_{33} = a_{11}a_{22} - a_{12}a_{21}$. (*Hint:* Keep A_1 in place $= A_1'$, A_2' on the intersection of A_1A_2 with the polar π_1' of A_1', A_3' on the intersection of $x_4 = 0$, π_1' and the polar π_2' of A_2'.) See Jacobi, *Werke III*, p. 590.

9. *Hexagons on a quadric.* A skew hexagon on a quadric can be obtained by taking alternately a side on one and then the other of the two reguli. If the sides of a skew hexagon are 1,2,3,4,5,6, then we call it a *Pascal hexagon* if the lines in which the planes (12),(45), the planes (23),(56), and the planes (34),(61) intersect, are in a plane π. Show that every hexagon on a quadric is a Pascal hexagon, and conversely.

10. If the lines connecting the vertices (12),(45); (23),(56); and (34),(61) of a skew hexagon intersect in a point P, we have a *Brianchon hexagon*. Show that every Pascal hexagon is also a Brianchon hexagon and conversely, and that P and π (Ex. 9) are pole and polar with respect to the quadric (Hesse).

11. Show that a ruled quadric can be represented by the equations $x_1:x_2:x_3:x_4 = u:v:uv$, where u and v are parameters.

12. Show that a quadratic cone can be represented by the equations $x_1:x_2:x_3:x_4 = 1:u:u^2:v$, where u and v are parameters.

13. If two quadrics have two intersecting lines in common, then their full intersection consists of these lines and a conic. Prove.

14. If two quadrics have a conic C_1 in common, then they have another conic C_2 in common. Prove. Can C_1 be identical with C_2? (See Sec. 10–7.)

15. If two quadrics have two skew lines in common, then their full intersection is a skew quadrilateral, that is, a quadrilateral in which the four sides do not lie in a plane. Prove.

16. Show that through nine points in a general position we can lay one and only one quadric.

17. If the equation of the quadric is written in the form $ax_1x_3 + bx_2x_4 = 0$, find the relation between the coordinate tetrahedron and the surface.

18. Show that the lines connecting the vertices A_λ of a tetrahedron with those of its polar tetrahedron B_λ with respect to a quadric form a hyperboloid set. Take the vertices different from each other. (Comp. Ex. 8, Sec. 5–7.)

CHAPTER 10

AFFINE AND EUCLIDEAN THEORY OF QUADRICS

10–1 Center and conjugate directions. The affine theory is obtained from the projective theory by singling out the special plane $x_4 = 0$ as the plane at infinity. Let us first suppose that this plane is not tangent to the quadric. Its pole C is not at infinity and has the property that every chord through it intersecting the quadric is bisected at C. This point is called the *center*. A line through it is a *diameter*, a plane through it a *diametral plane*. Quadrics with a center are called *central quadrics*.

We introduce affine coordinates x,y,z; $x:y:z:1 = x_1:x_2:x_3:x_4$. The equation of the quadric can then be written:

$$F(x,y,z) \equiv a_{11}x^2 + 2a_{12}xy + \cdots + a_{33}z^2 + 2a_{14}x + 2a_{24}y + 2a_{34}z + a_{44}$$
$$\equiv a_{ij}x_ix_j + 2a_{i4}x_i + a_{44} = 0 \quad (i,j = 1,2,3), \tag{1-1}$$

where we have written x_i for (x,y,z).

We move the (oblique) axes parallel to themselves to the center $C(x_0,y_0,z_0)$:

$$x = x_1 + x_0, \quad y = y_1 + y_0, \quad z = z_1 + z_0. \tag{1-2}$$

The x_1,y_1,z_1 are the new coordinates. The equation of the surface in the new coordinates has no linear terms, since changes from x_1,y_1,z_1 into $-x_1,-y_1,-z_1$ must leave the equation unchanged. For the coordinates of C we thus find the equations

$$a_{11}x + a_{12}y + a_{13}z + a_{14} = 0,$$
$$a_{12}x + a_{22}y + a_{23}z + a_{24} = 0 \quad \text{or} \quad a_{ij}x_j + a_{i4} = 0 \quad (i,j = 1,2,3), \tag{1-3}$$
$$a_{13}x + a_{23}y + a_{33}z + a_{34} = 0,$$

where we have changed (x_0,y_0,z_0) into (x,y,z). These equations can be written

$$\frac{\partial F}{\partial x} = 0, \quad \frac{\partial F}{\partial y} = 0, \quad \frac{\partial F}{\partial z} = 0. \tag{1-4}$$

The form (1–4) is also obtained by expanding $F(x_1 + x_0, y_1 + y_a, z_1 + z_0) = 0$ into a Taylor series with respect to the variables x_1,y_1,z_1.

The Eqs. (1–3) have one solution, provided that $D_3 \neq 0$:

$$D_3 = \begin{vmatrix} a_{11} & a_{12} & a_{13} \\ a_{12} & a_{22} & a_{23} \\ a_{13} & a_{23} & a_{33} \end{vmatrix}. \tag{1–5}$$

The inequality $D_3 \neq 0$ is therefore the condition that $x_4 = 0$ is not tangent to the conic. (See Ex. 3, Sec. 10–2.) The number D_3 is, like D_4, a relative affine invariant. When, under changes of axes $x'_i = c_{ij}x_j + c_i$, $F(x,y,z) = 0$ changes into $a'_{ij}x'_i x'_j + 2a'_{i4}x'_i + a'_{44} = 0$, D_3 changes into

$$D'_3 = D_3 C^2 \quad [C = \text{Det } c_{ij}]. \tag{1–6}$$

In the new coordinates, the surface has the equation

$$a_{11}x^2 + 2a_{12}xy + \cdots + a_{33}z^2 + F(x_0,y_0,z_0) \doteq 0, \tag{1–7}$$

where we have changed x_1,y_1,z_1 into x,y,z. Because of Eqs. (1–3) and of Eq. (1–2) of Chapter 9,

$$\begin{aligned} F(x_0,y_0,z_0) &= x_0(a_{11}x_0 + a_{12}y_0 + a_{13}z_0 + a_{14}) + y_0(a_{12}x_0 + a_{22}y_0 \\ &\quad + a_{23}z_0 + a_{24}) + z_0(a_{13}x_0 + a_{23}y_0 + a_{33}z_0 + a_{34}) \\ &\quad + a_{14}x_0 + a_{24}y_0 + a_{34}z_0 + a_{44} \\ &= a_{14}x_0 + a_{24}y_0 + a_{34}z_0 + a_{44} = -D_4/D_3, \end{aligned}$$

so that Eq. (1–7) can be written

$$a_{11}x^2 + 2a_{12}xy + \cdots + a_{33}z^2 - D_4/D_3 = 0. \tag{1–8}$$

To the point of infinity of a diameter as pole belongs a *diametral plane*, the *conjugate* plane of this diameter. If the coordinates of such a point in projective coordinates are $(y_1:y_2:y_3:0)$, then its polar plane with respect to the quadric $a_{\lambda\mu}x_\lambda x_\mu = 0$ $(\lambda,\mu = 1,2,3,4)$ has the equation

$$\begin{aligned} (a_{11}y_1 + a_{12}y_2 + a_{13}y_3)x_1 + (a_{12}y_1 + a_{22}y_2 + a_{23}y_3)x_2 \\ + (a_{13}y_1 + a_{23}y_2 + a_{33}y_3)x_3 + (a_{14}y_1 + a_{24}y_2 + a_{34}y_3) = 0. \end{aligned} \tag{1–9}$$

Passing to affine coordinates with the center C as origin, we deduce from Eq. (1–9) that a diameter d_1 given by $x:y:z = \lambda_1:\lambda_2:\lambda_3$ has a conjugate plane π_1:

$$(a_{11}\lambda_1 + a_{12}\lambda_2 + a_{13}\lambda_3)x + (a_{12}\lambda_1 + a_{22}\lambda_2 + a_{23}\lambda_3)y$$
$$+ (a_{13}\lambda_1 + a_{23}\lambda_2 + a_{33}\lambda_3)z = 0. \qquad (1\text{--}10)$$

If we take a diameter d_2 in this plane, then its conjugate plane π_2 intersects plane π_1 in a diameter d_3, of which the conjugate plane π_3 passes through d_1 and d_2. The three diameters d_i form a set of *conjugate diameters*, their planes π_i a set of *conjugate diametral planes*. With the plane $x_4 = 0$ they form a self-polar tetrahedron. There are ∞^3 such tetrahedra.

Chords parallel to a diameter are bisected by the conjugate plane. Each line direction is conjugate to a conjugate plane direction, and conversely. Each plane has its pole on the conjugate diameter, each point P has its polar plane conjugate to the direction CP. Moreover:

The tangent planes at the points where a diameter intersects the quadric are parallel to the conjugate plane through the center.

10–2 The affine normal forms. When we take a set of conjugate diameters as our coordinate system, we derive from Eq. (1–10) that $a_{12} = a_{13} = a_{23}$. This also follows directly from the projective normal forms of Sec. 9–4. We obtain, after appropriate choice of the unit measure on the new coordinate axes, the following affine normal forms.

1. The surface has no real points at infinity. Case (B) of Sec. 9–4 gives the normal form either as

$$x^2 + y^2 + z^2 = -1, \qquad (2\text{--}1)$$

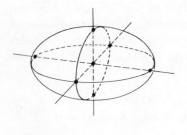

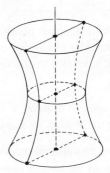

FIG. 10–1   FIG. 10–2

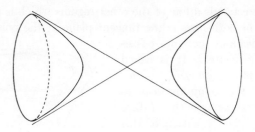

Fig. 10–3

which has no real points, or as

$$x^2 + y^2 + z^2 = 1, \qquad (2\text{--}2)$$

the *ellipsoid* (Fig. 10–1).

2. The surface has a real nonsingular conic at infinity. Case (C) gives the normal form as

$$x^2 + y^2 - z^2 = 1, \qquad (2\text{--}3)$$

the *hyperboloid of one sheet* (Fig. 10–2), or as

$$x^2 - y^2 - z^2 = 1, \qquad (2\text{--}4)$$

the *hyperboloid of two sheets* (Fig. 10–3). For the ellipsoid and the hyperboloid of two sheets $D_4 < 0$; for the hyperboloid of one sheet $D_4 > 0$. This relation is invariant under the choice of affine axes. The case $D_4 = 0$, rank 3, hence $D_3 \neq 0$, offers no further difficulties. Its normal form can be obtained from case (B) and is either

$$x^2 + y^2 + z^2 = 0, \qquad (2\text{--}5)$$

the *imaginary cone*, or

$$x^2 + y^2 - z^2 = 0, \qquad (2\text{--}6)$$

the *real cone*, consisting of lines through the origin, which is the vertex. These lines are the *generating* lines of the cone.

From Eq. (1–8) follows that a geometrical interpretation of $D_4 = 0$, $D_3 \neq 0$ is that *the center lies on the quadric*.

The hyperboloid of one sheet contains real lines, which form two reguli. The lines of these reguli are paired, since to each line of one regulus corresponds a line of the other regulus which is parallel to it. The plane of both lines is the tangent plane at the point at infinity of these lines and therefore passes through the center. It is called the *asymptotic tangent plane*. These planes envelop the *asymptotic cone*, tangent to the surface at infinity. The equation of this cone is (2-6), because the tangent plane to surface (2-3) at $(a:b:c:0)$, $a^2 + b^2 - c^2 = 0$, is $ax + by - cz = 0$, which is also the tangent plane to cone (2-6) at any point of the line $x:y:z = a:b:c$ (Fig. 10-4). A hyperboloid of two sheets has also an asymptotic cone with center at the center of the surface.

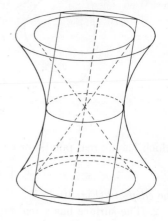

Fig. 10-4

EXERCISES

1. Show that the diametral plane conjugate to the diameter $x:y:z = a:b:c$ of the quadric $x^2 + y^2 + z^2 = 1$ has the equation $ax + by + cz = 0$.

2. Prove algebraically that the conjugate planes of the points on a diameter of the quadric $x^2 + y^2 + z^2 = 1$ are parallel to each other.

3. Show that $D_3 = 0$ means that the ideal plane is tangent to the quadric.

4. Show that all parallel sections of an ellipsoid or a hyperboloid are similar.

5. At all points of a generating line of a cone the tangent plane is the same. Prove algebraically that it is conjugate to the generating lines.

6. Find the equation of the tangent planes to the ellipsoid and the hyperboloids at an arbitrary point (x_0, y_0, z_0).

7. Which direction is conjugate to the asymptotic tangent plane?

8. Show that the volume of the parallelepiped formed by the tangent planes at the points where three conjugate diameters intersect an ellipsoid is the same for all conjugate sets.

10-3 Paraboloid and cylinder. When the special plane $x_4 = 0$ is tangent to the quadric, we select a particular type of self-polar tetrahedron; it has its vertex A_1 at the point of contact of $x_4 = 0$ and its vertex A_4 at another point of the quadric; the tangent plane at A_4 will be the plane $x_4 = 0$. On the intersection of $x_1 = 0$ and $x_4 = 0$ we select A_2; A_3 then appears as the pole of plane $A_1A_2A_4$ or $x_3 = 0$ on this same intersection.

Then $a_{11} = a_{12} = a_{13} = a_{24} = a_{44} = a_{23} = 0$ and the equation of the quadric takes the form

$$a_{22}x_2^2 + a_{33}x_3^2 + 2a_{14}x_1x_4 = 0,$$

or, in affine coordinates:

$$a_{22}y^2 + a_{33}z^2 + 2a_{14}x = 0. \qquad (3\text{--}1)$$

The direction of A_1A_4 is that of a *diameter*, it is the direction of the x-axis. For surfaces with D_4 of rank 4 we have a_{22}, a_{33}, a_{14} all $\neq 0$. There are two normal forms depending on the sign of $a_{22}a_{33}$:

$$y^2 + z^2 = x, \qquad (3\text{--}2)$$
$$y^2 - z^2 = x. \qquad (3\text{--}3)$$

The first is that of the *elliptic paraboloid*, which has no real lines on it (Fig. 10–5). The second is that of the *hyperbolic paraboloid* (Fig. 10–6). The elliptic paraboloid intersects the plane at infinity in two imaginary lines, the hyperbolic paraboloid in two real lines, which are the lines at infinity of the two families of parallel planes $y \pm z =$ constant. These planes are called the *directrix planes;* they intersect in lines which have the direction of the diameter. There

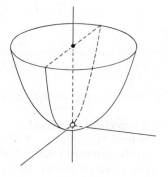

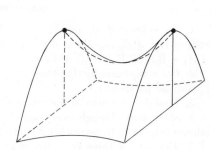

FIG. 10–5   FIG. 10–6

are two reguli on the hyperbolic paraboloid, and since all lines of one regulus intersect the lines at infinity of the other regulus, all lines of one regulus are parallel to a family of ∞^1 parallel planes, the corresponding family of directrix planes.

Three skew lines parallel to a plane determine a hyperbolic paraboloid, since the lines of the regulus determined by them intersect the line at infinity of this plane. This plane at infinity has therefore a line, and hence two lines, in common with the quadric determined by the given three skew lines, which shows again that the plane at infinity is a tangent plane to the quadric.

Every tangent plane to the elliptic paraboloid has only one real point in common with the quadric, every tangent plane to the hyperbolic paraboloid has two real lines in common with the quadric.

A particular form of the cone appears when the vertex is at infinity. Normal form (B) then gives the equation of the *elliptic cylinder*,

$$x^2 + y^2 = 1,$$

and the *hyperbolic cylinder*,

$$x^2 - y^2 = 1.$$

In these cases the plane at infinity is not a tangent plane. When this is the case, we have to select our coordinates in such a way that we obtain Eq. (3–1). For D_4 of rank 3 we have a_{22} (or a_{33}) = 0 and find the *parabolic cylinder*

$$y^2 = x.$$

EXERCISES

1. Three lines of one regulus on the hyperbolic paraboloid intersect the lines of the other regulus in segments of constant ratio (Fig. 10–7: A_1A_2 : $A_2A_3 = B_1B_2 : B_2B_3 = C_1C_2 : C_2C_3 = \cdots$). Prove.

2. Prove algebraically that three skew lines parallel to a plane determine a hyperbolic paraboloid.

3. Find the equations of the two reguli on a hyperbolic paraboloid.

4. Show that through every skew quadrilateral (Ex. 15, Sec. 9–5) an infinite number of hyperboloids and one hyperbolic paraboloid can be laid.

5. Two sets of three conjugate diameters of a central quadric lie on a quadratic cone. Prove.

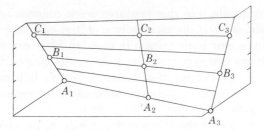

Fig. 10–7

10–4 The S-equation. We introduce a Euclidean metric, and consider first the case $D_3 \neq 0$, that of the central quadric. The normal forms of Sec. 10–2 must now be modified, since we are no longer free to select our own appropriate unit of measure in the three axis directions. The normal forms of ellipsoid, hyperboloid, and real cone can now be written in the classical forms

$$\frac{x^2}{a^2} + \frac{y^2}{b^2} + \frac{z^2}{c^2} = 1, \quad \frac{x^2}{a^2} + \frac{y^2}{b^2} - \frac{z^2}{c^2} = 1,$$
$$\frac{x^2}{a^2} - \frac{y^2}{b^2} - \frac{z^2}{c^2} = 1, \quad \frac{x^2}{a^2} + \frac{y^2}{b^2} - \frac{z^2}{c^2} = 1. \tag{4–1}$$

The coordinate axes are here conjugate diameters. Let us investigate these quadrics with the aid of rectangular systems of axes (x,y,z) which pass into each other by orthogonal transformations $x_i' = c_{ij}x_j$. Since the determinant $C = \text{Det}(c_{ij}) = \pm 1$, both D_3 and D_4 are not changed at all under these transformations [see Eq. (1–6)]; they are *orthogonal invariants*.

We shall now show that it is possible in at least one way to select a rectangular coordinate system in which the equation of the quadric retains the normal forms (4–1). This means that *there is at least one set of three conjugate diameters which is mutually orthogonal.* These diameters are the *principal axes.* This also means, in projective language, that there exists at least one self-polar triangle to two given conics, one of which is nonsingular (in this case the absolute conic). Stated in this way, it is an immediate result of the theory of two conics presented in Sec. 5–9, at any rate for the case (a) that the two conics have four distinct points in common, and (b) that the conics touch in two points. In case (a) there is one common self-polar triangle formed by the diagonal points of the complete quadrangle formed by the four basic points; in case (b) there are ∞^1 such triangles with one common vertex and one common opposite side, the line connecting the two points of contact. We shall proceed without referring to this result, and obtain the mutually orthogonal conjugate diameters algebraically.

The condition that the diameter $x:y:z = \lambda_1:\lambda_2:\lambda_3$ is perpendicular to its conjugate plane follows from Eq. (1–10) and is

$$\frac{a_{11}\lambda_1 + a_{12}\lambda_2 + a_{13}\lambda_3}{\lambda_1} = \frac{a_{12}\lambda_1 + a_{22}\lambda_2 + a_{23}\lambda_3}{\lambda_2}$$
$$= \frac{a_{13}\lambda_1 + a_{23}\lambda_2 + a_{33}\lambda_3}{\lambda_3}. \tag{4–2}$$

It is customary to denote the common value of the fractions in these Eqs. (4–2) by S. Then Eqs. (3–2) are equivalent to the set of three equations

$$\begin{aligned}
(a_{11} - S)\lambda_1 + a_{12}\lambda_2 + a_{13}\lambda_3 &= 0, \\
a_{12}\lambda_1 + (a_{22} - S)\lambda_2 + a_{23}\lambda_3 &= 0, \\
a_{13}\lambda_1 + a_{23}\lambda_2 + (a_{33} - S)\lambda_3 &= 0.
\end{aligned} \tag{4–3}$$

To every solution S of the determinant equation

$$\begin{vmatrix}
a_{11} - S & a_{12} & a_{13} \\
a_{12} & a_{22} - S & a_{23} \\
a_{13} & a_{23} & a_{33} - S
\end{vmatrix} = 0 \tag{4–4}$$

we have one solution $\lambda_1:\lambda_2:\lambda_3$, hence one diameter perpendicular to its conjugate diametral plane. The existence of at least one set of these conjugate diameters is now guaranteed by the theorem:

The roots of the S-equation are real.

A proof of this theorem can be based on the remark that since all a_{ij} are real, at least one solution $S = S_3$ of Eq. (4–4) is real. Let the other roots be S_1,S_2 and let us suppose that they are complex: $S_1 = p + iq$, $S_2 = p - iq$. To S_1 belongs the solution $\lambda_1:\lambda_2:\lambda_3$, to S_2 the solution $\mu_1:\mu_2:\mu_3$. These solutions are also complex conjugate. We multiply the terms of the three equations

$$a_{i1}\lambda_1 + a_{i2}\lambda_2 + a_{i3}\lambda_3 = S_1\lambda_i \quad (i = 1,2,3), \tag{4–5}$$

by μ_1,μ_2,μ_3 respectively, and add. Similarly, we multiply the terms of the three equations

$$a_{i1}\mu_1 + a_{i2}\mu_2 + a_{i3}\mu_3 = S_2\mu_i \tag{4–6}$$

by $\lambda_1,\lambda_2,\lambda_3$, respectively, and add. We obtain

$$S_1(\lambda_i\mu_i) = S_2(\lambda_i\mu_i),$$

hence, since $S_1 \neq S_2$,

$$\lambda_i\mu_i = \lambda_1\mu_1 + \lambda_2\mu_2 + \lambda_3\mu_3 = 0. \tag{4–7}$$

Since λ_i is the complex conjugate of μ_i, the products $\lambda_1\mu_1, \lambda_2\mu_2, \lambda_3\mu_3$ are all positive, which contradicts the condition (4–7). Hence S_1 and S_2 must be real, which means that all roots of Eq. (4–1) are real.

There exist many demonstrations of this theorem. Perhaps the first was that of Lagrange, in a paper of 1773 on the rotation of a body (*Oeuvres* 3, p. 695). The proof which we have given is due to Cauchy, *Exercises d'Analyse* III (1828). Cauchy gave another proof in *Exercises* IV (1829), which is found in many textbooks. This proof is based on the fact that if the S-equation in n rows and columns, Det $(a_{\alpha\beta} - S\delta_{\alpha\beta})' = 0$ $(\alpha,\beta = 1, \ldots, n; \delta_{\alpha\beta}$ the Kronecker symbol, see Sec. 8–6), has unequal roots, they are separated by those of the S-equation: Det $(a_{pq} - S\delta_{pq}) = 0$ $(p,q = 1, \ldots, n - 1)$. This proof needs some amplification for the case of equal roots (Cauchy, *Oeuvres* Ser. 2, Vol. 8, pp. 14–18; Vol. 9, pp. 174–195). Cauchy's paper of 1829 has the title: *Sur l'équaticn à l'aide on détermine les inégalités séculaires des mouvements des planètes*, which may be the reason that the S-determinant is known as the *secular determinant*. For another proof, see O. Staude, *Math. Annalen* **61** (1905), pp. 392–396. The proof for the reality of the roots requires that the $a_{\alpha\beta}$ be real and symmetric: $a_{\alpha\beta} = a_{\beta\alpha}$. It also holds for equations of the form Det $(a_{\alpha\beta} - Sb_{\alpha\beta}) = 0$, provided the $b_{\alpha\beta}$ are symmetric and the quadratic form $b_{\alpha\beta}x_\alpha x_\beta$ is *definite*, that is, maintains the same sign for all real $x_\alpha \neq 0$ (e.g., $x_1^2 + x_2^2 + x_3^2$ is definite; $x_1^2 + x_2^2 - x_3^2$ is indefinite).

Let us first suppose that the roots S_1,S_2,S_3 of the S-equation are different from each other. Then there exist three directions $(\lambda_1,\lambda_2,\lambda_3)$, $(\mu_1,\mu_2,\mu_3),(\nu_1,\nu_2,\nu_3)$ such that, according to Eq. (4–7),

$$\lambda_i\mu_i = 0, \quad \lambda_i\nu_i = 0, \quad \mu_i\nu_i = 0. \tag{4–8}$$

This means that these directions are mutually perpendicular, and we have thus demonstrated that *in the case that the S-equation (4–4) has different roots, there exists one and only one system of perpendicular conjugate directions.* We take these axes as the new x-, y-, and z-axes. Then the four normal forms (4–1) will now have a unique meaning: *they are the equations of the central quadrics with respect to their principal axes.*

The actual computation of the coefficients of x^2, y^2, z^2 is facilitated by the following theorem:

The S-equation is invariant under orthogonal transformations of a rectangular system of axes.

To prove it, consider the form $F \equiv a_{ij}x_ix_j + S(x_1^2 + x_2^2 + x_3^2)$. The coordinates x_i are rectangular coordinates (x, y, z). After an orthogonal transformation of the x_i the form will be $F' \equiv a'_{ij}x'_ix'_j + S(x_1'^2 + x_2'^2 + x_3'^2)$, where the S is the same in both cases, since $x_1^2 + x_2^2 + x_3^2 = x_1'^2 + x_2'^2 + x_3'^2$. The condition that F and F' can be split into two linear factors is given exactly by the S-equation, in a_{ij}, a'_{ij} respectively, according to Sec. 5–2. The S-equation therefore has the same roots before and after transformation.

The S-equation can be written in the form

$$S^3 - D_1S^2 + D_2S - D_3 = 0, \qquad (4\text{–}9)$$

where

$$\begin{aligned} D_1 &= a_{11} + a_{22} + a_{33}, \\ D_2 &= \alpha_{11} + \alpha_{22} + \alpha_{33}, \end{aligned} \qquad (4\text{–}10)$$

α_{ij} being the cofactor of a_{ij} in $D_3 = \mathrm{Det}\,(a_{ij})$. The quantities D_1 and D_2 are therefore orthogonal invariants, just as are D_3 and D_4.

Applying the theorem of the invariance of the S-equation to the normal form,

$$a_{11}x^2 + a_{22}y^2 + a_{33}z^2 + a_{44} = 0, \qquad (4\text{–}11)$$

we find that the roots of the S-equation after, and hence before, transformation are

$$S_1 = a_{11}, \quad S_2 = a_{22}, \quad S_3 = a_{33},$$

so that *in the case that $D_3 \neq 0$ and $D_4 \neq 0$ the final result of the translation of the origin to the center and the rotation (with or without reflection)*

*of coordinate axes into the principal axes is that the following equation
of the quadric is obtained:*

$$S_1 x^2 + S_2 y^2 + S_3 z^2 - \frac{D_4}{D_3} = 0. \tag{4-12}$$

This theorem has been proved for the case that S_1, S_2, S_3 are different. We
shall see that it also holds for the case of equal roots.

From Eq. (4–12) follows that

$$\begin{aligned}
D_1 &= S_1 + S_2 + S_3, \\
D_2 &= S_1 S_2 + S_2 S_3 + S_3 S_1, \\
D_3 &= S_1 S_2 S_3.
\end{aligned} \tag{4-13}$$

The rotation about the center leading from the original axes to the
principal axes is given by the formulas

$$\begin{aligned}
x &= x' \cos \alpha_1 + y' \cos \beta_1 + z' \cos \gamma_1, \\
y &= x' \cos \alpha_2 + y' \cos \beta_2 + z' \cos \gamma_2, \\
z &= x' \cos \alpha_3 + y' \cos \beta_3 + z' \cos \gamma_3; \\
x' &= x \cos \alpha_1 + y \cos \alpha_2 + z \cos \alpha_3, \\
y' &= x \cos \beta_1 + y \cos \beta_2 + z \cos \beta_3, \\
z' &= x \cos \gamma_1 + y \cos \gamma_2 + z \cos \gamma_3,
\end{aligned} \tag{4-14}$$

where

$$\begin{aligned}
\lambda_1 : \lambda_2 : \lambda_3 &= \cos \alpha_1 : \cos \alpha_2 : \cos \alpha_3, \\
\mu_1 : \mu_2 : \mu_3 &= \cos \beta_1 : \cos \beta_2 : \cos \beta_3, \\
\nu_1 : \nu_2 : \nu_3 &= \cos \gamma_1 : \cos \gamma_2 : \cos \gamma_3.
\end{aligned}$$

Hence $\cos \alpha = \lambda_1 / \sqrt{\lambda_1^2 + \lambda_2^2 + \lambda_3^2}$, etc.

The labeling of the principal axes as x-,y-,z-axes depends on the
way we associate the angles $\alpha_i, \beta_i, \gamma_i$ with the coordinate axes.

EXAMPLE. $F(x,y,z) = 7x^2 + 6y^2 + 5z^2 - 4xy - 4yz - 10x - 8y + 4z + 3 = 0.$

Center:
$$\begin{aligned}
7x - 2y - 5 &= 0, \\
-2x + 6y - 2z - 4 &= 0, \\
-2y + 5z + 2 &= 0.
\end{aligned}$$

Hence center $C(1,1,0)$, and $F(1,1,0) = -6$. Equation when the center is
the origin:

$$7x^2 + 6y^2 + 5z^2 - 4xy - 4yz - 6 = 0.$$

S-equation:
$$\begin{vmatrix} 7 - S & -2 & 0 \\ -2 & 6 - S & -2 \\ 0 & -2 & 5 - S \end{vmatrix} = 0,$$

or

$$S^3 - 18S^2 + 99S - 162 = (S - 3)(S - 6)(S - 9) = 0.$$

Normal form: $3x^2 + 6y^2 + 9z^2 - 6 = 0$, ellipsoid.

To obtain the principal planes, we solve

$$7\lambda_1 - 2\lambda_2 \qquad\qquad = S\lambda_1,$$
$$-2\lambda_1 + 6\lambda_2 - 2\lambda_3 = S\lambda_2,$$
$$\qquad\quad - 2\lambda_2 + 5\lambda_3 = S\lambda_3.$$

For

$$S_1 = 3: \quad \lambda_1:\lambda_2:\lambda_3 = 1:2:2,$$
$$S_2 = 6: \quad \mu_1:\mu_2:\mu_3 = 2:1:-2,$$
$$S_3 = 9: \quad \nu_1:\nu_2:\nu_3 = 2:-2:1.$$

The principal planes are therefore (C is a point of all three planes):

$$x + 2y + 2z = 3, \quad 2x + y - 2z = 3, \quad 2x - 2y + z = 0.$$

Since $\sqrt{1 + 4 + 4} = 3$, the rotation about C which turns the given coordinate axes into the principal axes is

$$3x = x' + 2y' + 2z',$$
$$3y = 2x' + y' - 2z',$$
$$3z = 2x' - 2y' + z'.$$

10–5 Double roots of the S-equation. When the S-equation has a double root, $S_1 = S_2$, then we solve first the equations for $\nu_1:\nu_2:\nu_3$ belonging to S_3. When the corresponding diameter is made into the new z-axis, then the line $(0:0:1)$ and the plane $z = 0$ are conjugate, hence $a_{13} = a_{23} = 0$. The S-equation becomes

$$\begin{vmatrix} a_{11} - S & a_{12} & 0 \\ a_{12} & a_{22} - S & 0 \\ 0 & 0 & S_3 - S \end{vmatrix} = 0,$$

so that the equation $(S - a_{11})(S - a_{22}) - a_{12}^2 = 0$ must have a double root. This means that $(a_{11} + a_{22})^2 - 4(a_{11}a_{22} - a_{12}^2) = 0$, or

$$(a_{11} - a_{22})^2 + 4a_{12}^2 = 0.$$

The reality of the surface demands $a_{11} = a_{22}$, $a_{12} = 0$, or $S_1 = S_2 = a_{11} = a_{22}$. The equation of the surface is therefore

$$S_1x^2 + S_1y^2 + S_3z^2 - D_4/D_3 = 0$$

for any choice of the x- and y-axes in the plane $z = 0$. When $S_1S_3 \neq 0$, the quadric is a *surface of revolution*, either a hyperboloid or an ellipsoid when $D_4 \neq 0$, and a cone of revolution when $D_4 = 0$. The single root belongs to the *axis of rotation*. All rectangular coordinate systems with this axis as one of the coordinate axes are equivalent. Their multiplicity is ∞^1.

EXAMPLE. $xy + yz + zx = a$.

S-equation: $\quad \begin{vmatrix} -S & 1 & 1 \\ 1 & -S & 1 \\ 1 & 1 & -S \end{vmatrix} = -S^3 + 3S + 2 = 0.$

$$S_1 = S_2 = -1, \quad S_3 = 2.$$

Normal form: $-x^2 - y^2 + 2z^2 = 2a$.

For $a > 0$ we obtain a hyperboloid of two sheets, for $a < 0$ a hyperboloid of one sheet. The surface is obtained by rotating the hyperbola $y^2 - 2z^2 = -2a$ about the z-axis (since $a_{13} = a_{23} = 0$). For $a = 0$ we have a cone obtained by rotating the two lines $y \pm z\sqrt{2} = 0$ about the z-axis. For $S_3 = 2$ we obtain the line $x:y:z = 1:1:1$, which is the axis of rotation.

When the S-equation has a triple root $\neq 0$, then we obtain, by a reasoning similar to that conducted for the case of a double root, that the normal form is now

$$S(x^2 + y^2 + z^2) = D_4/D_3 \quad (S \neq 0).$$

This is the case of the *sphere*. Here all ∞^3 sets of mutually orthogonal directions through the origin are conjugate.

We are now able to see how this theory is related to that of pairs of conics in the projective plane. The absolute circle is a nonsingular curve. In case (a), it has four distinct points in common with the conic at infinity of the quadric. This is the case of ellipsoids, hyperboloids and cones with S_1,S_2,S_3 unequal. In case (b), the absolute circle and the conic at infinity touch in two distinct points. This is the case of the quadrics of revolution. The pole of the line connecting the points of contact is the point at infinity of the axis of rotation, the line itself is the line at infinity of the planes in which the circles of the surface lie. In the case of the sphere, the conic at infinity coincides with the absolute.

10–6 Paraboloids. We now take $D_3 = 0$, so that the Eqs. (1–3) for the center have no solution. Starting with the general Eq. (1–1) we therefore first rotate the coordinate axes so as to obtain a new system of orthogonal conjugate lines through O. This leads to the S-equation (4–4). Let us again suppose first that there are three different roots S_1, S_2, S_3. Since $D_3 = 0$, one of these roots, S_3, vanishes. The equation of the quadric then takes the form

$$S_1 x^2 + S_2 y^2 + 2a_{14}x + 2a_{24}y + 2a_{34}z + a_{44} = 0.$$

It is now possible by a translation of the axes

$$x' = x + x_0, \quad y' = y + y_0, \quad z' = z + z_0$$

to reduce this equation to the normal form (we drop the primes for x, y, z):

$$S_1 x^2 + S_2 y^2 + 2a'_{34}z = 0,$$

which in the case that $S_1 S_2 > 0$, $a'_{44} \neq 0$, represents an elliptic paraboloid; $S_1 S_2 < 0$, $a'_{44} \neq 0$, a hyperbolic paraboloid, and in the case that $a'_{44} = 0$, represents two planes, real or imaginary. We can show, as we did before, that a double root $S_1 = S_2$ leads to the normal form

$$S_1(x^2 + y^2) + 2a'_{34}z = 0, \tag{6-1}$$

which in the case $a'_{44} \neq 0$ represents a paraboloid of revolution.

The computation of a'_{34} can be facilitated by the remark that D_4 is a rotation invariant. For the normal form its value is $-S_1 S_2 a'^2_{34}$. Hence

$$a'^2_{34} = -D_4 / S_1 S_2. \tag{6-2}$$

Only in the case that $S_1 S_2$ and D_4 have opposite sign is the value of a'_{34} real. In this case the sign of a'_{34} is immaterial, since it only indicates the sense of the new z-axis. We also see that for an elliptic paraboloid $D_4 < 0$, for a hyperbolic paraboloid $D_4 > 0$. The point (x_0, y_0, z_0) lies on the surface; it is the *vertex* of the paraboloid. At this point the diameter is perpendicular to the tangent plane; it is the *axis* of the surface. The directrix planes through the axis are the *principal planes;* they are only real in the case of the hyperbolic paraboloid.

EXAMPLE. $5x^2 - y^2 + z^2 + 4xy + 6xz + 2x + 4y + 6z = 8.$

Here $D_4 = 16$, $D_3 = 0$; the S-equation is

$$S^3 - 5S^2 - 14S = S(S - 7)(S - 2) = 0,$$
$$a_{34}'^2 = (-16):(-14), \quad a_{34}' = \tfrac{2}{7}\sqrt{14}.$$

The normal form is

$$7x^2 - 2y^2 + \tfrac{2}{7}z\sqrt{14} = 0;$$

the quadric is a hyperbolic paraboloid.

The three directions perpendicular to the perpendicular planes are found by solving Eqs. (4–3) for the computed values of S_1, S_2, S_3. We obtain $(1:2:-3)$ for the axis direction, $(4:1:2)$ and $(1:-2:-1)$ for the other two directions. Hence the rotation is given by

$$x'\sqrt{21} = 4x + y + 2z, \quad y'\sqrt{6} = x - 2y - z, \quad z'\sqrt{14} = x + 2y - 3z.$$

With the aid of this transformation the given equation can be written in the form

$$7\left(x + \frac{12}{7\sqrt{21}}\right)^2 - 2\left(y - \frac{1}{2}\sqrt{6}\right)^2 - \frac{2}{7}\sqrt{14}\left(z - \frac{293}{392}\sqrt{14}\right) = 0,$$

from which we see that the vertex is at $\left(-\dfrac{12}{7\sqrt{2}}, \dfrac{1}{2}\sqrt{6}, \dfrac{293}{392}\sqrt{14}\right)$.

We conclude with the following classification of quadrics with the aid of the invariants D_1, D_2, D_3, D_4:

Ellipsoids: imaginary $D_4 > 0$, $D_3 \neq 0$, $D_2 > 0$, $D_1 D_3 > 0$
      real $D_4 < 0$, $D_3 \neq 0$, $D_2 > 0$, $D_1 D_3 > 0$

Hyperboloids: two sheets $D_4 < 0$, $D_1 D_3$ and D_2 not both positive
     one sheet $D_4 > 0$, $D_1 D_3$ and D_2 not both positive

Paraboloids: elliptic $D_4 < 0$, $D_3 = 0$
    hyperbolic $D_4 > 0$, $D_3 = 0$

Cones: imaginary $D_4 = 0$, $D_1 D_3 > 0$, $D_2 > 0$
   real $D_4 = 0$, $D_1 D_3$ and D_2 not both positive

Pairs of intersecting planes:

   imaginary   rank of D_4 is 2, $D_2 > 0$
   real   rank of D_4 is 2, $D_2 < 0$

Coinciding planes: rank of D_3 and D_4 is 1

For the classification of cylinders we need the quantity $D_5 = \alpha_{11} + \alpha_{22} + \alpha_{33}$, where $\alpha_{\lambda\mu}$ is the cofactor of $a_{\lambda\mu}$ in D_4:

Cylinders: imaginary $\quad D_4 = 0, \quad D_3 = 0, \quad D_2 > 0, \quad D_1D_5 > 0$
$\qquad\qquad$ elliptic $\qquad D_4 = 0, \quad D_3 = 0, \quad D_2 > 0, \quad D_1D_5 < 0$
$\qquad\qquad$ hyperbolic $\quad D_4 = 0, \quad D_3 = 0, \quad D_2 < 0$
$\qquad\qquad$ parabolic $\quad D_4 = 0, \quad D_3 = 0, \quad D_2 = 0, \quad D_1D_5 < 0$

For the classification of parallel planes we need

$$D_6 = \begin{vmatrix} a_{11} & a_{14} \\ a_{14} & a_{44} \end{vmatrix} + \begin{vmatrix} a_{22} & a_{24} \\ a_{24} & a_{44} \end{vmatrix} + \begin{vmatrix} a_{33} & a_{34} \\ a_{34} & a_{44} \end{vmatrix}.$$

Pairs of parallel planes: rank of D_4 is 2, $\quad D_2 = 0, \quad D_6 > 0$
$\qquad\qquad\qquad\qquad\qquad$ rank of D_4 is 2, $\quad D_2 = 0, \quad D_6 < 0$

We can add, if we consider Euclidean geometry as part of projective geometry:

Finite and infinite planes: $(x_1x_4 = 0)$: $a_{ij} = 0$, $i,j = 1,2,3$

Infinite plane counted twice: $(x_4^2 = 0)$: only $a_{44} \neq 0$, all other $a_{\lambda\mu} = 0$.

EXERCISES

1. Classify the following surfaces (name, normal form):
(a) $x^2 + y^2 + z^2 - 4x + 6y - 14z + 37 = 0$.
(b) $xy - xz + yz - 5y = 0$.
(c) $y^2 + z^2 - 2yz + 4xy - 4 = 0$.
(d) $4x^2 - 2y^2 - 12z^2 + 12yz + 4xy + 4x + 2y + 3z = 0$.
(e) $2x^2 + 2y^2 + 5z^2 - 2xy - 4xz + 4yz - 2x + 6z - 4 = 0$.

2. Find the type of surface represented by the equation

$$a(x^2 + 2yz) + b(y^2 + 2zx) + c(z^2 + 2xy) = 1.$$

3. Show that the equation $S \equiv x^2 + y^2 + z^2 + Ax + By + Cz + D = 0$ represents a sphere. Find its center and radius and the condition that the sphere is real. When is the sphere a *null sphere*, that is, a sphere with radius zero?

4. Extend the theory of Sec. 6–6 to a *pencil of spheres* $S_1 - \lambda S_2 = 0$, $S_a = x^2 + y^2 + z^2 + A_ax + B_ay + C_az + D_a = 0$, $a = 1,2$. If $S(x,y)$ is the *power* of a point (x,y) with respect to a sphere $S = 0$ (Ex. 3), find the locus of the points of equal power with respect to two spheres (the *radical plane*).

5. Extend the theory of inversion to the sphere, interpreting the formulas relating $\mathbf{r}$ and $\mathbf{r}'$ of Ex. 1 of the Problems on Inversion, following Sec. 6–6.

6. Find the spheres tangent to the coordinate planes and passing through the point (1,2,1).

7. Find the equation of the tangent plane to a sphere $(x - a)^2 + (y - b)^2 + (z - c)^2 = r^2$ at the point (x_0,y_0,z_0) on the sphere.

8. Show that two spheres $S_2 \equiv x^2 + y^2 + z^2 + A_a x + B_a y + C_a z + D_a = 0$, $a = 1,2$ intersect orthogonally (that is, the tangent planes at a point of intersection are orthogonal, if $A_1 A_2 + B_1 B_2 + C_1 C_2 = 2(D_1 + D_2)$).

9. Find the spheres through the circle intersecting OX,OY,OZ at distance p from O and tangent to the line $x + y - z = p$, $x - y = 2p$.

10. Given two spheres $S_1 = 0$, $S_2 = 0$ (Ex. 4). (a) Show that the three radical planes of three spheres (not belonging to a pencil) taken in pairs pass through a line, the *radical line*. (b) Show that the six radical planes of four spheres (none of which passes through the two real or imaginary points of intersection of the three others) pass through a point, the *radical point*.

11. Show that two polar lines with respect to a sphere are perpendicular.

12. The four altitudes of a tetrahedron form a hyperboloid group, unless at least one pair of opposite edges is perpendicular. Prove. What happens in this exceptional case?

13. *Apollonius' method of generating conics.* Take a quadratic cone (which Apollonius obtains by joining the vertex by lines to the points of a circle in a plane not containing this vertex). Intersect the cone by planes not through the vertex. The intersections are the (nonsingular) conics. Find the conditions under which we obtain an ellipse, a parabola, and a hyperbola. This method of obtaining these curves explains the name *conic sections* (German: *Kegelschnitte;* French: *sections coniques*).

14. A line skew to the z-axis rotates about the z-axis. Prove that it generates a hyperboloid of one sheet.

15. Let a point A move on a given line l and B on another given line m skew to l and not perpendicular to l. Let C be the center of the common perpendicular to l and m. Show that the surface generated by line AB when $\angle ACB = 90°$ is a hyperboloid of one sheet.

16. Show that there are two reguli on the sphere, each consisting of isotropic lines.

10–7 Pencils of quadrics. Two quadric surfaces, $Q_1 = 0$ and $Q_2 = 0$, have a curve in common, which may be real or imaginary, and may consist of one or more parts. A plane intersects $Q_1 = 0$ in a conic and $Q_2 = 0$ in a conic. These two conics have four points in common (which may be real, imaginary, coincident, at infinity). Every plane has therefore four points in common with the curve of intersection. Since we call an algebraic space curve which has n points in common with a plane *a space curve of degree n*, we can state that two quadrics intersect in a *space curve of degree four*, or a *quartic space curve*. An example is the intersection of the ellipsoid $x^2/a^2 + y^2/b^2 + z^2/c^2 = 1$ and the hyperboloid $x^2/a'^2 + y^2/b'^2 - z^2/c'^2 = 1$ (the curve may consist of two parts).

This biquadratic curve can split into a line and a *cubic curve*, into two conics, into four lines. When, for instance, two cones have a generating line in common, their remaining intersection is a cubic space curve. Two cones with the same vertex have four lines in common, which may partly or totally coincide. *When two quadrics have a conic in common, then the other part of the intersection is also a conic*, since every space curve of degree 2 is plane and therefore a conic (Ex. 14, Sec. 9–5). This follows immediately from the fact that a space curve of degree 2 must have at least three points in common with any plane through three of its points, and therefore lies entirely in the plane.

The *pencil of quadrics* $Q_1 + \lambda Q_2 = 0$ consists of ∞^1 quadrics all passing through the same quartic space curve of common intersection. We see that through the intersection of two quadrics one and only one quadric can be laid passing through a given arbitrary point not on the intersection.

As an application, we ask whether it is possible to intersect a quadric by a plane in such a way that the intersection is a circle. Such intersections are called *circular sections*. Since the intersections of a quadric with a family of parallel planes are all similar curves (Ex. 4, Sec. 10–2), all planes parallel to one circular section also produce circular sections.

We first take the ellipsoid $x^2/a^2 + y^2/b^2 + z^2/c^2 = 1$. Then the pencil formed by this surface and the sphere with radius r and center at the origin,

$$\frac{x^2}{a^2} + \frac{y^2}{b^2} + \frac{z^2}{c^2} - 1 + \lambda(x^2 + y^2 + z^2 - r^2) = 0,$$

contains one quadric passing through the center, namely, that for which $\lambda r^2 + 1 = 0$:

$$x^2 \left(\frac{1}{a^2} - \frac{1}{r^2} \right) + y^2 \left(\frac{1}{b^2} - \frac{1}{r^2} \right) + z^2 \left(\frac{1}{c^2} - \frac{1}{r^2} \right) = 0.$$

This surface is a cone. This cone degenerates into two intersecting planes if its equation splits up into two linear factors or, according to Sec. 5–2, if

$$\left(\frac{1}{a^2} - \frac{1}{r^2} \right) \left(\frac{1}{b^2} - \frac{1}{r^2} \right) \left(\frac{1}{c^2} - \frac{1}{r^2} \right) = 0. \tag{7–1}$$

Let $a^2 > b^2 > c^2$. Then the only value of r^2 which gives a real solution is $r^2 = b^2$:

$$-x^2 \left(\frac{1}{b^2} - \frac{1}{a^2} \right) + z^2 \left(\frac{1}{c^2} - \frac{1}{b^2} \right) = 0,$$

or

$$\frac{x}{z} = \pm \frac{a}{c} \sqrt{\frac{b^2 - c^2}{a^2 - b^2}}. \tag{7–2}$$

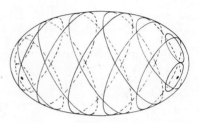

Fig. 10–8

These two planes intersect the ellipsoid in the intersection with a sphere, which means that the intersections are circles. All planes parallel to the planes (7–2) are the circular sections. The planes (7–2) are planes through the middle axis of the ellipsoid (Fig. 10–8); the tangent planes in their direction touch the ellipsoid in the four *umbilics*.

The Eq. (7–1) gives two other sets of circular sections, one parallel to planes through the largest axis, another parallel to planes through the smallest axis. These sections are imaginary.

We find in a similar way the circular sections of the hyperboloid of one sheet. Again we find three sets, of which one is real. In the case of a hyperboloid of two sheets there is a set of real planes through the center which do not intersect the surface in real points, but planes parallel to these planes do give circles as intersections.

To solve the corresponding problem for the paraboloids, we form the pencil

$$px^2 + qy^2 + rz + (Ax + By + Cz)(A_1x + B_1y + C_1z) = 0$$

of the quadrics passing through the intersections of the paraboloid $px^2 + qy^2 + rz = 0$ and two planes through the vertex, in which we expect to find the circular sections. In this case, these sections must lie on a sphere intersecting the quadric. Hence there must be values of A, B, C for which

$$p + AA_1 = q + BB_1 = CC_1,$$
$$0 = AB_1 + A_1B = AC_1 + A_1C = BC_1 + B_1C.$$

The second set of equations is equivalent to

$$\frac{A}{A_1} = -\frac{B}{B_1}, \quad \frac{B}{B_1} = -\frac{C}{C_1}, \quad \frac{C}{C_1} = -\frac{A}{A_1}.$$

This is impossible unless some quantities vanish. We take first $B = B_1 = 0$. Then $p + AA_1 = q = CC_1$, $0 = AC_1 + A_1C$ or $AA_1 = q - p$, $CC_1 = q$. Hence

$$\frac{A}{C} \cdot \frac{A_1}{C_1} = q(q - p), \quad \frac{A}{C} = -\frac{A_1}{C_1}, \quad \text{or} \quad \frac{A}{C} = -\frac{A_1}{C_1} = \pm \sqrt{q(p - q)},$$

which gives for the circular sections, $z = \pm x\sqrt{q(p - q)}$. These sections are real for $q > 0$, $p > q$, or $q < 0$, $p < q$, which happens for an elliptic paraboloid. We get similar results for $A = A_1 = 0$ and $C = C_1 = 0$, but only one set of circular sections is real. The hyperbolic paraboloid has no real circular sections.

D'Alembert was one of the first to comment on circular sections, for the case of a general ellipsoid [*Opusc. Mathem.* **7** (1780), p. 163]; the case of all center quadrics was studied by Monge and Hachette, *Journ. Ec. Polyt.*, cah. 11 (1802), p. 161.

By cutting out circles of the right size in parallel planes and putting them together, we can obtain models of surfaces of the second degree formed by two sets of parallel circles. They have the property that they do not determine the surface fully, so that one model can be made to represent a whole series of quadrics. These models were suggested by O. Henrici and constructed by A. Brill (1874). See O. Staude, *Analytische Geometrie* (Leipzig, 1910) p. 308.

Henrici also showed (1874) that the same property holds for models of hyperboloids of one sheet constructed with straight wires representing the two reguli. If these wires are made in such a way that they can turn about their points of intersection but cannot slide, then the hyperboloid is flexible. The hyperboloids thus obtained are confocal (see Sec. 10–8; see also O. Staude, *loc. cit.*, pp. 339, 714).

10–8 Confocal quadrics. A special example of a pencil of class quadrics is the set

$$a^2u^2 + b^2v^2 + c^2w^2 - \lambda(u^2 + v^2 + w^2) = 0, \qquad (8-1)$$

consisting of all quadrics tangent to the figure enveloped by the tangent planes common to the ellipsoid $a^2u^2 + b^2v^2 + c^2w^2 = 1$ and the absolute conic conceived as a class quadric. These quadrics therefore admit ∞^1 imaginary tangent planes which intersect the plane at infinity in tangent lines to the absolute conic. The equation of these quadrics in point coordinates is

$$\frac{x^2}{a^2 - \lambda} + \frac{y^2}{b^2 - \lambda} + \frac{z^2}{c^2 - \lambda} = 1. \qquad (8-2)$$

In analogy to the confocal conics in the plane (Sec. 6–7), we call this family of quadrics a *confocal* system. The name, however, is somewhat misleading, since there are in general no points which can be fully considered as analogues of the foci of the conics (comp. Ex. 3 below).

Let $a^2 > b^2 > c^2$. Then for $\lambda < c^2$ we have ellipsoids, for $c^2 < \lambda < b^2$ hyperboloids of one sheet, for $b^2 < \lambda < a^2$ hyperboloids of two sheets. For $\lambda > a^2$ the quadrics are imaginary.

Through every point of space passes one and only one quadric of each type. To show it, let us write Eq. (8–2) in the form $f(\lambda) = 0$, where

$$f(\lambda) = (a^2 - \lambda)(b^2 - \lambda)(c^2 - \lambda) - x^2(b^2 - \lambda)(c^2 - \lambda)$$
$$- y^2(a^2 - \lambda)(c^2 - \lambda) - z^2(a^2 - \lambda)(b^2 - \lambda).$$

We find by substitution,

$$f(-\infty) = +, \quad f(c^2) = +, \quad f(b^2) = -, \quad f(a^2) = +, \quad f(+\infty) = -,$$

so that there are three real roots, one $< c^2$, one between c^2 and b^2, and one between b^2 and a^2. They correspond to three quadrics.

The three quadrics of a confocal system which pass through one point intersect orthogonally.

Indeed, the tangent planes through a point $P(x_0, y_0, z_0)$ to the three quadrics given by $\lambda_1, \lambda_2, \lambda_3$, have the equations

$$\frac{xx_0}{a^2 - \lambda_i} + \frac{yy_0}{b^2 - \lambda_i} + \frac{zz_0}{c^2 - \lambda_i} = 1 \quad (i = 1,2,3). \quad (8\text{-}3)$$

But the λ_i are roots of Eq. (8-2) for $(x,y,z) = (x_0,y_0,z_0)$:

$$\frac{x_0^2}{a^2 - \lambda_i} + \frac{y_0^2}{b^2 - \lambda_i} + \frac{z_0^2}{c^2 - \lambda_i} = 0. \quad (8\text{-}4)$$

Subtracting Eq. (8-4) for λ_i from that for λ_j, $\lambda_i \neq \lambda_j$, $i,j = 1,2,3$, we obtain, since λ_1 and λ_2 are unequal,

$$\frac{x_0^2}{(a^2 - \lambda_i)(a^2 - \lambda_j)} + \frac{y_0^2}{(b^2 - \lambda_i)(b^2 - \lambda_j)} + \frac{z_0^2}{(c^2 - \lambda_i)(c^2 - \lambda_j)} = 0,$$

which are the conditions that the three planes (8-3) are perpendicular.

The three types of quadrics pass into each other at the limiting cases $\lambda = a^2$, $\lambda = b^2$, $\lambda = c^2$. We obtain three cylinders:

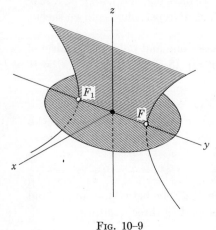

FIG. 10-9

$$\frac{x^2}{a^2 - c^2} + \frac{y^2}{b^2 - c^2} = 1,$$

$$\frac{x^2}{a^2 - b^2} - \frac{z^2}{b^2 - c^2} = 1, \quad (8\text{-}5)$$

$$\frac{y^2}{a^2 - b^2} + \frac{z^2}{a^2 - c^2} + 1 = 0,$$

of which the cross sections in the coordinate planes are conics; the first is an ellipse in the XOY-plane, the second a hyperbola in the XOZ-plane. The third is an imaginary conic. They are called the *focal conics*. The (real) focal ellipse has its foci at $(\pm \sqrt{a^2 - b^2}, 0, 0)$.

The foci of the focal ellipse are the vertices of the focal hyperbola on its real axis, the foci of the focal hyperbola are the vertices of the focal ellipse on its major axis (Fig. 10-9).

EXERCISES

1. A plane intersects a pencil of point quadrics in a pencil of point conics in which there are three singular conics forming a complete quadrangle. The diagonal points of this quadrangle are conjugate with respect to all conics of the pencil. By dualizing this theorem, prove that the three quadrics of a confocal system passing through a point are orthogonal.

2. If the quadrics of a confocal system through a point (x,y,z) are given by $\lambda_1, \lambda_2, \lambda_3$, show that

$$x^2 = \frac{(a^2 - \lambda_1)(a^2 - \lambda_2)(a^2 - \lambda_3)}{(a^2 - b^2)(a^2 - c^2)}, \quad y^2 = \frac{(b^2 - \lambda_1)(b^2 - \lambda_2)(b^2 - \lambda_3)}{(b^2 - a^2)(b^2 - c^2)},$$

$$z^2 = \frac{(c^2 - \lambda_1)(c^2 - \lambda_2)(c^2 - \lambda_3)}{(c^2 - a^2)(c^2 - b^2)}.$$

The λ_i are called the *elliptic coordinates* of the point.

3. If we define a *focus* of a quadric as the vertex of a null sphere tangent to the quadric at two (imaginary) points P,Q, show that the focal conics are the loci of the foci. The tangent to a focal conic at a point F on it has PQ as its polar line d with respect to the quadric. This line d is the *directrix* corresponding to the focus F.

4. Show that the directrix is perpendicular to the principal plane of the corresponding focus F, and that it intersects this plane in the pole G of the tangent at F of the focal conic with respect to the principal section of the quadric.

5. Show that FG is normal to the focal conic.

6. Show that the cone $x^2/a^2 + y^2/b^2 - z^2/c^2 = 0$, $a^2 > b^2$, has the focal lines $x^2/(a^2 - b^2) - z^2/(b^2 + c^2) = 0$, $y = 0$.

7. Show that the prolate ellipsoid of rotation and the rotation hyperboloid of two sheets have two foci, while the oblate ellipsoid of rotation and the rotation hyperboloid of one sheet have a focal circle obtained by rotation of the corresponding conic.

8. All quadrics passing through seven given points in a general position pass through an eighth point. Prove.

9. A quadric passing through seven of the vertices of two self-polar tetrahedra also passes through the eighth. Prove.

CHAPTER 11

TRANSFORMATIONS OF SPACE

11-1 Collineations. A linear homogeneous point transformation in projective space P_3,

$$\rho x'_\lambda = c_{\lambda\mu} x_\mu \quad (\lambda,\mu = 1,2,3,4), \tag{1-1}$$

is called a *collineation* (comp. Sec. 4–2). To every point $P(x_\lambda)$ corresponds a point $P'(x'_\lambda)$. When $C = \text{Det } (c_{\lambda\mu})$ is $\neq 0$, the collineation is nonsingular; in this case there is a point P corresponding to every point P',

$$\sigma x_\lambda = \gamma_{\mu\lambda} x'_\mu, \quad \gamma_{\lambda\mu} = \text{cofactor of } c_{\lambda\mu} \text{ in } C. \tag{1-2}$$

The points in a plane $\pi(u_\lambda)$ are transformed into the points of a plane $\pi'(u'_\lambda)$, and conversely:

$$\rho_1 u'_\mu = \gamma_{\lambda\mu} u_\lambda; \quad \sigma_1 u_\lambda = c_{\mu\lambda} u'_\mu. \tag{1-3}$$

Under a collineation, points pass into points, planes into planes, and lines into lines. Incidences are preserved; the transformation is one-to-one. Five independent points P_α, $\alpha = 1,2, \ldots, 5$, and another set of five independent points P'_α determine one and only one nonsingular collineation by means of which P_1 passes into $P'_1, \ldots$, and P_5 into P'_5. This follows from the properties of linear homogeneous transformations explained in Chapter 8 (comp. also Sec. 4–2).

These properties, translated from a passive to an active point of view, also show that a nonsingular collineation establishes a projectivity on two corresponding point ranges on a line or on two corresponding plane pencils. Moreover, two planes which correspond by means of a nonsingular space collineation are also related by means of a plane collineation. This can be established algebraically by taking one plane as $x_4 = 0$ and the other as $x'_4 = 0$, an assumption which can be made without loss of generality. Equation (1–2) then gives the projectivity for λ,μ ranging from 1 to 3. Another way to prove it is by invoking the fundamental property of projectivities (Sec. 1–8).

The dual proposition is that a collineation establishes a projectivity between the planes of two families of the ∞^2 planes each passing through a point. Then the relation between the ∞^2 lines passing through the points can also be considered as a projectivity. The intersections of these lines with a plane establish a collineation in the plane.

Collineations can be classified by means of their fixed points. We refer to Chapter 4, where a similar procedure is sketched for the plane. Since the condition for fixed points is the same as that for fixed planes, we can state that every collineation has as many distinct fixed planes as fixed points, as many pencils of fixed planes as lines of fixed points, and as many sets of ∞^2 fixed planes through a point as planes of fixed points.

The classification of collineations can be undertaken with the aid of elementary divisors. We give only two illustrations of nonsingular collineations.

(I) $\rho x_1' = ax_1, \quad \rho x_2' = bx_2, \quad \rho x_3' = cx_3, \quad \rho x_4' = dx_4 \quad (a,b,c,d \text{ different}).$

The vertices of the basic tetrahedron are isolated fixed points and its faces are isolated fixed planes. The choice of corresponding unit points determines a,b,c,d and hence the collineation.

(II) $\rho x_1' = ax_1, \quad \rho x_2' = ax_2, \quad \rho x_3' = ax_3, \quad \rho x_4' = dx_4 \quad (a,d \text{ different}).$

There is an isolated fixed point A_4, and a plane of fixed points $x_4 = 0$. Every point P is transformed into another point P' on a line through A_4. This is sometimes called a *homology*.

The full classification gives 14 types of nonsingular collineations. There are many more singular ones.

A full classification is given in F. S. Woods, *Higher Geometry* (1922), §101. A general discussion of collineations, for any number of dimensions, is given in J. A. Todd, *Projective and Analytical Geometry* (1946), Ch. V.

EXERCISES

1. Find the fixed points and planes of the collineation derived from Type I by (a) taking $a = b$, $c = d$, and (b) $a = b$, $c \neq d$.

2. Show that the collineation

$$\rho x_1' = ax_1 + x_2, \quad \rho x_2' = ax_2 + x_4, \quad \rho x_3' = ax_3, \quad \rho x_4' = ax_4,$$

has a line of fixed points and a pencil of fixed planes.

3. Consider a translation as a collineation. What are its fixed elements?

4. Consider a rotation of the XOY-plane about the z-axis in Euclidean space as a collineation. What are its fixed elements?

5. Show that all nonsingular collineations form a group.

11–2 Central projection. When the collineation is singular and the determinant C is of rank 3, space is transformed into a plane (comp. Sec. 4–3). Such a representation of space on a plane is the object of *descriptive geometry*, and is basic to photography and painting, although here nonlinear elements may enter, especially in painting. The collineations in this case are not performed in projective but in Euclidean space, so that questions concerning the mapping of parallel lines, of angles, and of length must be answered.

We shall discuss here a few fundamental principles characteristic of the most common types of descriptive geometry, without going into details of the constructions, which are adequately treated in the special textbooks on this subject. These types are *central projection*, with *perspective* as a slight modification, and different forms of parallel projection, notably *oblique projection*, *axonometry*, and *orthographic projection*.

In *central projection* all points P of space are connected with a fixed point C outside a plane π, the point of intersection P' of CP with π is called the (central) projection of P on the *plane of projection* π. The point C is called the *center of projection*. Lines in space are projected into lines of π, such as l through P is projected into l' through P' (Fig. 11–1). The projection establishes a perspectivity

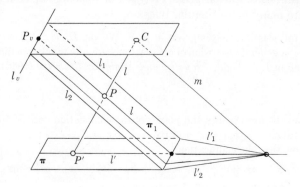

Fig. 11–1

on the lines l, l' (Secs. 1–5, 2–7), and a particular nonsingular projectivity between π and any plane π_1 through l not through C. The space transformation is a singular collineation; if C is taken as point $A_4\,(0:0:0:1)$ of a basic tetrahedron of which $\triangle A_1 A_2 A_3$ lies in π, then the central projection can be given by

$$\rho x_1' = x_1, \quad \rho x_2' = x_2, \quad \rho x_3' = x_3, \quad \rho x_4' = 0. \qquad (2\text{–}1)$$

In affine and Euclidean geometry, central projection ceases to be entirely one-to-one, since the line l_v of a plane π_1', in a plane through C parallel to π, has no projection on π (projectively speaking: it projects into the ideal line of π).

Parallel lines $l_1, l_2, l_3, \ldots$ in π_1 project into lines in π all passing through the point in which the line m through C parallel to these lines l intersects π (Fig. 11–1). This point is the *vanishing point* of l', through it passes the *vanishing line* of π_1 parallel to l_v. *This mapping of parallel lines into converging lines through a point is the typical feature of central projection* in affine and Euclidean space.

11–3 Perspective. We call a central projection *perspective* when the plane of projection π is conceived as the vertical plane, the objects to be projected are placed on a horizontal plane π_1 on one side of π, and when the center of projection or *eye* C is on the other side of π. The distance CC_1 from C to π is the *distance*. The plane through C parallel to π_1 intersects π in the vanishing line h of π_1; this line is here called the *horizon*. Parallel lines l in π_1 and lines parallel

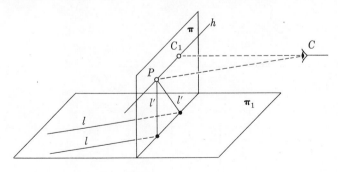

Fig. 11–2

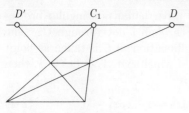

FIG. 11-3

to them in space project into lines l' passing through a point P on the horizon, the *vanishing point* of these lines (Fig. 11–2). The projection C_1 of C is the vanishing point of all lines $\perp \pi$. The vanishing points of lines in π_1 and parallel to them making an angle of 45° with π are two points D and D' at distance $|CC_1|$ on the horizon from C; they are the *distance points*. Figure 11–3 shows how a square in π_1 projects on π; Fig. 11–4 shows the perspective of a cube.

A perspective figure gives a fairly good representation of a figure in space as seen by one eye, especially at some distance. We do see the parallel lines of a big building, the parallel tracks of a railroad line, or the bordering rims of a straight highway all as converging to a "vanishing" point on the "horizon." It was for this reason that perspective was first developed, mainly by architects and painters of fifteenth century Italy.

The historical development of perspective centered around the discovery of the vanishing point. The knowledge that all parallel lines in the object converge in the observation to one point then led to a correct approach to problems of foreshortening and the relative length and directions of line segments of the perspective projection in general. There is no

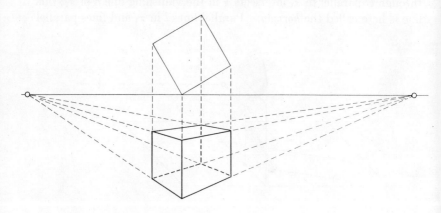

FIG. 11-4

evidence that the Ancients knew about the vanishing point, although we must keep in mind that only few vestiges of their paintings remain. The first book explaining some of the fundamental principles of perspective is *Trattato della Pittura* by the Florentine artist and scholar Leon Battista Alberti (1435, modern ed. by G. Papini, 1913); a full treatise was later written by the Urbino painter Piero Della Francesca, *De Prospectiva Pingendi* (c. 1470), published in 1899 by C. Winterberg. We can study the progress of perspective in the paintings and other pictures of the period. Where Giotto's knowledge of perspective (c. 1300) is still naive, we find in the work of Paolo Uccello (c. 1400) already a complete mastery of the subject, as can be seen from his remarkable "Mazocchio," a form of turban, of which the cross sections are regular hexagons whose corresponding vertices form regular polygons of 32 sides. On the rectangles at the front are four-sided pyramids. The perspective drawing is exact (Fig. 11-5).

The leading artists of the early sixteenth century knew the laws of perspective very well, as can be seen from an examination of the works of such men as Leonardo Da Vinci, Raphael, and Albrecht Dürer. In 1525 Dürer published a book with a good deal of pertinent information on the mathematics of drawing: *Messung mit dem Richtscheid*. An example of his art can be studied in Fig. 11-6.

During the sixteenth and seventeenth centuries systematic texts began to be published, among them the *Perspective* of A. Bosse, to which Desargues contributed. Desargues, who had already come close to the principles of projective geometry, was led to them by the study of perspective. Some of these ancient books have magnificent engravings; it is clear that artists enjoyed the mathematics of projection.

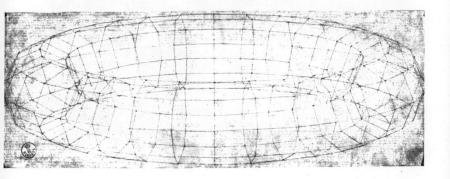

FIG. 11-5

Fig. 11–6

11–4 Parallel projection. When the points P of space are projected on a plane into points P' such that the lines PP' have the same direction, we speak of *parallel projection*. A common form is *oblique parallel projection*, in which the objects are placed on a horizontal plane and projected on a vertical plane of projection π. Let P (Fig. 11–7) be a point in the horizontal plane σ, which is projected in the direction PP' on π, and similarly for Q in the same direction QQ'. The triangles PAP' and QBQ' are similar. If the plane σ is turned about the axis AB into π, then P turns into P_r and Q into Q_r (Fig. 11–8); the $\triangle\triangle P_r A P'$ and $Q_r B Q'$ are again similar. When we give $\triangle A P_r P'$, then the projection of every point in σ can be found by drawing similar triangles. Now the projection of any point in space can also be found, since a line parallel to π maintains both direction and length. This projection preserves parallelism and the ratio of line segments in the same direction, and therefore produces a nonsingular affinity between a plane of space not in the direction of projection and its projection on π. The line AB is the *axis of affinity*.

As an example, we show the projection of a pentagonal prism (Fig. 11–9). This mapping of space on a plane is a singular affine transformation with a determinant of rank 2, which by choice of origin can be represented in rectangular coordinates in the form

$$x_i' = c_{ij}x_j \quad [C = \mathrm{Det}\ (c_{ij})\ \text{of rank 2}]. \quad (4\text{–}1)$$

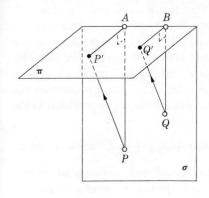

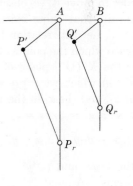

Fig. 11–7   Fig. 11–8

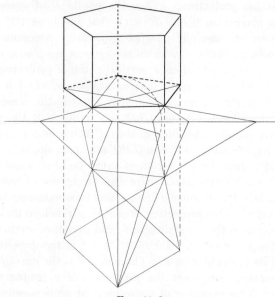

Fig. 11–9

It can also be shown that the converse theorem holds in the form that *every transformation (4–1) can be represented by a parallel projection followed by a similitude.*

In order to prove it, we observe that the determinant C is of rank 2, which means that there exists one linear relation between the x_i' (Sec. 3–8). Let this relation be $a_i x_i' = 0$. It is the equation of the plane π into which the points of space are transformed. We take this plane as the $X''OY''$ plane of a new rectangular coordinate system (x'', y'', z'') in which we express the points x_i'. Then, expressing the x'' in the x_i', and the x_i' in the x_i, we obtain the transformation in the form $(x_1 = x, x_2 = y, x_3 = z)$:

$$x'' = d_{11}x + d_{12}y + d_{13}z, \quad y'' = d_{21}x + d_{22}y + d_{23}z, \quad z'' = 0, \quad (4\text{–}2)$$

where the (xyz) and $(x''y''z'')$ refer to different rectangular coordinate systems. A point (x_0'', y_0'') in π is the transform of all points on the line of intersection of the planes $x_0'' = d_{11}x + d_{12}y + d_{13}z$, $y_0'' = d_{21}x + d_{22}y + d_{23}z$. When the point in π changes, these lines change into parallel ones. Every line of space in a given direction is thus mapped into a point of the plane.

Moreover, every free vector **v** of space is transformed by (4–2) into a free vector **v'** of π, and $p\mathbf{v} + q\mathbf{w}$ is transformed into $p\mathbf{v'} + q\mathbf{w'}$.

In particular, if we take three unit vectors of space $(1,0,0),(0,1,0)$, $(0,0,1)$, then they transform into the three vectors of π: (d_{11},d_{12}), $(d_{12},d_{22}),(d_{13},d_{23})$. These vectors of π can be arbitrarily given, but since the rank of the matrix of the d_{ai} is 2, they cannot all be in the same direction and at most one can vanish. If we give the vectors **d**, then the transformation (4–2) is determined. Three such vectors can therefore always be considered as the transforms of three mutually perpendicular unit vectors of space. This transformation is not necessarily a parallel projection. However, if we could find a plane π_1 (and then also ∞^1 such planes parallel to π_1) with a rectangular coordinate system (ξ,η) such that the parallel lines

$$d_{11}x + d_{12}y + d_{13}z = \xi, \quad d_{21}x + d_{22}y + d_{23}z = \eta \qquad (4\text{–}3)$$

intersect in the point (ξ,η), then the vectors $(1,0,0),(0,1,0),(0,0,1)$ would be projected on this plane into the three vectors **d**. Although this is not possible, it is possible to find an appropriate factor λ such that the lines (4–3) intersect in the point $(\lambda\xi,\lambda\eta)$. This is equivalent to the theorem that a triangular prism can be intersected by a plane in an isosceles rectangular triangle (Ex. 8, this section); for this prism we take a figure whose edges are given by (ξ,η) equal to $(0,0),(0,1),(1,0)$, respectively. Our result is expressed by the *theorem of Pohlke*:

Three arbitrary plane vectors can always be considered as the oblique parallel projection of three mutually orthogonal vectors of equal length, provided that at least two of the plane vectors are different from zero and not all vectors have the same direction.

The proof is not necessarily dependent on the orthogonality of the coordinate axes, so that Pohlke's theorem can be stated in the following form due to Schwarz:

A given tetrahedron can always be mapped by oblique parallel projection into a figure similar to any given quadrangle with its diagonals.

This theorem, sometimes called the fundamental theorem of oblique axonometry, was formulated by K. Pohlke c. 1853. After Steiner had expressed certain doubts, Pohlke proved it in his *Lehrbuch der darstellenden Geometrie* (1860), p. 109. Several proofs have been given, none of which is simple, because they also give the method by which we can construct the direction of projection. See H. A. Schwarz, *Ges. mathem.* Abh. 2, pp. 1–7; A. Emch, *Amer. Journ. of Mathem.* **40** (1918), pp. 366–374 (with bibliography). Our way of reasoning follows F. Klein, *Elementary Mathematics from an Advanced Point of View* II.

Parallel projection is common in Chinese and Japanese prints.

EXERCISES

1. Construct the parallel projection of a circle. Find the conjugate diameters of the projection.

2. Prove that the contour of the parallel projection of any given ellipsoid upon a plane may be similar to any given ellipse.

3. Find the analogue of Pohlke's theorem for an affine mapping of the plane on a straight line.

4. A cube is given with its faces parallel to the coordinate planes. Construct its parallel projection if (a) the projected axes make angles of 90°, 145°, 145°; (b) 120°, 120°, 120°; (c) 100°, 120°, 140° (measured from $OX \to OY \to OZ$).

5. Central projection is expressed by a projective transformation $x' = c_{\lambda\mu}x_\mu$ with determinant C of rank 2. Can every such transformation be considered as a central projection?

6. Construct the perspective of a cube of side a standing on the horizontal plane with a face parallel to the plane of projection (a) when the eye is at distance $\frac{1}{2}a$ above the horizontal plane, (b) when this distance is a, (c) when it is $2a$. Compare the resulting figures.

7. Characterize the affinity between a plane π in space and its oblique parallel projection on a plane π_1 as a collineation, when π is rotated into π_1 about the line of intersection of π and π_1.

8. Show that a triangular prism can be intersected by a plane in an isosceles rectangular triangle.

11–5 Orthogonal axonometry. In *axonometry*, we place the object on the XOY plane and map it by parallel projection on a plane π intersecting the three rectangular coordinate axes in the vertices of an acute triangle ABC. We usually project orthogonally, and the term axonometry then means this orthogonal axonometry (Fig. 11–10). Here the origin O is projected into a point O' such that the

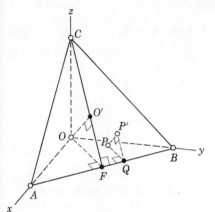

FIG. 11–10

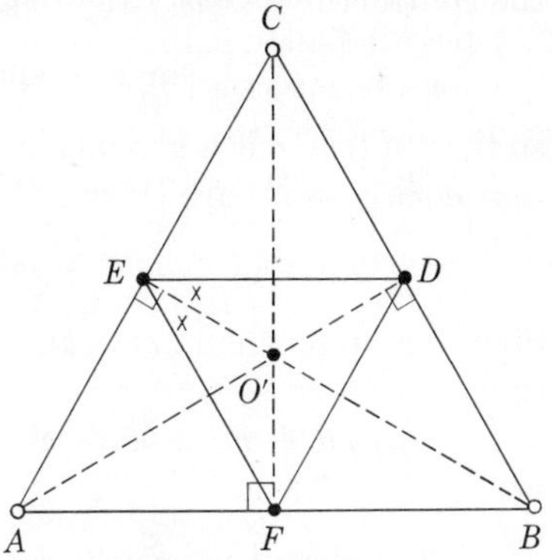

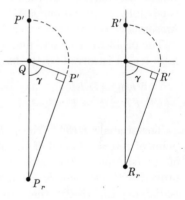

FIG. 11–11

projections of the three axes on π are the three altitudes of $\triangle ABC$, intersecting at O' (Fig. 11–11). The unit length in space appears in different ratios along the projected OX, OY, OZ directions. When these ratios are given, the projection of the unit length in all other directions is determined. When α, β, γ are the angles of OO' with the positive x-, y-, and z-axes, then we call $\sin \alpha : \sin \beta : \sin \gamma$ the *contraction ratio*, and we have such relations as $O'A = OA \sin \alpha$. Each

FIG. 11–12

sine is called a *contraction*. When P is a point in the XOY plane and P' its projection, then if $PQ \perp AB$, $P'Q$ also $\perp AB$, so that $P'Q = PQ \cos \gamma$. If we rotate XOY about AB into π, P becomes P_r, and if γ is given, P' follows from the construction of $\triangle P_r Q P'$ (Fig. 11–12). If $\triangle P_r Q P'$ is given, then the projection of all points R in plane XOY follows from the construction of similar triangles. Since

$$\cos^2 \alpha + \cos^2 \beta + \cos^2 \gamma = 1,$$

the contractions satisfy the relation

$$\sin^2 \alpha + \sin^2 \beta + \sin^2 \gamma = 2, \qquad (5\text{--}1)$$

so that, if $l:m:n$ is a given contraction ratio, $l = a \sin \alpha$, $m = a \sin \beta$, $n = a \sin \gamma$ (a an arbitrary constant), and

$$l^2 + m^2 + n^2 = 2a^2.$$

Since a is larger than l,m,n, and none of the angles α,β,γ is 90°, we find that

$$l^2 + m^2 > n^2, \quad m^2 + n^2 > l^2, \quad l^2 + n^2 > m^2, \qquad (5\text{--}2)$$

or:

> *It is always possible to construct a triangle with the squares of the contractions as sides.*

A contraction ratio 5:4:6 is possible; a ratio 5:4:7 is impossible. Within the limits set by the inequalities (5–2) every contraction ratio is possible. A usual one is 1:1:1, which gives *isometric* axonometry. Anisometric contraction ratios in use are 5:4:6, 9:5:10, 7:6:8.

The problem of how to find a triangle ABC by a given contraction ratio $l:m:n$ is solved by the *theorem of Weisbach:*

> *When AD,BE,CF are the altitudes of a triangle ABC, then $EF:FD:DE = l^2:m^2:n^2$ (Fig. 11–11).*

The triangle DEF is the *pedal triangle* of triangle ABC, and the point of intersection O' of the altitudes of triangle ABC is the point of intersection of the bisectors of triangle DEF, as can be readily proved with elementary geometry. When therefore $l:m:n$ is given [satisfying Eq. (5–2)], then we can always construct triangle DEF; the bisectors of this triangle then give the directions of the projections of OX,OY,OZ. The triangle of which these bisectors are the altitudes is the triangle of projection.

Weisbach's theorem can be demonstrated by taking $x \cos \alpha + y \cos \beta + z \cos \gamma - p = 0$ as the equation of plane ABC. Then we find successively, using Eq. (5–1):

$$O'(p \cos \alpha, p \cos \beta, p \cos \gamma),$$
$$A(p \sec \alpha, 0, 0),$$
$$B(0, p \sec \beta, 0),$$

$C(0, 0, p \sec \gamma)$,

$D(0, p \cos \beta \operatorname{cosec}^2 \alpha, p \cos \gamma \operatorname{cosec}^2 \alpha)$,

$E(p \cos \gamma \operatorname{cosec}^2 \beta, 0, p \cos \alpha \operatorname{cosec}^2 \beta)$,

$F(p \cos \alpha \operatorname{cosec}^2 \gamma, p \cos \beta \operatorname{cosec}^2 \gamma, 0)$,

$EF = \sin \alpha \operatorname{cosec} \beta \operatorname{cosec} \gamma$,

$FD = \sin \beta \operatorname{cosec} \gamma \operatorname{cosec} \alpha$,

$DE = \sin \gamma \operatorname{cosec} \alpha \operatorname{cosec} \beta$,

from which the theorem of Weisbach follows.

We thus see that in oblique axonometry we can give three arbitrary plane vectors as the projection of a set of mutually orthogonal vectors of equal length, while in orthogonal axonometry we can only give the length of these vectors arbitrarily [taking the inequalities (5–2) into account].

The theorem is found in Julius Weisbach, *Anleitung zum axionometrischen Zeichnen* (Freiberg, 1847); it is also called after O. Schlömilch [*Zeitschr. für Mathem. u. Physik* **4** (1859), p. 361]. Another simple method to find the triangle *ABC* for given contraction ratios is due to J. Tesař, *Sitzungsber. Akad. Wien* **81**, II (1880), pp. 453–478. See G. Loria, *Vorlesungen über darstellende Geometrie I* (Leipzig-Berlin, 1907), pp. 164–176 and H. De Vries, *Leerboek der beschrijvende meetkunde I*, 2d ed. (Delft, 1913), pp. 193–199.

11–6 Orthographic projection.   Another orthogonal projection is the orthographic or Monge projection.   It is so widely used that the name "descriptive geometry" is sometimes exclusively used for this type of projection.   Here we take the *ZOY* plane of a rectangular coordinate system as the plane of projection π; since the planes $\perp$ *ZOY* now project into lines, we add a second orthogonal projection, that on the *XOY* plane.   In this method we therefore project a point *P* of space into P_3 in the *XOY* plane, and into P_1 on the *ZOY* plane (Fig. 11–13).   Then the *XOY* plane is rotated about the *y*-axis into the *ZOY* plane (sometimes the *ZOY* plane is rotated into the *XOY* plane).   In the plane of projection P_1P_3 *is then perpendicular to the y-axis.* Very often the projection P_2 of *P* on the *ZOX* plane is also considered, in which case the *ZOX* plane is rotated about the *z*-axis into the *YOZ* plane (Fig. 11–13).   Points on the *x*-axis are therefore reproduced twice, once on the *x*-axis as part of the *XOY* plane, and

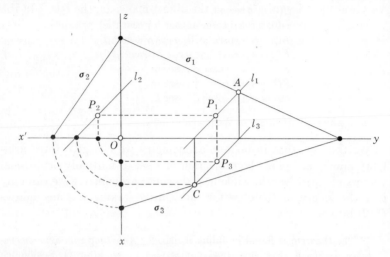

Fig. 11–13

once on the x-axis as part of the XOZ plane (OX and OX' in Fig. 11–13). These corresponding points are connected by circular arcs with O as center. A line l through P intersecting the XOY plane in C and the YOZ plane in A (A,C are the *traces* of l) is projected into the lines l_1, l_3; P_1 lies on l_1, P_3 on l_3. The projection l_2 can then be determined. A plane σ is given by its lines of intersection (*traces*) $\sigma_1, \sigma_2, \sigma_3$ with the three coordinate planes, a line AC in σ has its point of intersection A with YOZ on σ_1, and similarly its point of intersection C with XOY on σ_3. A theorem useful for this type of projection is the following:

The orthographic projections l_i of a line l perpendicular to a plane σ are perpendicular to the corresponding traces σ_i of the plane.

The proof can readily be obtained by elementary means.

The three orthographic projections are in affine relationship. Two projections are sufficient to determine uniquely the spatial relationships, including angles and distances, since two points P_1, P_3 on a line ⊥ y-axis determine uniquely the point P.

Orthographic projection is very convenient for the construction of rather complicated figures, but the projection does not convey very well the visual impression the object makes on the eye.   In this respect it is far inferior to axonometry or parallel projection. The latter projections are therefore most commonly used for the illustration of geometrical texts, and we have also used them for that purpose.

Orthographic projection appears first in Dürer (1525, see Sec. 11–3), but its systematic development is due to Monge. His presentation, developed from lectures first at the military school in Mézières, and after 1795 at the Ecole Normale and the Ecole Polytechnique in Paris, can be studied in his *Leçons de Géométrie Descriptive* [1st ed., 1795; 7th ed., 1847; English transl. by J. F. Heather, new ed., 1851; English adaptation by W. H. Roever, *The Mongean Method of Descriptive Geometry* (New York, 1933, 141 pp.)]. The modern exposition of the methods of orthographic projection differs little from that of Monge. Modern authors tend to stress the relationship of descriptive and projective geometry, see, e.g., W. Fiedler, *Die darstellende Geometrie in organischer Verbindung mit der Geometrie der Lage* (Leipzig, 3d ed., 1883). Textbooks in English usually stress the graphical rather than the theoretical aspects; see, e.g., E. F. Watts-J. T. Rule, *Descriptive Geometry* (New York, 1946).

EXERCISES

1. The necessary and sufficient condition that the orthogonal projection of a right angle is again a right angle is that one side of the angle is parallel to the plane of projection. Prove.

2. Is the orthogonal projection of an acute angle larger than, smaller than, or equal to the angle?

3. Prove by the use of vectors that the orthogonal projection l' of a line l perpendicular to a plane σ is perpendicular to the trace (see Sec. 10–6).

4. Prove Desargues' theorem with the aid of orthographic projection.

5. *Relief perspective.* Show that the collineation

$$x' = \frac{(1+k)x}{z+k}, \quad y' = \frac{(1+k)y}{z+k}, \quad z' = \frac{(1+k)z}{z+k}$$

for $k > 0$ represents the whole of space behind the plane $z = 1$ on a relief of depth k. This type of perspective is useful in sculpture. What happens when $k = 0$, $k = -1$?

6. *Numbered projections.* In this system, used in the sectional United States topographic maps, a point is given by its projection on a plane π and a number k indicating its altitude above the plane. Points of a figure at

equal altitudes h are projected in *contour lines*. We usually draw the contour lines of equal increment in altitude h. Project in this way a right circular cone with its axis (a) perpendicular to π, (b) at angle α to π. This method is called in French that of "projections cotées." See Martin Pernot, *Géométrie Cotée* (Paris, 1903).

7. *Anaglyphs.* An anaglyph consists of two projections of an object in space in central perspective; they are drawn in complementary colors (red and green). They are viewed through a pair of eyepieces of corresponding complementary colors (green and red). The resulting picture, obtained by the amalgamation of the two pictures, gives the impression of a black figure in three dimensions.

If the point $P(x,y,z)$ is projected from the eyes $O_1(0,0,d)$ and $O_2(a,0,d)$ as the XOY plane in $P_1(x_1,y_1,0)$, $P_2(x_2,y_2,0)$, respectively, prove that

$$x_1 = \frac{dx}{d - z}, \quad y_1 = \frac{dy}{d - z}.$$

When O_1 is removed from $(0,0,d)$ to an arbitrary eye $O_1'(x_0,y_0,z_0)$ and O_2 to $(x_0 + a_1', y_0, z_0)$, then show that the images P_1, P_2 now represent a point $(x'y'z')$ for which

$$x' = \frac{a'dx + ax_0z}{a'd + (a - a')z}, \quad y' = \frac{a'dy + ay_0z}{a'd + (a - a')z}, \quad z' = \frac{az_0z}{a'd + (a - a')z}.$$

Show that this is an affine transformation for $a = a'$, and for $a \neq a'$ a projective transformation. Ordinary anaglyphs are viewed with a pair of eyepieces $a = $ about $2\frac{1}{2}$ inches apart; when we move them parallel to the plane of the anaglyph the space figure we see is subjected to an affine transformation. See H. Vuibert, *Les Anaglyphes Géométriques* (Paris, 1912); A. Graf, *Deutsche Mathem.* **4** (1939), pp. 432–448.

11–7 Drawing in solid geometry. We often like to draw figures of three-dimensional objects without using complicated projection methods, and yet sufficiently correct for the purpose of demonstrating an argument. Satisfactory results can often be obtained by following some simple projection rules, replacing the more involved constructions by approximations based on common sense. In the case of objects of unusual length, such as church spires or long stretches of highway, we can best use a simplified perspective, since an oblique projection of such an object as a church with a tower gives the impression of a toy. Such projections, however, rarely enter into the solid geometry discussed in our mathematical textbooks. In most cases we shall use a parallel projection, either oblique parallel projection or axonometry.

The following simple rules, based on the affine relationship underlying parallel projection, can easily be followed, even in freehand drawing.

1. Straight lines in the object remain straight lines in the projection, their intersections remain their intersections, hence tangency remains tangency.

2. Parallel lines remain parallel.

3. Ratios of line segments in the same direction (and sense) remain the same.

4. Equal lengths in different directions should not be equal, but not too different either, and should follow the same rule of continuity, based on the fact that the projection of a circle is an ellipse. The exact relation should be left to the geometric (and artistic) feeling of the designer. We are usually safe in presenting figures in the vertical plane in their natural shape, and representing segments perpendicular to the vertical plane at an angle of 30° and one-half of the true (relative) length.

These rules are sufficient to give reasonably correct figures of simple objects consisting of lines and planes, such as the common polyhedra. We should keep in mind such corollaries as the following:

(a) Parallel planes are intersected by a plane in parallel lines.

(b) A line is parallel to a plane if it is parallel to a line in the plane.

(c) A parallelogram circumscribed to a figure remains a parallelogram circumscribed to its projection.

A few more illustrations may clarify the application of the rules.

If in Fig. 10–7 the lines $a, b, c, \ldots$ connect the points $A_1, B_1, C_1, \ldots$ of line l_1 and the points $A_2, B_2, C_2, \ldots$ of a line l_2 skew to l_1, and are parallel to a plane, then the locus of the points $A_2, B_2, C_2, \ldots$, such that the ratios $A_1A_2 : A_3A_2 = B_1B_2 : B_3B_2 = C_1C_2 : C_3C_2 = \cdots$ are the same, is a straight line.

This example also shows how minor additions to the figure such as the "supporting" planes through l_1 and l_2 can give more reality to the figure.

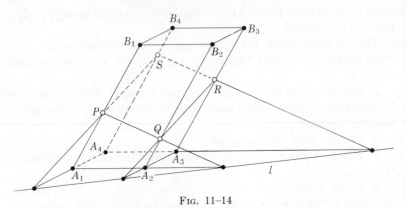

Fig. 11–14

To construct (Fig. 11–14) the intersection of a quadrangular prism $A_1A_2A_3A_4B_1B_2B_3B_4$ by a plane given by three points PQR; P on A_1B_1; Q on A_2B_2; R on A_3B_3. The point S in which plane PQR intersects A_4B_4 is constructed with the aid of the line l in which plane PQR intersects the base $A_1A_2A_3A_4$.

In cases where we have to pay more attention to the relative length or angles of the lines of the figure we can use the similar triangles described in connection with Figs. 11–9 and 11–13. It is also useful to remember that the apparent circumference of a sphere in axonometry is a circle, but in parallel projection it is an ellipse (but with small eccentricity).

It is not difficult to find in the literature figures which violate the elementary rules of projection. For instance, in figures such as Fig. 11–14, the four points $PQRS$, supposedly forming the cross section of the prism with a plane, are not always constructed in such a way that they lie in a plane at all, as can be seen when we try to construct the intersection of this "plane" with the base. The old adage that mathematics is the art of correct reasoning from wrong figures is occasionally taken more seriously than it deserves.

11–8 Correlations. The linear transformation

$$\rho u_\lambda' = c_{\lambda\mu}x_\mu, \quad (\lambda,\mu = 1,2,3,4) \tag{8–1}$$

associates with a point $P(x_\lambda)$ a plane $\pi'(u_\lambda')$. We take the determinant $C \neq 0$, in which case every plane π' is the transform of a point P. The points of the plane $(ux) = 0$ correspond to the planes through the point

$$\sigma x_\lambda' = \gamma_{\lambda\mu} u_\mu \quad (\gamma_{\lambda\mu} \text{ cofactor of } c_{\lambda\mu} \text{ in } C). \tag{8–2}$$

We express this by saying that with a plane $\pi(u_\lambda)$ a point $P'(x_\lambda')$ is associated, and conversely. Points on a line l are transformed into planes through a line l', so that we can also say that (8–1) transforms lines into lines, and intersecting lines l into intersecting lines l', the point of intersection of the l (or l') corresponding to the plane of l' (or l). The cross ratio of four planes through a line is equal to the cross ratio of the corresponding four points on the corresponding line. This transformation is a *correlation* (comp. Sec. 4–4). The Eqs. (8–1) can also be expressed by the single equation:

$$c_{\lambda\mu} x_\lambda' x_\mu = 0 \quad (\text{or } \gamma_{\lambda\mu} u_\lambda' u_\mu = 0), \tag{8–3}$$

which also expresses the condition that two points (or two planes) are *conjugate* in a null system (Sec. 11–9). A correlation followed by another correlation is a collineation. The classification of collineations thus offers an approach to the classification of correlations. The first question is that of involutory correlations. To answer it, let $P(x_\lambda)$ pass into $\pi'(u')$ by means of Eq. (5–1), and this plane π', considered as a plane π, pass into the point $P'(x_\lambda'')$:

$$\sigma x_\lambda'' = \gamma_{\lambda\mu} u_\mu' = \rho^{-1} c_{\mu\nu} x_\nu \gamma_{\lambda\mu},$$

or, since $\gamma_{\lambda\mu} c_{\lambda\kappa} = \delta_{\mu\kappa}$ (the Kronecker symbol, see Sec. 8–6) $(\kappa,\lambda,\mu = 1,\ldots,4)$,

$$\sigma c_{\lambda\kappa} x_\lambda'' = \rho^{-1} c_{\mu\nu} \delta_{\mu\kappa} x_\nu = \rho^{-1} c_{\kappa\lambda} \dot{x}_\lambda. \tag{8–4}$$

The correlation is involutory if point P' is the same as P. This happens if there exist values τ such that the equations

$$(c_{\lambda\mu} - \tau c_{\mu\lambda}) x_\mu = 0 \quad (\lambda = 1,2,3,4)$$

have a solution, and this takes place if

$$\text{Det } (c_{\lambda\mu} - \tau c_{\mu\lambda}) = 0. \tag{8–5}$$

The same equation is obtained if we repeat the reasoning for planes π instead of points P. This equation gives either four roots for τ, to which certain double elements correspond, or holds for all values of τ, in which case the correlation is involutory. Equation (8–4) shows that this holds if $c_{\lambda\mu}$ is a multiple of $c_{\mu\lambda}$. Suppose $c_{\lambda\mu} = mc_{\mu\lambda}$. Then also $c_{\mu\lambda} = mc_{\lambda\mu}$; therefore $m^2 = 1$, or $m = \pm 1$. Thus there are only two cases, that in which $c_{\lambda\mu} = c_{\mu\lambda}$ and that in which $c_{\mu\lambda} = -c_{\lambda\mu}$.

The first case, as comparison of Eq. (8–3) and Eq. (3–1) of Sec. 9–3 shows, is the polarity of point and plane with respect to the real or imaginary quadric $c_{\lambda\mu}x_\lambda u_\mu = 0$. The quadric, as point quadric, is the locus of all points P incident with their corresponding planes π', and as plane quadric, is the envelope of all planes π incident with their corresponding points P'.

11–9 Null system, projective theory. The second kind of involutory correlation, that in which $c_{\lambda\mu} = -c_{\mu\lambda}$, is given by the equations

$$\left.\begin{array}{l} \rho u_1' = c_{12}x_2 + c_{13}x_3 + c_{14}x_4, \\ \rho u_2' = -c_{12}x_1 + c_{23}x_3 + c_{24}x_4, \\ \rho u_3' = -c_{13}x_1 - c_{23}x_2 + c_{34}x_4, \\ \rho u_4' = -c_{14}x_1 - c_{24}x_2 - c_{34}x_3, \end{array}\right\} \quad \begin{array}{l} \rho u_\lambda' = c_{\lambda\mu}x_\mu, \\ c_{\lambda\mu} = -c_{\mu\lambda}. \end{array} \qquad (9\text{--}1)$$

This transformation has an inverse if the determinant

$$C = (c_{12}c_{34} + c_{13}c_{42} + c_{14}c_{23})^2 \qquad (9\text{--}2)$$

is $\neq 0$. Hence we assume that the quadratic inequality holds:

$$c_{12}c_{34} + c_{13}c_{42} + c_{14}c_{23} \neq 0. \qquad (9\text{--}3)$$

Since

$$u_\lambda' x_\lambda = c_{\lambda\mu}x_\lambda x_\mu = -c_{\mu\lambda}x_\lambda x_\mu = 0, \qquad (9\text{--}4)$$

every point is incident with its corresponding plane and, as $C \neq 0$, *every plane is incident with its corresponding point*. This correspondence is called a *null system*. In saying that a null system is involutory, we mean that when a point P corresponds to a plane π', this plane, taken as π, corresponds to point $P' = P$. We can thus write $P \leftrightarrow \pi$. To every plane π belongs one of its points P as its *pole*, and π is the *polar plane* of P. When a point P lies in a plane σ, then the pole S of σ lies in the polar plane π of P. To every line l belongs a corresponding *polar line* l', and this relation is again involutory: the two lines are polars of each other. When P runs along l, the corresponding π turns about l'.   If, therefore, l lies in π, l' must be identical with l: *all lines through a point P in its polar plane π are self-polar.*   They are the only self-polar lines: two polar lines l,l' which intersect do coincide; *two distinct polar lines are skew.*   Self-polar lines are also called *null lines.*

There are ∞^4 lines in space.   The null lines have the multiplicity of the points of space: there are ∞^3 of them.   Every system of ∞^3 lines is called a *line complex.*   The line complex of a null system has the special property that the lines passing through every point lie in a plane.   This line complex is therefore called *linear.*

A line can be defined (Sec. 8–3) by the ratio of six coordinates $p_{\lambda\mu} = -p_{\mu\lambda}$ between which a quadratic relation exists.   The linear relation

$$a_{\lambda\mu}p_{\lambda\mu} = 0, \qquad (9\text{--}5)$$

where the $a_{\lambda\mu} = -a_{\mu\lambda}$ are six arbitrary constants not all zero, represents ∞^3 lines, hence a complex.   When we write $p_{\lambda\mu} = x_\lambda y_\mu - x_\mu y_\lambda$, then Eq. (9–5) can be written

$$a_{\lambda\mu}x_\lambda y_\mu = 0, \quad a_{\lambda\mu} = -a_{\mu\lambda}, \qquad (9\text{--}6)$$

which is the equation of the null system in its form (8–3), provided the $a_{\lambda\mu}$ satisfy the inequality (9–3), with $a_{\lambda\mu}$ instead of $c_{\lambda\mu}$.   Equation (9–6) follows from Eq. (9–5) because

$$a_{\lambda\mu}x_\lambda y_\mu - a_{\lambda\mu}x_\mu y_\lambda = a_{\lambda\mu}x_\lambda y_\mu + a_{\mu\lambda}x_\mu y_\lambda = 2a_{\lambda\mu}x_\lambda y_\mu,$$

the indices μ and λ in $a_{\mu\lambda}x_\mu y_\lambda$ being summation indices, hence $a_{\mu\lambda}x_\mu y_\lambda = a_{\lambda\mu}x_\lambda y_\mu$.

In other words:

A null system defines a linear line complex, and conversely.

The lines of the complex are the null lines of the null system.

A null system leads to a remarkable space configuration which we obtain if we take four points P_1, P_2, P_3, P_4 with their polar planes $\pi_1, \pi_2, \pi_3, \pi_4$.   We select the points in such a way that they do not lie in the polar planes of the other points.   *The vertices of the tetrahedron $P_1P_2P_3P_4$ lie on the faces of the tetrahedron $\pi_1\pi_2\pi_3\pi_4$.*   But the vertex $(\pi_1\pi_2\pi_3)$ lies in the plane $(P_1P_2P_3)$, because the polar plane of every point in π_α passes through the corresponding P_α.   In the same way, we see that the vertex $(\pi_1\pi_2\pi_4)$ lies in the plane $(P_1P_2P_4)$, etc. *The vertices of the tetrahedron $\pi_1\pi_2\pi_3\pi_4$ lie on the faces of the tetrahedron $P_1P_2P_3P_4$.* These two tetrahedra are both inscribed and circumscribed, they form the *configuration of Möbius* $[8_4,8_4]$, which symbol means (in space) that there are 8 points, each lying in 4 planes, and 8 planes each passing through four points.

This configuration was discovered by Möbius in 1828 (*Werke I*, p. 439). He also discovered the null system (1833, *Ges. Werke I*, pp. 489–515). See also Möbius, *Lehrbuch der Statik* (1837). The study of linear complexes was undertaken by Plücker in the *Neue Geometrie des Raumes* (1868–69).

In the plane no triangles exist which can be inscribed and circumscribed at the same time (see Ex. 11, Sec. 3–7; no $[6_3]$ exists). But there exist systems of three triangles I,II,III such that the vertices of I lie on the sides of II, the vertices of II on the sides of III, and the vertices of III on the sides of I. This can be verified in the Pascal configuration $[9_3]$ (see Fig. 3–7; take, for example, $\triangle A_1B_2B_3$, $\triangle RB_1Q_1$, $\triangle A_2A_3P$).

11–10 Null system, affine and Euclidean theory. When we introduce the plane at infinity, π_∞, as the ideal plane, then its pole P_∞ determines a set of parallel lines, the *diameters* of the null system. The line conjugate to a diameter is in π_∞ and does not pass through P_∞, so that *to every diameter belongs a plane direction which does not contain a diametral direction* and, conversely, to every such plane direction belongs a diameter. When a plane is passed through a line l, not a diameter, and containing a diametral direction, then its line at infinity is self-polar and therefore contains the point at infinity of the line l' conjugate to l. This means *that every line l is parallel to the plane passing through its polar line l' and containing a diameter.*

Let us apply this theorem to a polyhedron $P_1P_2\ldots P_n$ with k faces. This has as its polar a polyhedron with k vertices $Q_1Q_2\ldots Q_k$ and n faces. The number of edges is the same in both polyhedra and they are polar in pairs. If we project these figures in the direction of a diameter on a plane not containing a diameter, then we obtain two polygons of which corresponding sides are parallel. When the first polyhedron has a solid angle at which m edges meet, then the

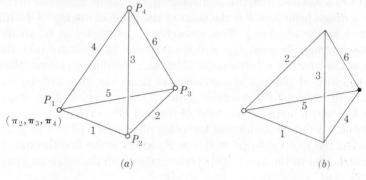

(a)

(b)

Fig. 11–15

second polyhedron has a polygon of m sides as its face. The projected figures correspond in such a way that if in the first projection there is a vertex P at which m sides meet, then to it corresponds a polygonal part bounded by m sides, each parallel to one of the sides at P. The same holds for a vertex Q at which m sides meet. We illustrate this in Fig. 11–15(a,b) for two tetrahedra of Möbius. As *reciprocal figures*, these figures play a central role in graphical statics.

We now take a diameter as the z-axis. Then the plane $(0:0:0:1)$ corresponds to the point $(0:0:1:0)$, hence $c_{13} = c_{23} = 0$ in Eq. (9–1). If we take the XOY plane as the polar plane of the origin $(0:0:0:1)$, then the line $x_1 = 0$, $x_2 = 0$ corresponds to the line $x_3 = 0$, $x_4 = 0$, which gives $c_{14} = c_{24} = 0$. The null system can then be written in the form

$$\rho u_1' = c_{12}x_2, \quad \rho u_2' = -c_{12}x_1, \quad \rho u_3' = c_{34}x_4, \cdot \rho u_4' = -c_{34}x_3,$$

or, in oblique Cartesian coordinates, writing $k = -c_{34}/c_{12}$:

$$u' = y/kz, \quad v' = -x/kz, \quad w' = 1/z,$$

or in one equation [comp. Eq. (9–4)]:

$$xy' - yx' - k(z - z') = 0. \tag{10–1}$$

The transformation to (10–1) can be performed in ∞^3 ways. The k can be reduced to 1 by choice of the measuring units.

When a Euclidean metric is introduced, then there exists one diameter d whose polar line d' is the polar of the point at infinity of d with respect to the absolute. This diameter is perpendicular to all the planes through its polar line and is called the *axis*. If we take the axis as the z-axis of a rectangular Cartesian coordinate system, then the equation of the null system assumes again the form (10–1), but now with respect to rectangular axes. This is possible in ∞^1 ways. The k is now a metrical invariant of the null system.

Equation (10–1) shows that the polar plane π of a point $P(x',y'\,z')$ contains the line $xy' - yx' = 0$, $z = z'$, which is the line through P perpendicular to the axis. This plane makes with the z-axis an angle α such that

$$\cos \alpha = \frac{k}{\sqrt{x^2 + y^2 + k^2}}, \quad \text{or} \quad \tan \alpha = \frac{r}{k}, \quad r = \sqrt{x^2 + y^2}, \quad (10\text{--}2)$$

where r is the distance of P to the axis. The plane corresponding to a point P on a line l perpendicular to the axis contains the axis; it is perpendicular to the axis if P is on the axis, and when P moves away from the axis the plane turns about l, the sense and amount of rotation depending on k. When P moves to infinity the corresponding plane moves parallel to itself.

We can thus obtain a null system by taking the planes through a line l perpendicular to the axis, according to (10–2), and then both rotating l about the axis and moving it parallel to itself. The meaning of Eq. (10–2) can be visualized by taking the circular helices

$$x = r \cos \phi, \quad y = r \sin \phi, \quad z = k\phi,$$

where r and ϕ are polar coordinates in the XOY plane. For $r =$ const. these equations give a circular helix on the cylinder $x^2 + y^2 = r^2$, which turns once around the cylinder when z moves up or down the distance $2\pi k$ (the *pitch* p). This helix is obtained by taking the diagonal of a rectangle with sides $ABCD$ ($AB = 2r$ and $BC = 2\pi k$) and winding it around a cylinder such that BC coincides with AD. The $\angle APQ$ is the angle which the tangent to the helix makes with BC. Since $\angle APQ = \angle BCA = \alpha$, $\tan \alpha = r/k$, we find the Eq. (10–2). *The normals to the polar planes of the points at distance r from the axis are therefore tangents to helices on cylinders of pitch $2\pi k$ and of radius r*

which have the central axis of the null system as axis. The null lines are the lines through the points of the helix perpendicular to the tangent. They form a linear line complex, and conversely; every nonspecial linear complex can be represented in this way as the complex of the normals to a system of coaxial circular helices.

EXERCISES

1. When XYZ is a right-handed coordinate system, show that $k > 0$ gives right-handed helices, $k < 0$ left-handed ones.

2. The lines of a linear complex may be considered as the tangents to the circular helices on circular coaxial cylinders of radius r with the central axis of the null system as axis, and a pitch of $2\pi r^2/k$, and making an angle β with the z-axis such that $\tan \beta = +k/r$. Prove.

3. Show that the equation of a null system can be cast into the form

$$\rho u_1' = x_3, \quad \rho u_2' = x_4, \quad \rho u_3' = -x_1, \quad \rho u_4' = -x_2,$$

and also into the form

$$\rho u_1' = x_2, \quad \rho u_2' = -x_1, \quad \rho u_3' = x_4, \quad \rho u_4' = -x_3.$$

4. Find examples other than the one mentioned in Sec. 11–9 of sets of three triangles in a Pascal [9_3] which are inscribed and circumscribed.

5. When two polar lines l, l' of a null system intersect a plane π, then the line connecting the points of intersection of the lines l, l' with π passes through the pole of π. Prove.

6. What is the polar polyhedron of a cube with respect to a null system? Project the cube and its reciprocal on a plane perpendicular to the axis and show how the projected figures correspond.

7. Show that a linear line complex $a_{\lambda\mu}p_{\lambda\mu} = 0$, where $a_{12}a_{34} + a_{13}a_{42} + a_{14}a_{23} = 0$, represents all lines intersecting the line with Plücker coordinates $a_{\lambda\mu}$. This is a *special* complex.

8. Discuss the correlation $\rho u_\lambda' = c_{\lambda\mu}x_\mu$, $c_{\lambda\mu} = -c_{\mu\lambda}$, $\lambda, \mu = 1, 2, 3, 4$, with $C = \text{Det}(c_{\lambda\mu}) = 0$.

9. Is it possible to establish an involutory correlation in the plane which associates to every line an incident point?

10. Two congruent regular tetrahedra $P_1P_2P_3P_4$, $Q_1Q_2Q_3Q_4$ are in such a position that Q_1 is the center of triangle $P_2P_3P_4$, P_1 the center of triangle $Q_2Q_3Q_4$, while their bases are turned 60° with respect to each other. Show that they are Möbius tetrahedra. [Other properties of such tetrahedra in W. Blaschke, *Projektive Geometrie* (Wolfenbüttel-Hannover, 1947), Ch. VII.]

11-11 Forces. When we pass from projective space to Euclidean space, then the coordinates of a line l, $p_{\lambda\mu} = x_\lambda y_\mu - x_\mu y_\lambda$, pass into

$$p_{23}:p_{31}:p_{12}:p_{14}:p_{24}:p_{34} = (x_2y_3 - x_3y_2):(x_3y_1 - x_1y_3) \\ :(x_1y_2 - x_2y_1):(x_1 - y_1):(x_2 - y_2):(x_3 - y_3), \quad (11\text{-}1)$$

where $P(x_i), Q(y_i)$, $i = 1,2,3$, are two points on the line given by rectangular Cartesian coordinates. These coordinates have a special meaning in Euclidean space. When $\overrightarrow{OP} = \mathbf{x}$, $\overrightarrow{OQ} = \mathbf{y}$, then the second set of coordinates represents the vector $\mathbf{v} = \mathbf{x} - \mathbf{y}$ and the first set the vector $\mathbf{M} = \mathbf{x} \times \mathbf{y}$. We assume first that $\mathbf{v}$ is not zero. Then this vector $\mathbf{v}$ has the direction of l, and $\mathbf{M} = \mathbf{x} \times \mathbf{v} = \mathbf{y} \times \mathbf{v}$ is the *moment vector* of l with respect to O, a vector independent of the choice of P on l. The quadratic relation between the $p_{\lambda\mu}$ now assumes the form

$$\mathbf{v} \cdot \mathbf{M} = 0. \quad (11\text{-}2)$$

The sense of $\mathbf{v}$ imparts to l a sense; the line has become a ray. *A ray is uniquely determined, for given origin, by the free vectors* $\mathbf{v}$, $\mathbf{M}$ *between which the relation* $\mathbf{v} \cdot \mathbf{M} = 0$ *exists.*

Indeed, if $\mathbf{v}$ and $\mathbf{M}$ are given, then the equation

$$\mathbf{x} = \frac{\mathbf{v} \times \mathbf{M}}{v^2} - \lambda\mathbf{v}$$

gives for variable λ all the points of the line. We indicate the ray by $(\mathbf{v},\mathbf{M})$. The expression $(k\mathbf{v},k\mathbf{M})$ indicates the same ray if $k > 0$; when $k < 0$ the sense of the ray is changed. This expression depends on the origin; if the origin O is removed to $O'(\mathbf{a})$, then $\mathbf{v}$ is unchanged, but the new $\mathbf{M}'$ and the old $\mathbf{M}$ are related by

$$\mathbf{M}' = \mathbf{M} + \mathbf{S} = \mathbf{M} - \mathbf{a} \times \mathbf{v}. \quad (11\text{-}3)$$

The vector $\mathbf{S}$ can be arbitrarily selected $\perp \mathbf{v}$ by choice of origin.

When we select one particular vector $\mathbf{F} = k\mathbf{v}$ in the direction of the ray, then a magnitude is assigned to the ray. In this case we speak of a *sliding vector* or *force* (also *spear*). *A force is determined by a line, a sense in the line, and a magnitude.* We can also express this by saying that a force is a vector which is only allowed to move in its own line, its *line of action.* A force is indicated by $(\mathbf{F},\mathbf{M})$, $\mathbf{F} \cdot \mathbf{M} = 0$ (origin given). There exist ∞^5 forces in space.

We now take the case that $\mathbf{v} = 0$. This case appears for lines lying in $x_4 = 0$. For such a line l_∞, we find from Eq. (11–1):

$$p_{23} : p_{31} : p_{12} : p_{14} : p_{24} : p_{34}$$
$$= (\alpha_2\beta_3 - \alpha_3\beta_2) : (\alpha_3\beta_1 - \alpha_1\beta_3) : (\alpha_1\beta_2 - \alpha_2\beta_1) : 0 : 0 : 0, \quad (11–4)$$

where $x_1 : x_2 : x_3 = \alpha_1 : \alpha_2 : \alpha_3$ and $y_1 : y_2 : y_3 = \beta_1 : \beta_2 : \beta_3$ are two lines in the plane π through O and l_∞. The first three terms represent a moment vector $\mathbf{M}$ perpendicular to π. When we assign a definite magnitude to $\mathbf{M}$, then we have obtained a quantity which can be written $(0, \mathbf{M})$. It is called a *couple*. *A couple is determined by a plane direction, a sense of rotation, and a magnitude, and is therefore identical with a free (axial) vector.* A couple has no line of action.

Let us now consider a linear complex, given by $a_{\lambda\mu}p_{\lambda\mu} = 0$ or, in the new symbolism [cf. Eqs. (9–5) and (11–1)]:

$$\mathbf{p} \cdot \mathbf{F} + \mathbf{q} \cdot \mathbf{M} = 0, \qquad (11–5)$$

where $\mathbf{p}$ and $\mathbf{q}$ are given vectors. When the linear complex is non-singular, $\mathbf{p} \cdot \mathbf{q} \neq 0$. Equation (11–5) therefore establishes ∞^4 forces, of which the lines of action are ∞^3 self-polar lines of a null system.

Equation (11–5) allows an interesting geometrical interpretation, for which we need the concept of the *moment* of the force $(\mathbf{F}, \mathbf{M})$ with respect to a line l given by the force $(\mathbf{G} \cdot \mathbf{N})$. When two points $\mathbf{x}, \mathbf{y}$ are selected on the line of action of force $(\mathbf{F}, \mathbf{M})$, $\mathbf{F} = \mathbf{x} - \mathbf{y}$, and the points $\mathbf{p}, \mathbf{q}$ are the projections of $\mathbf{x}, \mathbf{y}$ respectively on l, then we select $\mathbf{G} = \mathbf{p} - \mathbf{q}$ and define the moment as the volume of the tetrahedron formed by $\mathbf{x} \rightarrow \mathbf{y} \rightarrow \mathbf{p} \rightarrow \mathbf{q}$ (Fig. 11–16):

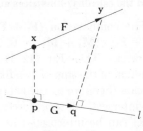

Fig. 11–16

$$\begin{vmatrix} x_1 & x_2 & x_3 & 1 \\ y_1 & y_2 & y_3 & 1 \\ p_1 & p_2 & p_3 & 1 \\ q_1 & q_2 & q_3 & 1 \end{vmatrix} = \tfrac{1}{6}(\mathbf{M} \cdot \mathbf{G} + \mathbf{N} \cdot \mathbf{F}). \qquad (11–6)$$

This moment does not depend on the particular choice of the points $\mathbf{x},\mathbf{y}$ on the line of action of $(\mathbf{F},\mathbf{M})$. When ϕ is the angle of the two rays and p their shortest distance, then the absolute value of the moment is equal to $\frac{1}{6}pFG \sin \phi$ (see Ex. 1, Sec. 11–12). The moment is therefore also independent of the choice of origin. It is zero if and only if the force either intersects the line or is parallel to it.

From Eq. (11–6) follows therefore that

$$\mathbf{F}_1 \cdot \mathbf{M}_2 + \mathbf{F}_2 \cdot \mathbf{M}_1 = 0 \qquad (11\text{–}7)$$

is the necessary and sufficient condition that the lines of action of two forces $(\mathbf{F}_1,\mathbf{M}_1),(\mathbf{F}_2,\mathbf{M}_2)$ *intersect.*

This means that for the case that $\mathbf{p} \cdot \mathbf{q} = 0$, Eq. (11–5) represents all forces whose lines of action intersect the line $(\mathbf{p},\mathbf{q})$. This is the case of a special complex (Ex. 7, Sec. 11–10). To obtain an interpretation of the case that $\mathbf{p} \cdot \mathbf{q} \neq 0$, we must attach a geometrical meaning to the combination $(\mathbf{p},\mathbf{q})$, when $\mathbf{p} \cdot \mathbf{q} \neq 0$. This is done by the introduction of the concept of the *sum of forces*.

11–12 Force systems. We call the *sum* of two forces $(\mathbf{F}_1,\mathbf{M}_1)$, $(\mathbf{F}_2,\mathbf{M}_2)$ the combination $(\mathbf{F}_1 + \mathbf{F}_2, \mathbf{M}_1 + \mathbf{M}_2)$:

$$(\mathbf{F}_1,\mathbf{M}_1) + (\mathbf{F}_2,\mathbf{M}_2) = (\mathbf{F}_1 + \mathbf{F}_2, \mathbf{M}_1 + \mathbf{M}_2). \qquad (12\text{–}1)$$

This corresponds to the addition of two sets $a_{\lambda\mu}, b_{\lambda\mu}$, each of them satisfying the quadratic relation. The concept of such summation is common to the calculus of matrices and tensors.

The combination $(\mathbf{F}_1 + \mathbf{F}_2, \mathbf{M}_1 + \mathbf{M}_2)$ only represents a force if $(\mathbf{F}_1 + \mathbf{F}_2) \cdot (\mathbf{M}_1 + \mathbf{M}_2) = 0$, that is, if the lines of action of the forces intersect. Then Eq. (12–1) is equivalent to the parallelogram construction of the sum of two forces. The combination $(\mathbf{L},\mathbf{R})$, $\mathbf{L} \cdot \mathbf{R} \neq 0$ appears therefore as the expression of the sum of two forces which do not intersect, of *skew* forces. We can show that every expression $(\mathbf{L},\mathbf{R})$ can be interpreted as such a sum by means of the following theorem:

Every combination $(\mathbf{L},\mathbf{R})$, $\mathbf{L} \cdot \mathbf{R} \neq 0$ *can be considered as the sum of two skew forces. The line of action of one force can be taken arbitrarily, provided it is not perpendicular to* $\mathbf{R}$ *or in the direction of* $\mathbf{L}$.

Indeed, let one force be arbitrarily given as $(\lambda\mathbf{i},\mathbf{M})$, $\lambda \neq 0$, $\mathbf{i} \times \mathbf{L} \neq 0$. Then λ can be determined from the equation

$$(\mathbf{L} - \lambda\mathbf{i}) \cdot (\mathbf{R} - \mathbf{M}) = 0 \quad (\mathbf{i} \cdot \mathbf{M} = 0),$$

or

$$\mathbf{L} \cdot \mathbf{R} - \mathbf{L} \cdot \mathbf{M} - \lambda\mathbf{i} \cdot \mathbf{R} = 0, \tag{12–2}$$

which determines λ uniquely provided $\mathbf{i} \cdot \mathbf{R} \neq 0$, in which case $\mathbf{M}$ cannot have the direction of $\mathbf{R}$ (the geometrical meaning of this condition will appear presently). The theorem is thus proved.

When $\mathbf{L} = 0$, then $(\mathbf{L},\mathbf{R})$ is the sum of two forces $(\mathbf{F}, \mathbf{R} - \mathbf{S})$, $(-\mathbf{F},\mathbf{S})$, provided $\mathbf{F} \cdot \mathbf{R} = 0$, $\mathbf{F} \cdot \mathbf{S} = 0$. *A couple can therefore be represented by two forces of equal magnitude and opposite sense in a plane $\perp R$.* They may be moved parallel to this plane, and rotated about any angle in their plane (since $\mathbf{S}$ is arbitrary).

We summarize our results in the following theorem, interpreting Eq. (11–5) for $\mathbf{p} \cdot \mathbf{q} \neq 0$:

Two arbitrary skew forces determine a null system, of which the self-polar lines are the lines for which the moment of the forces is zero.

For this reason the self-polar lines are called *null lines*. The lines of action of the forces are polar with respect to the null system, since all lines joining their points are null lines.

We can extend the concept of the sum of forces to any number of forces, but we can always replace this sum by the sum of two forces, except (a) in the case that the sum is a single force, or (b) that the sum is a couple.

When a force system is given, and we wish to decompose it into two forces of which one acts along a diameter, then the other force acts along the polar of the diameter, which is a line at infinity, l_∞. We have found that such a force is equivalent to a couple with its moment vector perpendicular to the plane of l:

$$(\mathbf{L},\mathbf{R}) = (0,\mathbf{R}) + (\mathbf{L},0) = (0,\mathbf{R} + \mathbf{S}) + (\mathbf{L},\mathbf{S}) \quad (\mathbf{L} \cdot \mathbf{S} = 0). \tag{12–3}$$

The $\mathbf{S}$ determines the diameter we select for the decomposition. *Every force system can therefore be decomposed into a force and a couple. The force has the direction $\mathbf{L}$ of the diameter of the null system.*

If we select as the diameter the axis of the null system, then the force and the couple have the same direction.

From the equation $(\mathbf{L},\mathbf{R}) = (0,\mathbf{R}) + (\mathbf{L},0)$ follows that at the origin the force system can be decomposed into a force through O along the diameter, and a couple in the plane $\perp R$. The line of action of the force is polar to the line at infinity of the plane $\perp R$. This shows what the condition $\mathbf{i} \cdot \mathbf{R} = 0$, introduced in the discussion of Eq. (12–2), means: The directions $\mathbf{i}$ are the null lines through O. We can therefore summarize our results as follows: *Every force system not reducible to one force can be considered as the sum of two skew forces. The line of action l of one force can be taken arbitrarily, but may not be a null line or a diameter. The line of action l' of the other force is polar to l. If the selected line of action is a diameter m, then the force system is the sum of a force along m and a couple in the plane through the polar line of m.*

This theory of force systems is the foundation of statics. It was developed by G. Monge, *Traité Elémentaire de Statique* (Paris, 1798; 8th ed., 1846); Möbius, *Lehrbuch der Statik* (Leipzig, 1837, *Werke III*); and many others. The terms *null system* and *null line* are due to Möbius, and refer to their occurrence in statics. Möbius was led to the discovery of the null system by the study of force systems. For a modern discussion, see C. J. Coe, *Theoretical Mechanics* (New York, 1938), Ch. VI.

For applications of projective geometry in mechanics, see also L. Cremona, *Graphical Statics* (Oxford, 1890) and A. Emch, *An Introduction to Projective Geometry and Its Applications* (New York, 1905).

EXERCISES

1. Prove that the moment (11–6) is equal to $\frac{1}{6}pFG \sin \phi$ by selecting the lines in an appropriate way.

2. *Dual numbers.* W. K. Clifford has introduced the complex numbers $a + \epsilon b$, where a,b are real numbers and $\epsilon^2 = 0$. If cos and sin are defined in the ordinary way by expansion in series, (a) show that $\cos \epsilon a = 1$, $\sin \epsilon b = \epsilon b$. (b) The combination $(\mathbf{L},\mathbf{R})$ is often written as a *dual vector* $\mathbf{D} = \mathbf{L} + \epsilon\mathbf{R}$. Given two dual vectors $\mathbf{D},\mathbf{D}_1$, representing forces, show that $\mathbf{D} \cdot \mathbf{D}_1 = 0$ means that the lines of action of $\mathbf{D}$ and $\mathbf{D}_1$ intersect.

3. Let $\mathbf{D},\mathbf{D}_1$ be unit dual vectors, hence $\mathbf{D} \cdot \mathbf{D} = \mathbf{D}_1 \cdot \mathbf{D}_1 = 1$. If we write $\mathbf{D} \cdot \mathbf{D}_1 = \cos (\phi + \epsilon p) = \cos \phi \cos \epsilon p - \sin \phi \sin \epsilon \phi$, show that ϕ is the angle of the lines of action of $\mathbf{D}$ and $\mathbf{D}_1$ and that p is their shortest distance.

4. Show that a force can be replaced by a parallel force of equal magnitude and direction, together with a couple.

SPECIAL EXERCISES

1. Every continuous one-to-one correspondence between the points of the complex line which preserves the harmonic relation between four points is a projectivity or an antiprojectivity. An antiprojectivity is defined by $\bar{\lambda}' = (a\lambda + b)/(c\lambda + d)$; $\bar{\lambda}$ complex conjugate of λ; a,b,c,d real.

This theorem supplements that of von Staudt, Sec. 1-8. It is still doubtful whether continuity is necessary. See C. Segre, *Atti R. Acc. Sc. Torino* **25** (1889), p. 291; J. L. Coolidge, *Geometry of the Complex Domain* (1924), p. 38; Veblen-Young II, p. 250.

2. *Tangent problem of Apollonius.* To determine all circles tangent to three circles.

This problem has eight (real or imaginary) solutions in the general case. It was published in the lost book on "Contacts" by Apollonius and has been preserved by Pappus. It has received the attention of Newton, Steiner, and many others. An elementary discussion is given, for example, in D. Davis, *Modern College Geometry* (Cambridge, Mass., 1949), pp. 199–204. See E. Kötter, *Entwicklung der synthetischen Geometrie*, Jahresber. Deutsch. Math. Ver. **5** (1901), Ch. XV; J. L. Coolidge, *Treatise on the Circle and the Sphere* (1916), Ch. III.

3. *Problem of Malfatti.* Given a triangle. To determine three circles, each of which is tangent to the two other circles and to two sides of the triangle.

This problem is due to G. F. Malfatti, *Mem. Soc. Ital. Modena* 10 (1803), p. 235, in the form: to cut three holes out of a triangular prism such that the cylinders and the prism have the same altitude and the volume of the cylinders be maximum. Steiner's solution in *Werke I*, p. 35; see *Crelle's Journal* **77** (1874), p. 230. See also R. C. Archibald, *Scripta Mathem.* **1** (1932), pp. 170–171.

4. *Theorem of Pompeiu.* The distances from the vertices of an equilateral triangle to a point of its plane are the sides of a triangle.

See D. Pompeiu, *Bull. Mathem. Phys. Ec. Polytechn. Bucharest* **6** (1936), pp. 6–7; also Thébault, *ibid.* **10** (1938–39), pp. 38–42; T. Popoviciu, *Bull. Mathem. Soc. Roumaine des Sc.* **43** (1941), pp. 27–43.

5. *Theorem of Morley.* The angles of a triangle ABC are trisected. Let A' be the intersection of those trisectors of $\angle B$ and $\angle C$ which lie nearest to

BC; B' of those trisectors of $\angle C$ and $\angle A$ nearest to CA; C' of those trisectors of $\angle A$ and $\angle B$ nearest to AB.   Then triangle $A'B'C'$ is equilateral.

See F. Morley-F. V. Morley, *Inversive Geometry* (Boston, 1933), p. 299; H. Lebesgue, *Enseignement Mathém.* **38** (1940), pp. 34–58; H. Lob, *Proc. Camb. Philos. Soc.* **36** (1940), pp. 401–413; H. F. Baker, *An Introduction to Plane Geometry* (Cambridge, 1943), p. 345, here we find the relation in the projective version of Ex. (23), Sec. 5–10.

6. *Chain of Miquel-Clifford.* Given n independent lines $1,2,\dots,n$. Let (pqr) be the circumcircle of the triangle formed by lines p,q,r. Take any four of the given lines, say 1,2,3,4. Then the four circles (123), (124), (234), (134) pass through one point, say (1234). Take any five of the given lines, say 1,2,3,4,5. Then the five points (1234), (1235), (1245), (1345), (2345) lie on a circle, say (12345). Six circles (12345), (12346), ..., (23456) pass through a point, say (123456). Seven points (123456), ..., (234567) lie on a circle, etc. The points and circles form a configuration $[(2^{n-1})_n, (2^{n-1})_n]$.

See W. K. Clifford (1877), *Coll. Papers*, pp. 38–54; J. L. Coolidge, *loc. cit.*, Special Ex. 2, p. 90; F. Morley, *Amer. Jour. of Math.* **51** (1929), pp. 465–472.

7. *Chain of De Longchamps.* Given n independent lines $1,2,\dots,n$. Let (pqr) be the center of the circumcircle (circumcenter) of the triangle formed by lines p,q,r. Take any four of the given lines, say 1,2,3,4. Then the four points (123), (124), (234), (134) lie on a circle of which (1234) is the center. Then the five points (12345), (1235), ..., (2345) lie on a circle of which (12345) is the center. Then the six points (12345), (12346), ..., (23456) lie on a circle, etc.

See De Longchamps, *Nouv. Corresp. de Mathém.* **3** (1877), pp. 306–312, 340–347; J. L. Coolidge, *loc. cit.*, Special Ex. 2, pp. 92, 603; H. W. Richmond, *Jour. London Math. Soc.* **14** (1939), pp. 78–80. For another chain, see M. D. Montesano, *Tohoku Math. Jour.* **20** (1921), pp. 41–43.

8. *A theorem of O. Nehring.* Let A_1, B_1, C_1 be points on the sides BC, CA, AB of a triangle ABC, and let 1 be a point on BC; 2 the intersection of $(1B_1)$ and (BA); 3 of $(2A_1)$ and (AC); 4 of $(3C_1)$ and (CB); etc. Then the cycle closes with $7 = 1$ if AA_1, BB_1, CC_1 pass through one point (the "Ceva condition," see Ex. 15, Sec. 3–7).

See O. Nehring, *Crelle's Journal* 184 (1942), pp. 129–137, where further relations are derived, obtained by taking points $1', 1''$ on BC, CA and constructing the points $2', \dots, 7'$; $2'', \dots, 7''$; etc.

9. *Theorem of Dandelin*. When a cone of revolution is intersected by a plane in an ellipse or a hyperbola, then the points of contact of the spheres inscribed in the cone and tangent to the plane are the foci of the intersection. The focus of a parabolic intersection is obtained in the same way.

This theorem, which seems to have escaped the Ancients, was first published by G. Dandelin, *Nouv. Mémoires Acad. Bruxelles* **2** (1822), p. 171. The theorem, useful in descriptive geometry, holds for all quadrics of revolution, as remarked by Dandelin, *ibid.* **3** (1826), pp. 1–14. See also H. Lebesgue, *Les Coniques* (Paris, 1942), Ch. I, p. 3.

10. *A problem of Pappus*. Given a right angle and a point A on its bi-sector. To construct a line through A intersecting the sides of the right angle in the points B and C such that BC has a given length.

On this problem a book has been written: A. Maroger, *Le problème de Pappus et ses Cent Premières Solutions* (Paris, 1925), 386 pp.

11. *Closure theorem of Poncelet*. When two conics C, C_1 are situated such that there exists one polygon inscribed in C and circumscribed to C_1, then there exist ∞^1 such polygons in the sense that every point of C can be taken as a vertex of such a polygon.

See Poncelet, *Traité* No. 565; Jacobi has discussed this problem with the aid of elliptic functions, *Werke I*, p. 284. See also H. Lebesgue, *loc. cit.*, Special Ex. 9, Ch. IV.

12. *A generalization of Pascal's theorem for space*. The edges of a tetrahedron intersect a quadric in six pairs of points. Through these points lying on edges through a vertex a plane is drawn; in this way four planes are obtained. The lines of intersection of each of these planes with the opposite face of the tetrahedron form a regulus.

See G. Salmon, *Analytic Geometry of Three Dimensions* (4th ed., p. 122).

13. *A theorem of R. A. Johnson*. If three equal circles are drawn through a point, the circle through their other three intersections is equal to each of them.

This elegant theorem seems to have first been published by R. A. Johnson, *Am. Math. Monthly* **23** (1916), p. 161. See A. Emch, *Scripta Mathematica* **16** (1950), pp. 61–66.

14. *Sarrus linkage*. Six plates A, B, R, S, T, U are hinged in such a way that the sets A, R, S, B and A, T, U, B are each joined by three parallel hinges, the two sets of hinges having different directions. The plates A and B then remain parallel. Show that if B is fixed, every point of A describes a straight line in space.

This linkage was proposed by P. F. Sarrus, *Comptes Rendus Acad. Paris* **36** (1853), pp. 1036, 1125, and therefore precedes that of Peaucellier (Ex. 10, Sec. 6–6). See G. T. Bennett, *Phil. Mag.* (6), **9** (1905), p. 803; M. Goldberg, *Nat. Mathem. Magazine* **16** (1942), pp. 323–332.

15. *A finite geometry.* A finite projective geometry is formed by a set of n (>2) points and subsets called lines, each of which contains at least three points, satisfying the following properties. (a) If A and B are two points, there is one and only one line containing A and B. (b) If A,B,C are non-collinear points and a line l contains a point D of line AB, and a point E of line BC, but does not contain A,B,C, then l contains a point F of line CA. Construct a finite geometry for $n = 7$ (7 lines of 3 points each) and $n = 13$ (13 lines of 4 points each).

See O. Veblen-W. H. Bussey, *Trans. Am. Math. Soc.* **7** (1906), pp. 241–259; H. F. MacNeish, *Am. Math. Monthly* **49** (1942), pp. 15–23; F. W. Levi, *Finite Geometrical Systems* (Calcutta, 1942).

16. *Desmic tetrahedra.* These are sets of three mutually self-polar tetrahedra (Sec. 8–3, Ex. 14). To obtain them, take two self-polar tetrahedra $A_1A_2A_3A_4$, $B_1B_2B_3B_4$. Let $P_1P_2P_3P_4$ be the intersections of lines A_1B_1, A_2B_1, A_3B_1, A_4B_1 with the faces $B_2B_3B_4$, $B_3B_4B_1$, $B_4B_1B_2$, $B_1B_2B_3$. Let C_1,C_2,C_3,C_4 be the harmonic conjugates of B_1 with respect to A_1P_1, A_2P_2, A_3P_3, A_4P_4. Then the tetrahedra $A_1A_2A_3A_4$, $B_1B_2B_3B_4$, and $C_1C_2C_3C_4$ are desmic. Any two tetrahedra of such a system are perspective (Sec. 8–3, Ex. 15), the centers of perspectivity being the vertices of the third tetrahedron, the planes of perspectivity being the respectively opposite faces of this third tetrahedron.

The name and description appear in C. Stephanos, *Bull. Sciences Mathem.* **3** (1879), pp. 424–456. See also N. Altschiller-Court, *Modern Pure Solid Geometry* (New York, 1935), p. 237.

17. *Photogrammetry.* The central problems of photogrammetry can be stated as follows. (a) Given the projections of a space figure from two different given centers. To determine the projection from a third center. (b) Given n projections from n unknown centers, can we find the position and the shape of the figure? The planes of projection may be the same or may be different. *Example:* Given two photographs of an object from different points, can we find its orthogonal projection on a given plane?

See G. Loria, *Vorlesungen über Darstellende Geometrie I* (Leipzig-Berlin, 1907), Ch. 5; F. Schilling, *Über die Anwendungen der Darstellenden Geometrie* (Leipzig-Berlin, 1904); M. Zeller, *Lehrbuch der Photogrammetrie* (Zürich, 1947).

18. *Apolarity.* Given two quadrics, $a_{\lambda\mu}x_\lambda x_\mu = 0$ in point coordinates, $b_{\lambda\mu}u_\lambda u_\mu = 0$ in plane coordinates. When $a_{\lambda\mu}b_{\lambda\mu} = 0$ there exist ∞^3 self-polar tetrahedra of the quadric $a_{\lambda\mu}x_\lambda x_\mu = 0$ circumscribed to the quadric $b_{\lambda\mu}u_\lambda u_\mu = 0$ and ∞^3 self-polar tetrahedra of the quadric $b_{\lambda\mu}u_\lambda u_\mu = 0$ inscribed in the quadric $a_{\lambda\mu}x_\lambda x_\mu = 0$. The two quadrics are called *apolar*. When $b_{\lambda\mu}u_\lambda u_{\cdot\iota} = 0$ represents two points we obtain the apolarity relation of Sec. 1–7. [Hesse, *Crelle* **45** (1853), p. 83; see also J. A. Todd, *loc. cit.* below, pp. 175, 253; J. G. Semple-G. T. Kneebone, *loc. cit.* below, p. 184.]

COLLATERAL READING

English

Excellent books for study and reference in analytic geometry are the two books by G. Salmon: *A Treatise on Conic Sections* (1848; 6th ed, London, 1879) and *Analytic Geometry of Three Dimensions* (1862, now 2 vols: I, 7th ed, 1928; II, 5th ed, 1915); supplemented by D. M. Y. Sommerville, *Analytic Geometry of Three Dimensions* (Cambridge, 1934). The standard work on projective geometry is O. Veblen-J. W. Young, *Projective Geometry* (2 vols: Boston I, 1910; II, 1918, quoted as Veblen-Young).

W. Graustein. *Introduction to Higher Geometry* (New York, 1930). (Recommended for beginners.)

F. S. Woods. *Higher Geometry* (Boston, etc., 1922).

E. A. Maxwell. *The Methods of Plane Projective Geometry Based on the Use of General Homogeneous Coordinates* (Cambridge, 1946).

J. W. Archbold. *Introduction to the Algebraic Geometry of a Plane* (London, 1948).

J. A. Todd. *Projective and Analytic Geometry* (New York, Chicago, 1946). (Deals with complex geometry, and is recommended for more advanced study.)

H. F. Baker. *An Introduction to Plane Geometry with Many Examples* (Cambridge, 1943). (This book may serve as an introduction to the author's six volumes *Principles of Geometry*, 1922–33.)

J. G. Semple-G. T. Kneebone. *Algebraic Projective Geometry* (Oxford, 1952).

C. W. O'Hara-D. R. Ward. *An Introduction to Projective Geometry* (Oxford, 1937).

Translations into English exist of books by Cremona, Klein, and Reye (see below).

German

Th. Reye. *Die Geometrie der Lage* (1866; Vol. I, 3d ed, 1886; Vol. II, 2d ed, 1882). Part. transl. as *Lectures on the Geometry of Position*, Part 1 (New York, 1898).

A. Clebsch-F. Lindemann. *Vorlesungen über Geometrie*. 2 vols (Leipzig 1875/76–1891, I, 2d ed, 1932).

The books of Reye and Clebsch-Lindemann are classical texts, the first a synthetic, the second an algebraic approach.

L. Heffter-C. Koehler. *Lehrbuch der analytischen Geometrie* I (Leipzig 1905, 2d ed, Karlsruhe, 1927). Vol. II by L. Heffter (Leipzig-Berlin, 1923).

A. Schönfliess-M. Dehn. *Einführung in die analytische Geometrie der Ebene und des Raumes* (Berlin, 1931).

W. Blaschke. *Projecktive Geometrie* (Wolfenbüttel-Hannover, 1947).

F. Klein. *Vorlesungen über höhere Geometrie* (2 vols, 3d ed, Berlin, 1926).

F. Klein. *Elementarmathematik vom höheren Standpunkte aus. II Geometrie* (3d ed, 1925). Transl. as *Elementary Mathematics from an Advanced Standpoint* (New York, 1939).

French

Briot-Bouquet. *Leçons de Géométrie Analytique* (1846, 14th ed, Paris, 1893). Transl. as *Briot and Bouquet's Elements of Analytical Geometry of Two Dimensions* (Chicago, New York, 1896).

N. Niewenglowski. *Cours de Géométrie Analytique* (3 vols, Paris, 1894–96).

L. Godeaux-O.Rozet. *Leçons de Géométrie Projective* (Paris, 2d ed, 1952).

Italian

L. Cremona. *Elementi di geometria proiettiva* (Torino, 1873). Transl. as *Elements of Projective Geometry* (3d ed, Oxford, 1913).

F. Enriques. *Lezioni di geometria proiettiva* (Bologna, 1904). Translations exist in French and in German.

G. Castelnuovo. *Lezioni di geometria analitica* (6th ed, Milano, 1928).

L. Bianchi. *Lezioni di geometria analitica* (Pisa, 1920).

A. Comessati. *Lezioni di geometria analitica e proiettiva* (Milano, 1930).

ON THE HISTORY OF THE SUBJECT

J. L. Coolidge. *A History of Geometrical Methods*, (Oxford, 1940).

J. L. Coolidge. *A History of the Conic Sections and Quadric Surfaces* (Oxford, 1945).

E. Koetter. "Die Entwicklung der synthetischen Geometrie von Monge bis Von Staudt," *Jahresber. Deutsch. Mathem. Verein.* **5** (1896).

M. Chasles. *Aperçu Historique sur l'Origine et le Développement des Méthodes en Géometrie* (1837, 2d ed, Paris, 1875).

G. Loria. *Il passato ed il presente delle principali teorie geometriche* (4th ed, Milano, 1930).

F. Amodeo. *Origine e sviluppo della geometria proiettiva* (Napoli, 1939).

See also the articles by C. B. Boyer, *Scripta Mathematica* **13** (1947), pp. 133–153; **16** (1950), pp. 141–157, 221–258; and of J. L. Coolidge, *Am. Math. Monthly* **55** (1948), pp. 76–86.

Section 1–3.

2. $x = 25/7$.

5. When P is an isodynamic point, and a,b,c are the sides of the triangle $PA:PB:PC = bc:ca:ab$.

9. $\begin{vmatrix} x_1 - x_2 & x_2 & 1 \\ x_1 - y_1 & y_1 & 1 \\ x_1 - y_2 & y_2 & 1 \end{vmatrix} = 0.$

Section 1–4.

6. $(AB,P_\infty P) = BP:AP$; $(P_\infty A,BP) = PA:BA$.

7. $\mu = 21/20, 1/21$, etc.; $(0,\infty\,; a,b) = a/b$; $(\infty,0; a,b) = b/a = (a,b;\,\infty,0)$.

8. $x = 15/7$.

10. Modify Fig. 1–5.

Section 1–6.

1. If $\alpha \neq 0$, multiply Eq. (5–1) by α and replace $\alpha\delta$ by $\beta\gamma$.

2. Substitute x from Eq. (2–2) into Eq. (5–6); $\alpha\delta - \beta\gamma = (\alpha_1\delta_1 - \beta_1\gamma_1)$ $(a - b)^2$.

4. Use Ex. 6, Sec. 1–4.

6. (a) $x + x' = 5$; (b) $x - x' = 0$; (c) $x + x' = 0$.

7. (a) $2x - x' + 3 = 0$; (b) $bx - ax' = 0$.

8. Write Eq. (6–3) in the form (6–1) and set up the proportionality between the coefficients.

10. $a = 2$, $b = 1$, $k = 2/3$ (or 3/2).

11. $\dfrac{x' - ia}{x' + ia} = -\dfrac{x - ia}{x + ia}.$ See further Eq. (7–5).

13. $\dfrac{x' - 2}{x' + 1} = -\dfrac{4}{5}\dfrac{x - 2}{x + 1}.$

14. Consider sign of cross ratio.

15. In general $PQ \neq QP$.

Section 1–7.

1. (a) $x^2 + x + x_1 - 35 = 0$; (b) $x + x_1 - 10 = 0$.

2. Central point at $x = -3/5$.

3. If they are in involution, then $(AB,CC') = (A'B',C'C)$ because of the projective relationship. Conversely, this relation expresses that in the projectivity in which A corresponds to A', B to B', C to C', the point C' corresponds to C. Hence one pair of corresponding points is in involution.

4. Follows from Ex. 3.

5. Follows from Fig. 1–9. Also algebraically from Eq. (7–1); if this equation is satisfied for x,x' and for y,x', x' is fixed.

6. Use the second identity of Ex. 7, Sec. 1–3. If A and B have a factor in common, at least one of these forms is a square.

8. Follows from the fact that all solutions of the equation $ax + by + cz = 0$ are linear combinations of two solutions.

9, 11. See Ex. 7.

12. The form $x^2 - 3x$ is apolar to $x^2 - 8x + 12$ and $x^2 + 2x - 3$, hence the points are 0,3.

13. $2x^2 - 6x + 3 = 0$.

15. Take the double point at infinity.

16. Let P transform A into A' and A' into A''. Then take for T' the involution with A' as double point transforming A'' into A.

Section 1–8.

3. When $(1,\lambda)$ and $(0,\infty)$ are separated harmonically by real points, $\lambda > 0$. Hence $+1, f(\lambda); 0,\infty$ are separated harmonically by real points.

Section 2–4.

3. (a) $x \cos 135° + y \sin 135° - 2\sqrt{2} = 0$; (b) $x \cos \alpha + y \sin \alpha - 1 = 0$, $\cos \alpha = -3/5$, $\sin \alpha = 4/5$; (c) $x \cos 315° + y \sin 315° - \frac{3}{2}\sqrt{2} = 0$.

5. (a) no; (b) yes; (c) parallel.

7. (a) $13y = 59$; (b) $13x + 13y = 127$; (c) $59x = 68y$.

8. $y(m_1 + m_2) = x(m_1 m_2 - 1)$.

9. Take $B(+a,0)$, $C(-a,0)$. When (x,y) are the coordinates of A, those of the center of the inscribed square are $(2ax/(y + 2a), ay/(y + 2a))$. A linear relation between x and y implies a linear relation between the coordinates of this center.

10. $6L_1 + 4L_2 - L_3 - 2L_4 = 0$.

11. Straight line through O.

12. Take P_1, Q_1 on x-axis, P_2 on y-axis.

13. Follows from $\lambda_1 L_1 + \lambda_2 L_2 \equiv \lambda_3 L_3 + \lambda_4 L_4$, $\lambda_1 L_1 + \lambda_2 L_2 \equiv \lambda_5 L_5 + \lambda_6 L_6$ by elimination of the λ.

Section 2–6.

2. When PP', QQ', RR' are parallel, and also $PQ, P'Q'$, as well as $QR, Q'R'$, then PR is parallel to $P'R'$.

5. $L_1 + L_3 - L_2 \equiv L_1 - L_2 + L_3 \equiv L_3 - L_2 + L_1$.

7. (a) The altitude through vertex (x_3, y_3) on the side through the vertices (x_1, y_1) and (x_2, y_2) is $x(y_2 - y_1) + y(x_2 - x_1) - x_3 y_2 + x_3 y_1 - x_2 y_3 + x_1 y_3 \equiv 0$. Permute the indices cyclically and add the three left-hand

members.   (b) Median through (x_3,y_3): $x(y_1 + y_2 - 2y_3) - y(x_1 + x_2 - 2x_3)$ $+ x_1y_3 + x_2y_3 - x_3y_1 - x_3y_2 = 0$.

8. (b) (3_2);   (c) $(4_3,6_2)$;   (d) $(6_2,4_3)$.

9. Each of the m lines is intersected once by every one of the $m - 1$ other lines; through each of the $m(m - 1)/2$ points of intersection pass 2 lines. The symbol $\binom{n}{k}$ stands for $\dfrac{n(n - 1) \ldots (n - k + 1)}{1 \cdot 2 \cdots k}$.

Section 2–7.

2. Show it by using the theorem that a point is uniquely determined if its cross ratio with respect to three points is given.

3. (a) 2/3;   (b) 5/8.

Section 2–9.

3. Projecting   from   3: $(AB',CC') = (42,SC')$;   projecting   from   1: $(42,SC') = (BA',CC')$, where S is intersection of (13) and (24).   See further Ex. 3, Sec. 1–7.

4. See Ex. 3.

5. Take two opposite sides as x- and y-axes.

6. Take the dual of the construction of Fig. 2–18.

7. Apply Desargues' theorem.

8. Intersect AR and PQ in S, then find fourth harmonic point to A with respect to R and S.

9. Take two sides as x- and y-axis.

Section 2–10.

1. Take P as one of the points through which the circles pass ($P = A$ in Fig. 1–9), then the line bisecting AB has either one ordinary or ideal point in common with l, or coincides with l.

Section 3–3.

1. (a) $(5/3,-2/3)$;   (b) ideal point of $y = x$;   (c) $(0,-\frac{1}{8})$.

3. $x - 17y - 44 = 0$ (observe that the sum of corresponding coefficients of this equation and of each of the given equations is zero).

7. If in a quadrangle we connect the centers of the opposite sides and the centers of the diagonals, then these three lines pass through one point at their center.

Section 3–7.

3. Take P as unit point and reason as in the text of Sec. 3–7.

5. $a_1(b_2 - b_3) - a_2(b_3 - b_1) - a_3(b_1 - b_2) = 0$.

6. Follows from $d_1/h_1 + d_2/h_2 + d_3/h_3 = 1$.

7. In barycentric coordinates take $P(x_i)$; we find for $P_1, P_2, P_3 : 0 : (2y_1 + x_1) : (2z_1 + x_1)$; $(2x_1 + y_1) : 0 : (2z_1 + y_1)$; $(2x_1 + z_1) : (2y_1 + z_1) : 0$. For the center of gravity of $\triangle P_1 P_2 P_3$ we then find $(4x_1 + y_1 + z_1) : (x_1 + 4y_1 + z_1) : (x_1 + y_1 + 4z_1)$. We have used Ex. 5 and Ex. 6.

9. Take $\triangle CA_1B_1$ as basic triangle, where C is the point of intersection of l and m.

11. Use Ex. 5, Sec. 2–9.

12. See Ex. 2, Sec. 2–7 and Sec. 2–9.

14. Take A_1 $(1:0:0)$, A_2 $(0:1:0)$, A_3 $(0:0:1)$, B_1 $(0:a_1:b_1)$, B_2 $(b_2:0:a_2)$, B_3 $(a_3:b_3:0)$. Then P_1 $(b_2b_3:a_2b_3:a_2a_3)$, P_2 $(a_3a_1:a_1b_3:b_3b_1)$, P_3 $(b_1b_2:a_1a_2:a_2b_1)$, and $(A_1B_1, P_2P_3) = b_1b_2b_3/a_1a_2a_3$.

15. Use Ex. 14.

16. Use Ex. 15 and Ex. 3.

18. Let 123 and $1'2'3'$ be two triangles such that $(11'), (22'), (33')$ pass through point A. Then introduce $S = [(13)(2'3')]$, $T = [(12')(33')]$, $U = [(12)(AS)]$, $V = [(1'2')(AS)]$. Apply Pascal's theorem first to the points $A22', 1S3$; then to $A11', 2'3'S$, then to $2'1T, SUV$, and derive from this that the points of intersection of $(12), (1'2')$; $(13)(1'3')$; $(23), (2'3')$ lie on a line. (H. S. M. Coxeter, *loc. cit.*, Sec. 1–8, has the figure on the frontispiece.)

19. Use Ex. 9.

22. If d_1, d_2, d_3 are the perpendiculars from P on the sides, then because of the collinearity of $L, M, N : d_1d_2 \sin A_3 + d_2d_3 \sin A_1 + d_3d_1 \sin A_2 = 0$ $(A_i:$ angles of the triangle). Since $d_i = \rho h_i x_i$, and $a_1 \sin A_1 = a_2 \sin A_2 = a_3 \sin A_3$, we have $x_1x_2h_1h_2a_3 + x_2x_3h_2h_3a_1 + x_3x_1h_3h_1a_2 = 0$. Divide by $h_1h_2h_3$ and use $h_1a_1 = h_2a_2 = h_3a_3$.

Section 4–4.

1. C_1C_2 is not necessarily $= C_2C_1$.

2. Fixed points $(1:0:0)$, $(0:0:1)$; fixed lines $x_2 = 0$, $x_3 = 0$.

3. $l: x_2 = x_3$; pole of pencil: $(1:0:0)$.

4. Fixed point $(1:0:0)$; fixed line $x_3 = 0$.

5. P $(0:0:1)$, l $(x_3 = 0)$; fixed points on l: $(1:0:0)$, $(0:1:0)$.

7. [1,1] elliptic or hyperbolic, [2] parabolic.

8. It is a one-to-one correspondence which transforms harmonic points on a line into harmonic points on the corresponding line.

9. Point (a_i) is transformed into $x_1a_2a_3 + x_2a_3a_1 + x_3a_1a_2 = 0$, where a_i are the sides of a triangle.

Section 4–6.

4. When OQ is the segment cut out from v^i given by $\overrightarrow{OP}$ by the doublet, $u_iv^i = OQ/OP$.

6. Use the theorem that ratios of segments are invariants.

8. AB is in general not $= BA$.

9. Translation: take $x_2 = 0$ as ideal line in Ex. 2, Sec. 4–4.

10. The correspondence is a projectivity under which the line at infinity is preserved.

11. Take AB, AC as x- and y-axis, and AA_1 as $y = mx$.

12. Transformation of the plane into an arbitrary line.

13. $v^i \rightarrow (5,8)$, $w_i \rightarrow (-\frac{1}{15}, \frac{2}{3})$.

Section 4–7.

1. The quadratic equation for μ obtained as the condition that $y = \mu x$ transforms into $y' = \mu x'$ gives two roots μ_1, μ_2 with $\mu_1\mu_2 = -1$ if $c_{12} = c_{21}$.

3. Take square with sides along $y = x \tan 60°$ and $y = -x \tan 30°$.

4. Use $x^2 + y^2 = x'^2 + y'^2$; prove that $(c_{11}c_{22} - c_{12}c_{21})^2 = 1$.

Section 4–9.

1. $c_{11}^2 - c_{21}^2 = c_{12}^2 - c_{22}^2$, $c_{11}c_{22} - c_{21}c_{22} = 0$.   Use $\cosh^2 \phi - \sinh^2 \phi = 1$.

4. A straight line.

5. (a) A circle; (b) an ellipse.

6. $\overrightarrow{OR} = (\lambda_1 \mathbf{w} + \lambda_2 \mathbf{v})/(\lambda_1 + \lambda_2)$.

10. $\frac{1}{2}|(\mathbf{v} \times \mathbf{w}) + (\mathbf{w} \times \mathbf{u}) + (\mathbf{u} \times \mathbf{v})| = $ abs. value of $\frac{1}{2} \begin{vmatrix} v_1 & v_2 & 1 \\ w_1 & w_2 & 1 \\ u_1 & u_2 & 1 \end{vmatrix}$.

11. The points $(a + ib, c + id)$, $(a - ib, c - id)$ lie on the line $dx - by + (bc - ad) = 0$.

12. A rotation about angle α counterclockwise followed by a reflection in the y-axis is a reflection in a line through O of slope $\cot \alpha/2$.

Section 5–4.

2. $\lambda = 17/6$, $3x_1 + 2x_2 + 6x_3 = 0$, $4x_1 + 3x_2 - 6x_3 = 0$;
$\lambda = -3$, $x_1 - x_2 + 2x_3 = 0$, $2x_1 - x_2 - 3x_3 = 0$.

3. $x_3 + \lambda x_1 = 0$, $x_3 + \mu x_2 = 0$, $a\lambda\mu + b\lambda + c\mu = 0$; conic: $x_3(ax_3 - bx_2 - cx_1) = 0$.

4. (a) $5u_1^2 + 5u_2^2 - u_3^2 = 0$.   (b) $u_1^2 + u_2^2 + u_3^2 - 2u_1u_2 - 2u_1u_3 - 2u_2u_3 = 0$.   (c) $(u_1 + u_2)^2 = 0$.   Check with Ex. 7.

8. A conic.   Take the four points as basic points and unit point.

9. Start with a point 1 on side A_1B_1 of the second given triangle, intersect A_1C_1 and $1A$ in 2, B_1C_1 and $2C$ in 3, A_1B_1 and $3B$ in 4.   Between 1 and 4 exists a projectivity, of which the double points must be found.   There are several possibilities.   The triangles are ABC and $A_1B_1C_1$.

11. If A,A' and B,B' correspond, and P is the pole of AB, P' of $A'B'$, consider the correlation determined by the three given pairs of points and of P,P'.

12. The pencils connecting A with $B',C',\ldots,$ and A' with $B,C,\ldots,$ are perspective. See Ex. 3, Sec. 2–10.

Section 5–7.

1. $(-5:7:1)$.

2. E.g., the basic triangle.

3. Any triangle with, e.g., $(1:0:0)$ and $(0:1:0)$ as vertices.

4. $x_1 - x_2 - x_3 = 0$, $2x_1 - x_2 - 5x_3 = 0$.

7. Take the four lines as basic lines and unit line. If the conic is $a_{ij}x_ix_j = 0$, then $a_{12} = a_{13} = a_{23}$.

8. Take one triangle as basic and let the polars of the vertices with respect to $a_{ij}x_ix_j = 0$ be $L_i = 0$. Then $a_{23}L_1 - a_{13}L_2 = 0$, $a_{13}L_2 - a_{12}L_3 = 0$, $a_{12}L_3 - a_{23}L_1 = 0$ are concurrent.

9. This is the converse of the theorem of Ex. 8. Take as basic points (Fig. 2–9) A,B, and the intersection S of BC and PP', and as unit point Q'. Then if PR is $a_ix_i = 0$, the conic for which $\triangle ABS$ is self-polar and for which PR is the pole of Q' is $a_1x_1^2 + a_2x_2^2 + a_3x_3^2 = 0$. Take $Q[(1 + \lambda):1:1]$ and prove that C is the polar of AQ and D of AR. Check up successively on the other combinations.

10. Take line as $x_1 = 0$.

11. With the aid of the fixed lines as basic lines $x_1 = 0$, $x_2 = 0$ write the conic as $a_{12}x_1x_2 + a_{13}x_1x_3 + a_{23}x_2x_3 = 0$. Then AB passes through the point of intersection of the tangents to the two other basic points $(a_{23}:a_{13}:-a_{12})$.

Section 5–8.

3. The condition that the line $a_1x_1 + a_2x_2 - a_3x_3 = 0$ has two real points in common with the conic is $a_1^2 + a_2^2 - a_3^2 > 0$.

4. Any elliptic point can be selected as $(0:0:1)$.

7. Substitute $(1:0:0)$, $(0:1:0)$, $(0:0:1)$ into $x_1^2 + x_2^2 - x_3^2$.

8. Take this self-polar triangle as basic triangle; then the polarity is $\rho u_1 = a_1x_1$, $\rho u_2 = a_2x_2$, $\rho u_3 = a_3x_3$. One other pair of conjugate elements determines a_1,a_2,a_3.

9. See Eq. (9–4).

Section 5–10.

5. Use the dual of the theorem on the pentagon stated in the text.

6. Take the line as $x_3 = 0$ and use the theory of apolarity, Sec. 1–7.

7. Use Ex. 6. The condition that a line be tangent to a point conic is thus a quadratic one.

8. Three linear and two quadratic relations. [Another method is by using Sec. 6–6, projecting two points into the isotropic points; there are four circles tangent to two lines and passing through a given point.]

9. Connect the given point P with one of the five points as the conic, say 1; find the second point, 6, of $P1$ with respect to 1 and 6. Repeat this with point 2 and thus find two points of the polar.

10. Take the triangle as basic, and the given conic as $b_{ij}u_iu_j = 0$. Then the required conic is $\beta_{22}\beta_{33}u_1^2 + 2\beta_{12}\beta_{33}u_1u_2 + \beta_{11}\beta_{33}u_2^2 + 2\beta_{13}\beta_{22}u_1u_3 + 2\beta_{23}\beta_{11}u_2u_3 + \beta_{11}\beta_{22}u_3^2 = 0$.

12. Let PQR and ABC be the self-polar triangles. Intersect CA and QR in L, BA and QR in M. Then L is the polar of PB and M of PC. Since polarity preserves cross ratios, the cross ratio $(PC,PQ; PR,PB) = (MR,QL)$. From this show that B,C,Q,R are the points of intersection of two projective pencils (P) and (A). Dual theorem similarly.

13. Take a vertex of each triangle. These vertices, joined to the four other vertices, form two projective pencils, which cut out two projective point sets on the sides opposite the vertices. Then use the theorem on the lines connecting such sets, Sec. 5–3.

15. Use Ex. 8, Sec. 5–8, and Ex. 12 of this section.

16. $a_1L_1^2 + a_2L_2^2 + a_3L_3^2 = 0$.

17. Use Steiner's construction, Ex. 13, Sec. 5–4.

18. (1) Linear (point conics), $r = 4$; (2) linear (class conics), $r = 4$; (3) linear (point and class conics), $r = 2$; (4) linear (point conics), $r = 3,2$; (5) no.

19. Basic triangle has $x_1 = 0$, $x_3 = 0$ as tangents, $x_2 = 0$ connecting tangent points; $\lambda = 0$ is $(0:0:1)$, $\lambda = \infty$ is $(1:0:0)$.

23. Take the triangle as basic triangle, and $T(a_i)$. Then the lines $l_1,l_2,\ldots,n_1n_2$ are $x_2 - \lambda_1x_3 = 0$, $a_3\lambda_1x_2 - a_2x_3 = 0$, $\ldots,a_2\lambda_3x_1 - a_1x_2 = 0$, respectively. Then proceed by proving Brianchon's theorem, numbering the lines $l_1,\ldots,n_2$ in different ways.

Section 6–3.

3. Take the x-axis through two points, the y-axis through the other two points. If the points are at distances a,b,c,d respectively from O, then $abcd > 0$.

4. (a) Connect the centers of parallel chords. For the points of intersection of the diameters with the conic, use Steiner's construction, Ex. 13, Sec. 5–4.

6. Only possible for hyperbola or ellipse.

7. Take the measure such that the ellipse is $x^2 + y^2 - 1 = 0$. Then

$$\begin{vmatrix} -mb & b & 1 \\ b & mb & 1 \\ 0 & 0 & 1 \end{vmatrix} = -1, \text{ independent of } m, \ b = \frac{1}{\sqrt{1 + m^2}}. \text{ See Sec. 4–5.}$$

11. Use the remark of Sec. 1–6 (Case II) on the roots of a quadratic equation.

12. Follows from theorem of Sec. 6–3. We can also prove it by using Ex. 11.

13. Follows from Pascal's theorem.

Section 6–5.

1. (a) $\dfrac{x^2}{10} - \dfrac{y^2}{10} = -1$, axes $x - y = 0$, $x + y + 2 = 0$, vertices $(-1 + \sqrt{5}, -1 - \sqrt{5})$; $(-1 - \sqrt{5}, -1 + \sqrt{5})$; (b) $\dfrac{x^2}{13} + \dfrac{y^2}{\frac{13}{4}} = 1$, vertices $(\frac{1}{2}, 3)$; $(-\frac{5}{2}, 4)$; $(1, -1)$; $(-3, 5)$; (c) $y^2 = 2x$, axis $3x + 4y + 5 = 0$, vertex $(-2\frac{1}{5}, \frac{2}{5})$, opening below x-axis.

2. Hyperbola $y^2 - 2xy + 2ax + 2ay - 2a^2 = 0$.

5. Follows from the normal form $D_2 S_1 x^2 + D_2 S_2 y^2 = D_3$; $S_1 S_2 = D_2$.

6. We must add the condition of reality.

8. Apply Ex. 7 repeatedly and perform the transition to a limit.

9. Find the conditions that the two intersections of $y - y_0 = \lambda(x - x_0)$ with the conic pass to infinity.

10. Find the condition that $y = \lambda x$ has two intersections with the conic.

11. (a) The directions of the tangents through the origin; (b) the axis direction of a parabola.

12. Use Ex. 22, Sec. 5–10. Result:

$$\alpha_{33}(x^2 + y^2) - 2\alpha_{13}x - 2\alpha_{23}y + \alpha_{11} + \alpha_{22} = 0 \ (\alpha_{33} = D_2).$$

In the case of the ellipse (4–1) this is $x^2 + y^2 = a^2 + b^2$.

14. Let $T = 0$ be the tangent at P to conic $C = 0$ and $L = 0$ be another line through P. Find the condition that the pencil $C + \lambda TL = 0$ contains a circle.

16. Follows from Ex. 9.

18. If two sides are $A = 0$, $B = 0$, and the altitudes on these sides $H = 0$, $L = 0$ respectively, then the pencil $AH + \lambda BL = 0$ contains two (singular) equilateral hyperbolas. Further, see Ex. 17.

19. (b) $x^2 - y^2 + \lambda xy - x + y = 0$.

Section 6–6.

2. $x^2 + y^2 + 3x + y - 30 = 0$.

3. $x^2 + y^2 - 2x + 5y - 20 = 0$.

6. See Ex. 5, Sec. 1–3.

7. Take the four vertices as $(a \cos \alpha_\lambda, a \sin \alpha_\lambda, \lambda = 1,2,3,4)$.

8. Use method of Ex. 7. A simple geometrical proof is also possible.

10. $(1, 1\frac{1}{2})$, $(4, 2)$.

11. $(x - 7)^2 + (y - 12)^2 = 206$.

12. Use Ex. 16, Sec. 5–10.

14. Use Ex. 12; $N_2N_3 \sin A_1 + N_3N_1 \sin A_2 + N_1N_2 \sin A_3$ for any three lines $N_i = 0$ represents twice the area of the triangle formed by the feet of the perpendiculars P_i which we let fall from P on the sides of $\triangle A_1A_2A_3$.

15. Projectively speaking, the line $x = p$ is a line passing through a diagonal point D of the complete quadrangle formed by the basic points of the pencil. Any line through D has as locus of the poles of its points the line connecting the other diagonal points.

16. The director circles of two conics intersect in two points P from which both conics are seen at right angles. Hence from P we can see all conics of the class-pencil of these conics at right angles. Now consider the singular conics of this pencil. This proof is due to Plücker.

17. Take as origin the radical center of the circles $C_i \equiv x^2 + y^2 + 2a_ix + 2b_iy + c_i = 0$, $i = 1,2,3$. Then $c_1 = c_2 = c_3$. The required locus is $x^2 + y^2 - c_1 = 0$.

Inversions

4. It is sufficient to prove the theorem for the angle of a line with the line through the center of inversion. Take this line as x-axis.

6. Use method of Ex. 7, Sec. 6–6; a simple geometrical proof is also possible by taking a point E on AC such that $\angle EDC = \angle BDA$.

7. Apply inversion with respect to D as pole and use Ex. 5.

8. Apply inversion with respect to P as pole.

Section 6–7.

1. Take F as origin and the directrix as $x = -p$; x-axis is perpendicular to directrix. Then the equation is $x^2(1 - e^2) + y^2 - 2pxe^2 - e^2p^2 = 0$. For $e^2 \neq 1$, move the origin to the center of the conic.

5. Take the equation as in Ex. 1 to obtain a solution for all conics together.

6. For the case of an ellipse or hyperbola, use the property of the bisectors of a triangle, proved in Sec. 1–3. For the ellipse, $|FP| = a - ex$, $|F'P| = a + ex$. In the case of a parabola, $|FP| = x + p/2$, if $y^2 = 2px$.

8. From Eq. (7–4), we find for the point of intersection (x_0,y_0) of parabolas $\lambda_1\lambda_2 : x_0^2 = -4\lambda_1\lambda_2$, $y_0 = -(\lambda_1 + \lambda_2)$. For the slopes m_1,m_2 of the tangents at (x_0,y_0), we find $m_1m_2 = x_0^2/4\lambda_1\lambda_2 = -1$.

10. The locus of P is a conic because its points are generated by projective pencils; when IJ is a tangent to the conic, these pencils are perspective. The conic passes through I and J.

11. To prove that AB (A,B different) has the same pole with respect to C and C_1, consider the tangents to C_1 at A and B.

13. Use Brianchon's theorem.

14. Follows from the dual to the theorem Ex. 13, Sec. 5–10.

15. (b) follows from (a) when A',B',C' are collinear; for (c) use Ex. 14.

16. Take tangent and normal as x- and y-axes. The theorem can also be proved by showing that the lines connecting corresponding points of an involution on a conic (Ex. 11, Sec. 5–4) pass through a point.

Section 7–6.

3. Take L $(\lambda:1:0)$, H $(\rho:1:0)$, $\rho = a_1/a_2$, $\angle PLH = \alpha$. Then, applying Eq. (2–5), we get $\tan^2 \alpha = 4a_1^2 a_3^2 \lambda/(\rho - \lambda)^2$, which increases uniformly from 0 to ρ.

5. The equation of the circles follows from Eq. (3–1) and is $(a_{ij}x_i y_j)^2 + \lambda(a_{ij}x_i x_j)(a_{ij}y_i y_j) = 0$, y_i constant.

6. Here $a_{ij}x_i y_j = 0$ is the tangent at P to the absolute. Let $\lambda(a_{ij}y_i y_j)$ approach a finite value when P moves to the absolute.

7. See Ex. 5; but take $P(y_i)$ now outside the absolute, and the given line as $a_{ij}x_i y_j = 0$.

9. Take $x_1^2 + x_2^2 + x_3^2 = 0$ as the absolute, $x_3 = 0$ as one side of the triangle.

10. For ϵ small $\sinh d/k$ in Eq. (3–2) may be replaced by d/k; let $ik\sqrt{\epsilon} \to 1$.

11. Take the absolute as $u_1^2 - u_2^2 = 0$. By using a method similar to that of Ex. 10, we find for the distance d, if $x_3 = 0$ is the ideal line, that $d^2 = (x_1 - x_2)^2 - (y_1 - y_2)^2$, and for the angle θ between the lines $a_a x + b_a y + c_a = 0$, $a = 1,2$, $\cosh \theta = \dfrac{a_1 a_2 - b_1 b_2}{\sqrt{a_1^2 - b_1^2}\,\sqrt{a_2^2 - b_2^2}}$.

Section 8–3.

10. Projection of the figure on a plane not through P gives a configuration of Pascal (Ex. 9, Sec. 3–7).

11. If the line through $P(a_\lambda)$ intersects l $(x_1 = 0, x_2 = 0)$ and m $(x_3 = 0, x_4 = 0)$, Q has the coordinates $a_1:a_2: -a_3: -a_4$.

12. If l intersects $A_1 A_2$ in P_1 and $A_3 A_4$ in Q_1, then m intersects $A_1 A_2$ in P_2, $A_3 A_4$ in Q_2 such that $(A_1 A_2, P_1 P_2) = (A_3 A_4, Q_1 Q_2) = -1$.

13. The polar plane of $P(a_\lambda)$ is $\phi(1/a_\lambda)$.

14. First prove that such tetrahedra exist. Start with a vertex P_1 of I and construct its harmonic conjugates P_2, P_3, P_4 with respect to the three pairs of opposite edges of II. Then $P_2 P_3 P_4$ is the polar plane of P_1, and similarly, $P_3 P_4 P_1$ the polar plane of P_2, etc. Then show that a vertex of II is the pole of its opposite face with respect to I.

15. Take one tetrahedron as basic and the point of intersection of the lines joining corresponding vertices as unit point. If the vertices of the second tetrahedron are $(1 + \lambda):1:1:1$, etc., the plane which contains the

intersections of corresponding faces is $\dfrac{x_1}{\lambda_1} + \dfrac{x_2}{\lambda_2} + \dfrac{x_3}{\lambda_3} + \dfrac{x_4}{\lambda_4} = 0$.

Section 8–5.

1. If the vertices are given by a_i, b_i, c_i, d_i, then the medians intersect in the point $\frac{1}{4}(a_i + b_i + c_i + d_i)$. Use Eq. (4–4).

3. If the arrow $\overrightarrow{OP}$ of v^i intersects the plane of w_i in Q, then $v^i w_i$ is the ratio of OP to OQ. When $v^i w_i = 0$ the plane of w_i is parallel to the arrow of v^i.

4. It is invariant and represents a volume.

6. (a) $(m - m_1)(b - b_1) = (n - n_1)(a - a_1)$; (b) take OP as line m, condition is $b(mx_0 - y_0) = a(nx_0 - z_0)$. Here we can also consider the pencil of planes through l: $(mx - y + a) + \lambda(nx - z + b) = 0$.

7. $z = -(Ap + Bq + D)/(Aa + Bb + C)$.

8. Take the lines as $y = mx, z = a$; $y = -mx, z = -a$; plane as $Ax + By + Cz = 0$.

Section 8–8.

4. Square of distance is

$$\frac{(x_0 - az_0 - p)^2 + (y_0 - az_0 - q)^2 + [b(x_0 - p) - a(y_0 - q)]^2}{a^2 + b^2 + 1}.$$

6. $\mathbf{x} = \mathbf{a} + \lambda(\mathbf{b} - \mathbf{a})$.

7. Take the plane segments as oriented parallelograms with a common side and common sense.

10. $x_3' = \frac{6}{7}x_1 + \frac{2}{7}x_2 - \frac{3}{7}x_3$.

13. $x_1' = -\frac{3}{5}x_1 + \frac{4}{5}x_2, x_2' = \frac{16}{25}x_1 + \frac{12}{25}x_2 - \frac{3}{5}x_3, x_3' = -\frac{12}{25}x_1 - \frac{9}{25}x_2 - \frac{4}{5}x_3$. $[C = 1]$

15. When $x_i' = c_{ij}x_j$, the rotation is about an axis

$$\mathbf{w}\left(\frac{c_{13} + c_{31}}{c_{12} - c_{21}}, \quad \frac{c_{12} + c_{21}}{c_{23} - c_{32}}, \quad \frac{c_{23} + c_{32}}{c_{31} - c_{13}}\right).$$

The angle θ is given by $2\cos\theta = c_{11} + c_{22} + c_{33} - 1$. The length of $\mathbf{w}$ is $\tan \theta/2$.

Section 9–5.

1. Derive the condition that an equation of the form $a_\lambda x_\lambda = 0$ is satisfied by the x_λ in Eq. (5–4), first for constant λ, then for constant μ.

2. Use the fact that a line having three points in common with the surface lies on it.

4. Use Eq. (5–4).

7. Apply Pascal's theorem.

9. A plane intersects the hexagon in 6 points on a quadric, which have a Pascal line. This line is intersected by the three lines under consideration. When we take another plane and repeat the reasoning, we obtain two Pascal lines both intersecting the three lines under consideration.

10. Apply a polarity in which the quadric passes into itself.

11. Change form (B_1) into $x_2^2 - x_1x_3 = 0$.

13. Prove that an algebraic curve in space intersected by a line in two (real, imaginary, coincident) points is a conic.

14. C_1 can be identical with C_2 (tangency along a common conic).

15. If P is a point in common to C_1 and C_2, then a line through P intersecting the two skew lines has three points in common with C_1 and C_2 and therefore is part of the intersection.

16. "In a general position" means that the nine equations for the ratio of the $a_{\lambda\mu}$ are independent. See Ex. 8, Sec. 10–8.

17. Four edges of the coordinate tetrahedron form a skew quadrilateral (Ex. 15) on the quadric.

18. Take one of the tetrahedra as the basic tetrahedron $A_1A_2A_3A_4$. If $P_\lambda = 0$ is the polar plane of A_λ with respect to $a_{\lambda\mu}x_\lambda x_\mu = 0$, then the line connecting A_1 $(1:0:0:0)$, with the pole B_1 of face $A_2A_3A_4$ is $x_2:x_3:x_4 = \alpha_{12}:\alpha_{13}:\alpha_{14}$ ($\alpha_{\lambda\mu}$ cofactors). Derive the conditions that an arbitrary line $P_\lambda x_\lambda = 0, Q_\lambda x_\lambda = 0$ intersects the four lines $A_1B_1, \ldots, A_4B_4$ and show that they are satisfied for ∞^1 lines.

Section 10–2.

4. Take one of the parallel planes as a coordinate plane and project the sections on it.

6. For the forms (2–2), (2–3), (2–4): $xx_0 + yy_0 + zz_0 = 1$, $xx_0 + yy_0 - zz_0 = 1$, $xx_0 - yy_0 - zz_0 = 1$.

7. The parallel generator of the asymptotic cone.

8. Equality of volume is defined in analogy to equality of areas, Ex. 7, Sec. 6–3 (also Sec. 8–5). Recall that $\begin{vmatrix} a_1 & b_1 & c_1 \\ a_2 & b_2 & c_2 \\ a_3 & b_3 & c_3 \end{vmatrix} = 1$ if $a_i^2 + b_i^2 + c_i^2 = 1$, $i = 1,2,3$; $a_ia_k + b_ib_k + c_ic_k = 0$, $i \neq k$.

Section 10–3.

1. Compare Ex. 4, Sec. 9–5.

2. Take the lines as $z = c, y = mx$; $z = 0, y = 0$; $z = -c, y = -mx$ (show that this does not affect the generality).

5. Show that the cone $Ayz + Bzx + Cxy = 0$ can contain the generators $x:y:z = a_i:b_i:c_i$, $i = 1,2,3$, if $a_ib_i + a_ic_i + b_ic_i = 0$.

Section 10–6.

1. (a) $x^2 + y^2 + z^2 = 25$, sphere.

(b) $2x^2 + 2y^2 - 4z^2 = 25$, rotation hyperboloid of one sheet; axis: $x = z$, $x + y = 5$, center $(2\frac{1}{2}, 2\frac{1}{2}, 2\frac{1}{2})$.

(c) $(-1 + \sqrt{3})x^2 - (1 + \sqrt{3})y^2 + 2z^2 = 4$, hyperboloid of one sheet.

(d) $(-5 + \sqrt{97})x^2 - (5 + \sqrt{97})y^2 - \frac{1}{2}z\sqrt{6} = 0$, hyperbolic paraboloid.

(e) $x^2 + y^2 + 7z^2 = 7$, rotation ellipsoid; axis: $-x = y - 1 = \frac{1}{2}(z + 1)$.

2. When $a = b = c$, parallel planes. Otherwise, if $a + b + c > 0$, hyperboloid of one sheet; $a + b + c < 0$, hyperboloid of two sheets; $a + b + c = 0$, cylinder with right section an equilateral hyperbola.

4. $S_1 - S_2 = 0$.

6. $x^2 + y^2 + z^2 - 2x - 2y - 2z + 2 = 0$, $x^2 + y^2 + z^2 - 6x - 6y - 6z + 18 = 0$.

7. $(x_0 - a)(x - a) + (y_0 - b)(y - b) + (z_0 - c)(z - c) = 0$.

9. $x^2 + y^2 + z^2 + 2px + 2py + 2pz - p^2 = 0$, $2x^2 + 2y^2 + 2z^2 - px - py - pz - p^2 = 0$.

12. First show that the three planes through the edges at a vertex perpendicular to the opposite face pass through a line (the orthocentric line of the trihedron). Then show that an orthocentric line intersects all altitudes. In the exceptional case, either the altitudes form two intersecting pairs, or all altitudes pass through one point. (This second case happens when two pairs of opposite edges, and hence all three pairs, are perpendicular.)

15. Take the lines l and m as $y = mx$, $z = a$; $y = -mx$, $z = -a$.

Section 10–8.

1. Dualize in space, so that a point conic corresponds to a cone.

3, 4. When (p,q,r) is a focus, the equation of the quadric must be cast into the form $(x - p)^2 + (y - q)^2 + (z - r)^2 = V_1 V_2$, where $V_1 = 0$, $V_2 = 0$ are the equations of two planes through the directrix PQ. If the quadric is taken as $x^2/a^2 + y^2/b^2 + z^2/c^2 = 1$, take PQ parallel to the z-axis. The locus of the foci appears in the form $\dfrac{p^2}{a^2 - c^2} + \dfrac{q^2}{b^2 - c^2} = 1$, the directrix as $x = \dfrac{a^2}{a^2 - c^2}\, p$, $y = \dfrac{b^2}{b^2 - c^2}\, q$.

7. Study Eq. (8–5) for such substitutions as $a^2 = b^2$.

Section 11–1.

1. (a) Two fixed lines A_1A_2, A_3A_4 of fixed points; two pencils of fixed planes with axes A_1A_2, A_3A_4 (the common line of a pencil of planes is its *axis*).

(b) Isolated fixed points A_1, A_2; a line of fixed points A_3A_4; two isolated fixed planes $A_1A_3A_4, A_2A_3A_4$; and the pencil of fixed planes with axis A_1A_2.

3. $\rho x_1' = ax_1 + x_4$, $\rho x_2' = ax_2$, $\rho x_3' = ax_3$, $\rho x_4' = ax_4$ has a plane π of fixed points and a linear set of ∞^2 planes with the vertex in π (a *bundle* of planes).

4. $\rho x_1' = ax_1 + bx_2$, $\rho x_2' = -bx_1 + ax_2$, $\rho x_3' = x_3$, $\rho x_4' = x_4$, $a^2 + b^2 = 1$ has two isolated fixed points I $(1:i:0:0)$, J $(1:-i:0:0)$; two isolated fixed planes A $(x_3 = 0)$, B $(x_4 = 0)$; a line of fixed points AB; and a pencil of fixed planes with axis IJ $(x_3 + \lambda x = 0)$.

Section 11-4.

2. Consider the rectangular parallelepiped circumscribed to the ellipsoid.

3. Two directed segments on a line (not both of zero length) can be considered as the parallel projection of two orthogonal vectors in a plane through the line.

5. To every point of space corresponds a point P in a plane π, to every point P in π a line of space passing through a fixed point C, which intersects π in a point P'. Between P and P' exists a collineation. The transformation is therefore a central projection followed by a plane collineation.

7. It is a homology. The intersection of π and π_1 is the *axis of affinity*, the fixed point is at infinity.

8. Take a rectangular cross section as the XOY plane, an edge as z-axis. There are two solutions, symmetric with respect to the XOY plane.

Section 11-6.

2. All possibilities exist.

3. When l has the direction of $\mathbf{n}$, and the plane of projection is $\perp \mathbf{i}$, then l' has the direction of $\mathbf{n} - (\mathbf{n} \cdot \mathbf{i})\mathbf{i}$ and the trace of σ that of $\mathbf{n} \times \mathbf{i}$.

4. Consider the traces of three planes intersecting in a point.

5. Central perspective for $k = 0$; $k = -1$ is trivial.

Section 11-10.

2. Take a line of the complex as $x - x' = m(z - z')$, $y - y' = n(z - z')$, then, according to Eq. (10-1), $my' - nx' = k$. The shortest distance to the z-axis is $r = k/\sqrt{m^2 + n^2}$; its angle α with the z-axis is $\tan \alpha = \sqrt{m^2 + n^2}$.

5. Show that the line connecting the points of intersection is self-polar.

7. Prove that when and only when two lines $p_{\lambda\mu}$ (in point coordinates), $q_{\lambda\mu}$ (in plane coordinates) intersect [Eqs. (3-1) and (3-2) in Sec. 8-3] $p_{\lambda\mu}q_{\lambda\mu} = 0$. For this, take in this Eq. (3-1), $x_1 = 0$, $x_2 = 1$, $y_2 = 0$.

8. Write $c_{\lambda\mu} = v_\lambda w_\mu - v_\mu w_\lambda$ (plane coordinates). To every point belongs a plane through a fixed line.

9. Reasoning as in Sec. 11-8, we find that the transformation is singular.

INDEX